TWO BLADES OF GRASS

With best Wishes

Peter

TWO BLADES OF GRASS
The Story of the Cultivation of Plants

Peter Thoday

And he gave it for his opinion, that whoever could make two ears of corn or two blades of grass grow upon a spot of ground where only one grew before, would deserve better of mankind, and do more essential service to his country than the whole race of politicians put together.

– Jonathan Swift, *Gulliver's Travels*, "A Voyage to Brobdingnag"

THODAY ASSOCIATES

TWO BLADES OF GRASS
THE STORY OF THE CULTIVATION OF PLANTS

Copyright © 2007 Peter Thoday

First published in Great Britain in 2007 by
Thoday Associates
Faircross House
Box Hill
Corsham
Wiltshire
SN13 8HA

ISBN 978-0-9557033-0-0
British Library Cataloguing in Publication Data:
1. Cultivation 2. Cultivation – History 3. Husbandry 4. Agriculture – History
5. Horticulture – History I. Title

Printed by
Short Run Press, Exeter

Distributed in the UK by:

Thoday Associates
Faircross House
Box Hill
Corsham
Wiltshire
SN13 8HA
Email: faircross@thodays.co.uk

and

Thin Read Line Books
11 St Andrews Road
Prenton
Birkenhead
Wirral
CH43 1TB

Email: richmond_dutton@hotmail.com

With love and gratitude to Anne, Nonny and Jennie.
Without their influence this book would not have been written.

CONTENTS

THANKS AND APOLOGIES

This book has grown out of a lifetime of contact with those who cultivate or study plants. Together they make a long list starting with my father and his staff, then the staff and students at the Cambridge University Botanic Garden followed by those at the long defunct Department of Horticulture of Bristol University. Next came Oaklands College of Agriculture and Horticulture and then for over 25 years colleagues both within and without the University of Bath. Finally there are all the professional friends and contacts made through the botanical and educational fraternities, the Institute of Horticulture and my own small consultancy Thoday Associates. Many have influenced my professional development but I would particularly thank Eric Coker, David Miller, Leonard Broadbent, Vic Fowler, Bill Bowen, Tony Kendle, Jane Stoneham and Mary Payne. Sadly some of them are no longer with us but I trust that those that are will find an echo of the information and ideas they have shared with me in the pages of this book.

Turning to those directly associated with this book my deep gratitude and thanks go to six people. All have been indispensable to the undertaking: Peter McLoughlin for his unwavering encouragement and draft reading, Richmond Dutton for his enthusiasm, scholarship and ability to supply a stream of exactly the books I needed, and Di Vaz for her patient, tolerant, and always obliging provision of secretarial and computing skills. More recently Mark Hendy entered the saga, initially to edit the manuscript, but then to guide the book through all its final stages and above all to greatly improve the text through kindly advice unstintingly given from his near bottomless scholarship. Without Lars Stenberg illustrations might well have remained the missing ingredient. Many approaches were considered but proved either unattainable or unaffordable until the combination of his artistic skills and fertile imagination provided the ideal introduction to each chapter. The last great hurdle, the index, would have proved beyond our DIY abilities if Ken Payne, with endless patience and kindness, had not linked his computing skills to his accountant's discipline to garner and order the entries.

The cover illustration is from a watercolour *Fields in the Severn Vale* by Jean Martin, artist, friend and wonderful person.

Above all my thanks go to my wife Dr Anne Thoday for her endless tolerance of my obsession, her ever friendly welcome to all concerned and her unwavering support in spite of five years of domestic disturbance and the inevitable costs to our exchequer.

There remains one other but unknown key contributor; the compiler of my spell-checker. As a dyslectic I would never have had either the courage or cheek to have shown anyone my unchecked manuscript.

I apologise and make no excuses for any mistakes or gross inaccuracies but I ask indulgence over the matter of generalisations. It is my hope that no matter how small the readership it will include a good percentage from outside the professions now referred to in official circles as "the land-based industries". I believe that the over zealous pursuit of detail across such a broad canvas would have been inhibiting. Those seeking deeper enlightenment may find both the glossary (entries designated [g] in the text) and the bibliography of value, in which case their thanks should in great part be directed towards Mark Hendy.

PETER THODAY
2007

GLOSSARY

abiotic Pertaining to the non-living (physical and chemical) components of an ecosystem.

ablaqueation The removal of soil from around roots typically prior to root pruning.

anatomy The internal structure of a plant.

aquifer A water-bearing stratum of rock on or below the soil surface.

assarting Clearing land for cropping; usually woodland.

auxin Hormone-like substance produced by plants which controls growth and development.

balk A strip or ridge of land left unploughed between two arable areas which at times served to demarcate ownership.

beetle bank Strip of uncultivated land left between arable fields to support a fauna of beneficial insects and other invertebrates.

bightle A small field or enclosure close to a croft

biological control The use of a living agent to control a pest, weed or disease organism.

biota The plant and animal species found in a specific place.

biotic Pertaining to the living components (plant and animal) of an ecosystem.

biotope An environmental region characterised by its own abiotic and biotic make-up.

bi-specific hybrid A hybrid resulting from a cross between species in the same genus.

bout A term used in land tillage to indicate the work achieved or area covered in a round trip "up and back" across a field.

break crop A crop inserted into a long sequence of cereal production to introduce some of the advantages gained from a traditional rotation; nitrogen-fixing legumes are often used.

bulk A strip of land forming a boundary within an arable field.

bulk density The density of a material as used, hence including any water- or air-filled spaces between the solids.

butt A small piece of land in an open field.

byland A headland.

canopy Area covered by the foliage of a group or an individual tree or shrub.

cench A strip of land in an arable field.

champion Land in open fields divided into strips.

close An enclosed field.

cotyledons "Seed leaves", the first leaves formed as part of the embryo. Most appear above ground; others remain within the seedcoat.

coulter The knife-like blade mounted in front of a ploughshare to produce a vertical cut through the soil.

croft A small enclosure next to a dwelling.

crop group A collection of crops with certain affinities; examples are cereals, legumes, and oil-seed crops.

cross-pollination The transfer of pollen between related taxa; often deliberately employed in an attempt to widen the gene base, i.e. introduce new genetic material into the resultant hybrid.

crumbs See soil crumbs

cultivar A cultivated variety arising from either a single species or a hybrid between species and selected for its desirable properties.

dioecious Having male and female flowers on different specimens.

esculent An item fit for food.

evapotranspiration The combined total of the water loss from the soil surface and the surfaces of the living plant(s) growing upon it.

feering The first or marker furrow made at the start of ploughing an area of ground.

field capacity The maximum amount of water that a freely draining soil holds against the pull of gravity.

flat A significant area of land within an open field.

frumentie/frumenty A dish of hulled wheat boiled in milk, sweetened and seasoned with spices.

garth An enclosed garden.

gas-water The liquid derived from the "washing" of coal gas by passing it through water to remove unwanted substances; some of these substances had insecticidal properties.

genotype The genetic make-up of an organism regardless of its appearance; in broad terms the nature of a specimen disregarding the effects of its nurture.

gore A triangular butt.

green manure Fresh plant material, specifically grown or crop debris, incorporated into soil to supply organic matter following its decomposition.

hand-barrow Flat topped stretcher on legs used in places unsuitable for wheelbarrows.

haulm The stems and leaves of various crop plants, generally used to describe such material when it represents a waste product at harvest.

headland The strip along the borders of a field on which tillage equipment is turned, typically cultivated last by working parallel to the field border.

heterozygous Having different alleles (forms of a given gene) at a particular gene locus; such plants are loosely referred to as "unfixed hybrids" which will not breed true.

hybrid A plant arising from the cross-fertilisation of two genetically distinct parents.

hypocotyl The transition zone that lies between the stem and the root in a seedling situated immediately below the cotyledons.

infield land The land nearest to a dwelling

inter-specific Between individuals of different species.

intra-specific Between individuals of the same species.

land An area of arable land of approximately half an acre.

landrace A primitive, often ancient crop plant cultivar; typically strongly heterozygous with a wide gene pool.

limiting factors The most deficient nutrient or component of the environment, and therefore the one that controls or prevents growth.

lount A strip of land separated from others by a ridge

macerated Fragmented, typically by vigorous stirring in water (referred to in cookery as "blitzing").

meristem A tissue in which cell division takes place, typically located in the stem and root tips and the cambium; hence "meristematic" describing tissue capable of such division.

messuage An ancient legal term for a dwelling with out-buildings and land.

microsite The immediate environment of a seed or plant whose conditions determine its wellbeing.

monoecious With male and female flowers on the same plant, the flowers being of separate sexes.

morphology The external form/shape of a plant (cf. anatomy).

oil cake The residue from the crushing of oil-bearing seeds compressed into a form suitable for stock feed.

outbreeding The crossing of distantly related individuals typically to widen the gene base (see cross-pollination).

overland Land on the margins of a common.

parcel An indistinct area of land.

ped Naturally occurring aggregation of soil particles found in a well-structured soil between whose cracks air and water move within the soil profile.

perennation The survival of a plant through a resting or dormant period, usually achieved through a specifically adapted organ, e.g. a bulb or corm.

permanent wilting point The degree of moisture in a soil at which a plant can no longer extract sufficient to sustain turgidity and ultimately life.

photosynthate The chemical product (compound) produced by photosynthesis other than water and oxygen; often used to embrace the carbohydrates so produced – first the sugars and then their derivatives such as starch.

photosynthesis The series of metabolic reactions that occur in green plants whereby organic compounds are synthesised by the reduction of carbon dioxide using the energy absorbed by chlorophyll from sunlight.

phytotoxic Poisonous to plants.

pit house A design of glasshouse with outer walls constructed partly below ground.

quillet A small plot or strip of land.

ramet An individual member of a clone, in agronomy often used to describe the fragments of a plant (stem, root or plantlet) used in the vegetative propagation of both weeds and cultivated plants.

ridge A strip in an open field.

rigg A raised area where sheaths were placed after harvesting.

roguing The removal of unwanted genetically or diseased off-types from a batch of plants.

rood A measure of land area approximately to 40 square poles.

rootball The soil-plus-roots that remain attached to a pot plant or transplant lifted from the open ground.

root/shoot ratio The comparison of the total amount of a plant found below and above ground.

rosary In this text, a rose garden.

rose A perforated cap fitted to the end of a watering can spout to produce a spray of water.

salicetum A planting of one or a collection of kinds of willow.

selion The basic unit within an open field; the strip of land.

shaduf A device for lifting water long used in the Middle East to supply irrigation channels.

shamba The Swahili word for a productive garden or smallholding.

shift A division of open fields to facilitate crop rotation.

shoddy The waste debris from the processing of wool, long used as an organic fertiliser.

shot A division of land within an open field.

soil crumb Naturally occurring aggregation of soil particles, the presence of which en masse is often referred to as "tilth" and is widely taken to indicate a good soil structure

soil moisture deficit The amount of water required to return a soil to field capacity.

sole The base of the plough body, situated behind the share, that slides along the bottom of the furrow.

stitch A strip or ridge of ploughed land between two furrows.

stomata The "breathing pores" in a leaf through which gases pass between the interior of the leaf and the external atmosphere.

taxon A unit of classification of any rank typically used to describe a recognisable set of individuals belonging to a species or sub-specific grouping.

terreau A French term describing the rich soil built up over time by deep cultivation and the addition of organic matter; most famously found in the market-gardens around large towns.

train oil Oil once derived from the processing of whale blubber; it was considered to have insecticidal properties; other light oils are still used and give fair results in the control of some stages in the life cycles of some pests.

undersowing The sowing of two crops on the same site; traditionally the lower undersowing would have been a grazing or forage crop and the taller "cover crop" a cereal.

understorey The vegetation growing below the tree canopy in a woodland

virgate An English land measure, typically 30 acres.

waste Uncultivated land situated beyond the arable fields surrounding a medieval village; regarded as common and used by all the villagers to graze their stock and in some cases gather such fuel as turf and furze.

went A portion of an open field separated by some barrier e.g. a road.

wick An enclosed piece of crop land.

wong A group of strips in the open field.

yardland A collection of strips under one management.

The arable fields of South Cambridgeshire at the end of the twentieth century. This study in intensive yet large-scale cultivation is based on an aerial photograph.

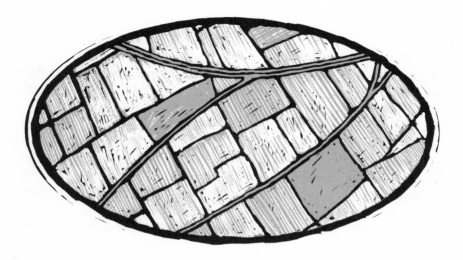

1 INTRODUCTION

Dem dat plants em is soon forgotten.
– *Ol' Man River*

This book celebrates man's skill in cultivating plants, an achievement upon which ninety-nine per cent of the world's population depends. From the start of the story some eleven thousand years ago agronomy in all its forms has been a long, slow process of increased understanding and the development of husbandry techniques. People tend to form their picture of man the cultivator depending on their background and interests. In the developed world, less than ten per cent of people grow anything and of those that do at least nine out of ten are amateur gardeners. The variously named professionals are spread over a wide range of locations: forests, arable farms, orchards, market-gardens, nurseries and glasshouses. At first glance they seem to have little in common with each other and even less to do with those who toil in suburban back gardens. I hope to show that in spite of the obvious differences in scale and equipment used the results are often very similar, and that the huge diversity of plants they grow have much the same basic needs and responses. This is not a social history, but no study of cultivation should disregard the cultivators, those countless generations of the ancestors of almost everyone alive today who tilled the land from childhood to old age. Inevitably in the story that follows it is the big names that get quoted, the famous agricultural scientists, the most progressive of the great landowners, the inventors of equipment and the owners of the most influential family firms. Before any of

1

these claim their place in the hall of fame let's pay our dues to the real men and women of the land, those who lived and died, typically in the humblest of circumstances within their society, with soil beneath their fingernails. This is their story too, the story of the countless generations of nameless peasants, cottage gardeners and farm labourers without whose skills civilisation could not have developed. Man's successful cultivation of plants over some eleven per cent of Earth's land surface is the worthy epitaph to their hardships and triumphs. It belongs as much to the Tolpuddle Martyrs as to their boyhood sovereign Farmer George.

The accompanying table is an attempt to put cultivation into its chronological place in the sequence of some of man's early major discoveries, based on developments in the Middle East. The dates for the domestication of plants and animals are those given by Professor Gordon Hillman. Professor Hillman and his team have spent over twenty years excavating and studying the tell at Abu Hureyra, an ancient settlement in Syria near Lake Assad on the Euphrates. Their work, which has skilfully brought together archaeology, palaeobotany, ethnobotany and ethnology, is referred to several times in this book. It has contributed much to our ideas on the origin of cultivation in the Middle East. The fruits of this work may be studied in depth in *Village on the Euphrates*. Other dates in the table also refer to developments in

CULTIVATION IN ITS CHRONOLOGICAL PLACE

Discovery	Years before present
First stone tools	>500,000
Use of fire	>400,000
Wooden spears	>300,000
Refinement of wood, bone and stone tools	500,0000 (onwards)
Cultivation of crop plants	**>11,000**
Domestication of dogs	>10,000
Construction of brick or stone walled buildings	10,000–9000
Domestication of sheep, goats and cattle	10,000
Pottery	>8000
Weaving using flax	7000
Basketry	7000
Wheel	5000
Metalworking	6000–5000
Writing	5000
Domestication of horses	4500

the Middle East from whence European civilisation spread. All are very approximate figures averaged from several sources.

Some writers on the theme of cultivation have concerned themselves mainly with technical developments, others have put a strong emphasis on the social and economic forces that appear to have stimulated and progressed change. Neither space nor expertise allows me to explore these underlying agencies in great depth but none of us should underestimate their pivotal role throughout man's conquest of the soil.

My main concern is with husbandry, which is the antithesis of the natural environment with its disinterested array of biotic [g] and abiotic [g] factors that make up the tools of Richard Dawkins's blind watchmaker. As wise Jane Wells Loudon wrote back in 1851, "When we [cultivators] attempt to imitate nature we should remember that the attempt is useless." Useless, let me add, on two counts: firstly we cannot do it, and secondly even if we could, with very few exceptions a return to nature would not produce the desired results.

As we know, in the myth of the Garden of Eden man did not have to cultivate; God did whatever was needed, for it is clear that the storytellers recognised that in this charmed habitat "someone" had overridden those natural forces against which they daily struggled in the real world.

Today the world faces a massive dilemma over how we use land. As a species we have become so numerous and so technically advanced that we have the power of life and death over virtually all other macroscopic life-forms. Historically we have "cherry-picked" across the globe, exploiting those sites that have most easily satisfied our social, industrial and agricultural needs.

Mankind has now reached virtually every branch and twig of that cherry tree; every fruit is within our grasp to the extent that we must face the awesome responsibility of being the stewards of the whole of the natural world. No wonder thinking people are so concerned about habitat and species conservation. But neither this concern nor a delight in the world's biodiversity and the scenery it helps create need blind us to man's triumph in discovering how to cultivate the crops of the field, forest and garden. We should remember that the very cultivation systems we have developed have produced their own much-loved national and regional landscape patterns. I despair at the division between "the greens" and "the cultivators". Both crop production and conservation are vital pursuits and I believe that my respect and enthusiasm for man's ability to cultivate land and produce crops is helped by my understanding of how plants grow in nature, and how both wild and cultivated plants are governed by the same "ecological dictates".

It may not be comfortable to see man's power over millions of other life-forms, but the truth is that we have already reached that terrifying responsibility for many of the larger-growing species of plant and animal. The husbandry of the future will inevitably have to embrace the stewardship of their homes by the way we manage both arable crop land and the pseudo-wild places of "our" nature reserves. Many of these sites are no longer stable ecosystems, so we will always have to "cultivate" them, albeit by covert means. If that sounds like something waiting in store for the distant future, it is not. That work is already under way every time a group of volunteers weeds out scrub on an English chalk downland reserve. Many people would go further than this and argue that room has to be made for "wildlife" around the edges and even within cropland. Such activities are actively encouraged by the Countryside Stewardship Scheme. Botanic gardens have for some years set up "biotopes" [g] in which they aim to establish and sustain a community of one or more species "growing as they would in the wild". Such areas can be successful but inevitably require the attention of skilled gardeners. Given such attention we should not be surprised at this success. As we will see later, both crop plants and weeds flourish under cultivation in locations far from their native homes.

Husbandry is the means by which cultivation is achieved. It encompasses man's efforts to adjust these conditions to the unique benefit of one species, the crop plant. We do this by adding or subtracting. Add more nutrients, add more water, subtract competing weeds, and subtract voracious caterpillars. In the wild, natural selection "uses" mutations to provide genotypes [g] more suited to their environment. In the same way, agronomists use plant breeding to produce cultivars [g] with a whole range of desirable traits. Nevertheless cultivation techniques can also change the shape and size of plants while carrying out the essential task of adjusting conditions to suit the crop.

The result of all this hard work enables people to grow plants on sites and in soils where they would fail in nature and to get far higher yields than the wild ancestors of our crops ever produced. By the time I was born in the mid 1930s British wheat farmers were getting a threefold increase compared with even the best wild stands gathered by our ancestors in the Middle East, an impressive figure but one that had taken over ten thousand years to achieve. Since then, mainly through the application of scientific research, increases have been truly staggering; in one lifetime yields have gone from 3 to 8 tonnes per hectare.

So what exactly is cultivation? Well surely there is no mystery here; most people with a back garden know what is involved. Every weekend throughout the growing season they deadhead the roses and edge the lawn or stake the runner beans. Fine: to have a prize-winning garden these tasks are important; but none of those kinds of activity get down to the really basic acts of husbandry that support plant growth, let alone make two blades of grass grow where one grew before.

Writing of basic acts prompts me to comment on the particular kinds of skill required. As with most crafts dexterity and good hand-to-eye coordination are high on the list, but above them I put judgement: judgement both to vary the treatment between individual plants or areas of a crop and above all to know when to set about a task and when to leave things as they are until another day if either the plants or the conditions are not right for the job. In 1813 Thomas Jefferson put it this way when discussing arable farm productivity with a friend:

> The spontaneous energies of the earth are a gift of nature, but they require the labor of man to direct their operation. And the question is so to husband his labor as to turn the greatest quantity of this useful action of the earth to his benefit.

In other words, natural forces are useful but they need our input to exploit them. The skill is to use your energy to get the maximum benefit from these natural processes.

I hope to show that cultivation touches our lives in many ways. But before setting off to the less obvious corners of this broad field I will identify the down-to-earth core of the craft, the main activities that together occupy most of a cultivator's working day world-wide, be he or she forester, farmer or horticulturist. In later chapters we will return to take a close look at each in turn. Of course none of the following activities are of any ultimate use unless the bit of plant you want can be harvested and as often as not stored. The story of harvesting and all the processes that follow it is outside the scope of this book unless the way it is done affects the subsequent growth of a perennial crop or the activity impinges on the husbandry of a following crop. What I am interested in here is the story of how we *grow* plants.

The near-universal acts of cultivation are:

Land drainage
Land tillage
Plant nutrition
Raising new stock by seed or vegetative means
Translocation – moving crop plants to new sites by sowing seed or transplanting
Crop spacing to control intra-specific [g] plant competition
Weed control to reduce inter-specific [g] plant competition
Irrigation
Plant manipulation by pruning and training
Control of pests and diseases.

To this list we must add two ancient and important man-made environments:

Cultivation in protected locations
Cultivation in containers

Most of these tasks appeared on the cultivator's worksheet very early on, if not at the very beginning of the story. As yet it is not possible to date the appearance of each, but what empirical evidence we have suggests that, as far as the Middle East is concerned, most if not all were being practised by the time urban settlements developed some five thousand years ago. They are still with us today, albeit no longer as hand-crafts but as highly mechanised crop production processes. Sometimes the changes from hand to machine have been slow, gradual developments with little altering on the ground for hundreds of years before a major innovation pushed the practice forward. I have in mind the cultivator's equivalent of "the great inventions that changed things forever", the kind of developments that used to be taught in elementary history classes and now make television programmes: the printing press, the spinning jenny and the steam engine.

The idea that the cultivator's equivalent of these breakthroughs had an instant impact on productivity is now regarded with suspicion by archaeologists and historians and it is certainly true

6

that agronomy, in common with most craft-based industries, has at times been slow to make very wide use of new knowledge, equipment and materials. Land workers, or more often their bosses, took time to adapt to each new way of working as it developed. In such ancient practices as irrigation and tillage, theory has now refined application but it lagged hundreds if not thousands of years behind their first use. In other areas such as the use of chemical fertilisers, herbicides, the biological control of pests, and the spacing of crops, it needed scientific research to improve our understanding before techniques could be successfully used in the field. Clearly the craft of cultivation is based on millennia of trial and error. As the following section indicates, it is only recently that these traditional practices have been influenced by scientific and technological developments to create modern agronomy.

SEMINAL EVENTS IN THE DEVELOPMENT OF CULTIVATION
Changes in cultivation have resulted from both discoveries that increased our understanding and inventions that directly impinged on working practices.

Although similar developments took place in other early centres of cultivation, the Middle East is recognised as the cradle of western agronomy, where, as already mentioned, cultivation is thought to have started around eleven thousand years ago, a date that has been revised backwards several times in the last half-century. With such remote origins it is not surprising that we are uncertain of both the dates and the sequence of introduction of the various practices. What is clear is that by 7000 to 5000 BP, when we have the first good evidence of agronomy as we now understand it, most of the basic activities noted above that together make up crop husbandry were being employed. It is very likely that by then they were already long and well established; however their use does not indicate an understanding of the reason why they were of value.

By early Roman times sophisticated husbandry and plant manipulation practices in both farming and gardening were well advanced and many of the hand-tools we know today had been invented. Britain's cultivation history is unusual in that many practices in agriculture and even more in horticulture were introduced by the Romans, but lost with their withdrawal only to be reintroduced, or in some cases reinvented, centuries later. The accompanying table groups the appearance of materials, methods, tools and equipment in the archaeological and/or historic record into three periods.

APPEARANCE OF MATERIALS, METHODS, TOOLS AND EQUIPMENT
IN THE ARCHAEOLOGICAL AND/OR HISTORIC RECORD

First evidence of cultivated plants in Middle East (c. 11,000 BP)
  Translocation: seed-sowing and crop-planting

Cultivation activities evident from first "civilisations" (c. 6000 BP)
  Sowing of stored seed
  Broadcasting seed into prepared seedbeds
  Vegetative propagation, including the use of tubers, rhizomes,
    cuttings and graftage
  Use of tillage hand-tools
  Ploughing by ard (primitive plough) using draught animals
  Use of organic manures
  Early forms of irrigation including use of water-lifting devices
  Hand-weeding
  Control of some pests
  Plant manipulation by pruning and training

Developments by or during classical times (c. 3000–2000 BP)
  Provision of well-designed seed stores
  Surface and simple subterranean land-drains
  Early form of mouldboard plough
  Spacing of crop plants
  Use of naturally occurring mineral fertilisers
  Inter-row cultivation by hoe
  Early forms of protected cultivation
  Cultivation in containers.

From this time on, progress was based not on new activities but on the introduction of improved equipment with which to do time-honoured tasks. This was a slow process. Even the seventeenth-to-nineteenth-century "revolution" in agriculture and commercial horticulture, with its changes to field patterns, cropping sequences, improved land drainage and the appearance of the seed drill, was primarily a socio-economic event. Indeed to those looking over the farm gate poor Hodge seemed to be doing what he had done for centuries and often with the same kinds of hand-tools. The real *cultivation* revolution took place in the mid twentieth century through mechanisation and the development of new materials. In a few short years it almost eliminated handwork and its associated skills to such an extent that hardly a trace of the old ways remains.

It is these that have resulted in huge increases in crop yield but also in disquiet as to their impact on matters as wide-ranging as the scenery, ecology and way of life of the countryside. These advances were closely linked with scientific progress. Developments in many fields from genetics and plant physiology to chemistry, entomology, pathology and metallurgy have all contributed both to the availability of novel aids and, through deeper understanding, to the better use of old skills. Many of the plethora of novelties that have come (and often gone) during the last 250 years are mentioned in the relevant chapters of this book. Setting precise dates against them is fraught with difficulties. The first appearance of items other than scientific discoveries and patented inventions cannot always be established, whilst even the approximate date when such introductions started to make a significant impact on practice varied greatly from place to place.

THE IMPACT OF CULTIVATION ON NATURE AND LANDSCAPE
The real landmarks

> The farm lands of England today are the work, literally, of men's hands. They represent the subjugation of nature by man, the result of an immense and continuous struggle carried on through the centuries, often with inadequate weapons and at a cost that it is impossible to measure. The struggle, once begun, has been and must always be continuous, for land in a state suitable for the practice of agriculture and horticulture is something entirely artificial, and Nature, never finally cowed, is ever awaiting the opportunity to shake herself free, to throw off the costume of civilisation in which man has clothed her, so that she may resume, once again, her first covering of woodland, water, and wild grass.
>
> – J. R. Bond, *Farm Implements and Machinery*

Bond may have used the poetic language of yesteryear but he understood both the British countryside and the nature of agronomy. What a contrast to Geoffrey and Susan Jellicoe's approach in *The Landscape of Man*. It is extraordinary to me that a book subtitled "Shaping the Environment from Prehistory to the Present Day" hardly mentions the impact of agronomy on our world. Perhaps it is a reflection of just how urban we have become. With little more than one per cent of the population of the developed world engaged in crop production the impact of cultivation on the lives of most people is through its effect on the scenery they traverse on their way to and from work or enjoy on holiday. There are however great designers who do approach the landscape with a greater understanding of the agronomist, and one such was Dame Sylvia Crowe. In *The Pattern of Landscape* she and her co-author Mary Mitchell expressed exactly such empathy for the cultivator's relationship with the land and the patterns it produces. The following quotations are taken from captions to the superb photographs in this deeply thoughtful book:

> Past generations of Englishmen, knowing the qualities of their land and careful for the continuity of its fertility, laid out their fields in sympathy with contours, soil and climate.

> Geometry, imposed by agricultural man, can create a patterned landscape giving character to the land.

> [I]t is possible for intensive use by men to produce a landscape of quality and lasting fertility.

So how would today's students of that study area where land use, plant geography and ecology come together express Mr Bond's thoughts on the British countryside? Surely they would note that cultivation has resulted in a huge reduction in the extent of several kinds of habitat and their characteristic species from native forest to wetland, heath and chalk downland; but a balanced commentator would point out that much of this change took place thousands of years ago and that by 1651 when John Ray made the first botanising excursions around Cambridge he was visiting mere fragments of wildscape and on many days none at all. Distribution maps in the *New Atlas of the British and Irish Flora* show our vegetation to be made up of a relatively small number of very common species that are found throughout the country and a much larger number of more uncommon species. Many of these are restricted to specific, small and scattered semi-natural and natural habitats. Any loss of any of these sites means the loss of their inhabitants, representatives of precisely those species that occur in small numbers.

The "artificial" habitat that each style of cultivation produced was aimed at providing the best conditions possible, as they were then understood, for just one plant – the crop – while the subsequent husbandry practices attempted to eliminate the competition from all other species to produce a pure stand. Today's ecologists would describe these activities as destruction of the "original" biodiversity. Quite so, but once the cultivators cleared the land and embarked on the operations discussed in this book they produced a "managed landscape" that offered opportunities for species that had previously had little chance to prosper. The same holds good within gardens; almost every lawn provides a home for the daisy but very few natural grasslands do. Taken together these successful species are the cultivator's weeds and the naturalist's "wild flowers"; not all are however truly native: a considerable number were accidentally introduced, mostly by farmers and gardeners! For millennia they held their own as commonplace members of our flora, some within the fields, many others in the man-made edge habitats such as verges, headlands, walls, hedges, banks and ditches. It is only in the last few decades with the increasing power of contemporary agronomy that anyone, from layman to ecologist, has seen the need to call for their protection; this must be done, sometimes for the good of other species because of the part the plants play in the ecosystem, sometimes because they are themselves becoming rare as a result of contemporary crop production and land management methods.

This short chapter does little more than touch on some very large and complex issues ranging from the origin and evolution of our lowland landscape to the drama of some of the world's large-scale farming systems. In a world in which vast tracts of arable land totalling some one thousand million hectares are producing crops it is inevitable that agronomists have had a major impact on the scenery we live in. In spite of all our civil engineering and large-scale industrial works the farmer remains the person that has by far the greatest impact on the landscape and endlessly re-forms that view from the car, train or aeroplane. We live in a cultivated landscape.

Perhaps as a reaction to this, holiday-makers and film-makers endlessly search for the wild and the remote. This near veneration of a world unsullied by man is laudable, but we may be in danger of loosing our long-held appreciation of the home-made, indeed handmade, agrarian heritage William Cobbett so loved. But such feelings go back far beyond the eighteenth century; as Simon Schama puts it in *Landscape and Memory*, "For a Roman the sign of a pleasing landscape was necessarily that which had been formed, upon which man had left his civilizing and fructifying mark." Sophisticated urban Romans may have thought themselves far above the rustics living in the vast stretches of country that lay within the empire, but the real division came at the frontier. It was here that both farming and the rule of Rome gave way to hunting and gathering barbarians living in what Tacitus damned as "*informem terris*", a shapeless, dismal land.

A few crops such as hops and conifer plantations are grown in such a way that their presence in the landscape is instantly recognisable. It would however be wrong to add too many crops to this list of indelible pattern makers. Production methods and the patterns they make change from place to place and from time to time. The wheat lands of the prairies could never be confused with the cereal fields of southern Italy. The geometry of a modern intensive apple plantation has little in common with the traditional Kentish orchard. Spanish vineyards look nothing like the desert grape fields of South Africa, and few brought up among the market-gardens of the Vale of Evesham would believe their eyes on first seeing a Californian lettuce "ranch"!

Like a painting in which an artist has reworked a detail but left other parts of his canvas unaltered, today's scenery is a patchwork record of agricultural history. I leave to such authorities as Christopher Taylor the field-by-field interpretation of that landscape, set as it has been in the social structure of its makers' lives. My aim is to remind us of the links between today's landscape and the history of crop cultivation: those crops that sustained our ancestors, and those that do so to this day.

Of all man's activities the keeping of domestic animals must have had the greatest impact on the world's landscape. Herded together, our livestock have grazed and browsed their way through huge areas of the world's flora, turning woods to grassland and scrub to desert. The graziers themselves may have had an even greater impact by their use of fire, axe and plough to provide better and more nutritional herbage. Recent research suggests they long ago changed the face of huge areas of Australia and the prairies of North America, whilst today the rainforests of South America are being turned into treeless cattle ranches.

FIELD PATTERNS

Sylvia Crowe and Mary Mitchell chose a photograph of arable fields for the cover of *The Pattern of Landscape*. Throughout the

12

book they remind us that the patterns made by the agronomist are key to our appreciation of much of the scenery of the inhabited world, providing, they suggest, an emotional bridge between the works of nature and mankind.

In spite of the graziers' impact, much of the view from the car or train window in rural areas of both the developed and the Third World is formed by arable and tree crops and the specific husbandry practices used to grow them. Productive land use typically starts with the painstaking clearance of the wild vegetation to create the space to plant and sow. The scale, thoroughness, permanence and shape of these clearings varies from place to place. In long-settled parts of the world one might expect to find that the first field patterns have long since disappeared, swept away by changes in farming practice. To the casual observer this is perhaps so – but cultivation leaves remarkably persistent traces. Many ancient field patterns are detectable by today's archaeologists and some, from the air, are clear to even the untrained eye, if conditions are right.

Land use in Britain faces an uncertain future. At the start of the new millennium there are around five million hectares of arable land, predominantly in the South and East with less in the cooler, wetter uplands of the North and West. Experts can still find traces of the boundaries and field patterns of at least five periods of arable land management spread over more than four thousand years. In general the older examples survive only as strong three-dimensional features in places avoided by subsequent arable farmers, while the best land is reworked over and over again. Very occasionally a new style of farming fits comfortably into a past layout and sometimes circumstances arise that redefine "best" land, as has happened on Salisbury Plain which after a rest of a thousand years has recently returned to growing cereal crops.

Apart from the obvious, massive change from woodland to pasture and arable fields, the first three thousand years of Britain's farming landscape takes a bit of finding. Perhaps the earliest landmarks are in the form of the mysterious parallel lines of the stone banks known as "reaves" visible on southern Dartmoor. Much more widespread but still needing a keen eye to find even from the air are the Neolithic, Bronze Age and Iron Age patches of cultivated land known to the layman collectively as "Celtic Fields", or as they are now called on Ordnance Survey maps, "ancient field systems". Considering the length of time these field systems span it is not surprising that they show variations in size and form; nevertheless most are small, neat, square or rectilinear features covering from a fifth to one and a half hectares. A square plan was logical for arable fields because the custom, as we shall see later, was to plough both ways, up and down and across the field. Some are particularly well preserved on the Land's End peninsula but their traces can be found, often with the aid of aerial photographs, scattered over thousands of hectares of chalk downland, heath and moor throughout Britain.

In spite of, or perhaps in some areas because of, their enthusiasm for order and their well-known liking for straight roads, the Romans left many of our fields much as they found them. Indeed in most parts of the country you need to go to areas they brought under the plough for the first time to see even a trace of their field layouts. The Fens qualify, but all that remains are crop marks within today's massive fields of our most industrialised arable farming.

Archaeological evidence suggests that a typical Romano-British villa estate's intensive cropping area had a field layout reminiscent of bonded brickwork, with mainly straight boundary hedges, fences or stone walls. However while "Roman order" was no doubt followed within the estate boundaries it seems much of the arable land around Romano-British homesteads continued to be cultivated without massive changes to farming methods, although it has been suggested that fields tended to get larger and somewhat more symmetrical. Following the withdrawal of Roman authority, this tenacity for the old ways of farming seems once again to have held good.

The Romans' successors the Saxons left us few agricultural features that we can easily detect as uniquely characteristic of the first half of their tenure. That being the case, we may pass forward to the later period of Saxon rule and one of the truly great upheavals that reshaped much of our countryside, particularly in the Midlands. This was the change that swept away those small, clearly defined fields to produce the open or common fields that dominated the landscape round thousands of English villages for between six and eight hundred years. Such "land-marks" as have survived give us an outline of the farming system that filled the people's breadbaskets but not what went into the stewpot to produce that ubiquitous medieval dietary item, pottage. The peasants grew their vegetables for that basic dish within their messuages [g] on the small areas of land surrounding their houses or, in the vernacular, the tofts around their cots. As William Langland tells us, his fourteenth-century fictional character Piers Plowman had "parsley, leeks and many cabbages". Truth to tell, England's famed "cottage gardens", with all their floral delights, started life as a place for the pig, privy and peas.

The fragments we now find of this revolution in farming are not field boundaries but the undulating surface of the ploughland appearing within later fields as the ridge-and-furrow patterns of those long-gone medieval "open fields". After centuries of use and custom it must have seemed that these were as permanent as the topography on which they sat, but eventually, at some point over a period of several hundred years, the geometry of enclosed fields returned to enfold our villages. It would be an exaggeration to add "as they had been before, during and after Roman times", because the second time around they were larger. Nevertheless their boundaries were definitely a case of déjà vu; back came the hedges and walls, the one trained and the other constructed just as they were first time around!

There is a strong, practical link between field shape and use. For more than a thousand years across Northern Europe the mouldboard plough, drawn by teams of oxen or horses, prepared the land for arable crops. Turning such teams is both laborious and time-wasting, so they work best when drawing long, reasonably straight furrows. Almost certainly these considerations produced long, and when small, narrow fields, typified by the oft mentioned but far less frequently found one-acre plot being "one chain wide by one furlong long" (22 by 220 yards), a ratio of 1:10. Similar field shapes still dominate the landscape of other parts of Europe such as North Belgium and the Rzeszow district in Poland but are rare in Britain, as, in part, the aerial views that make up the millennium publication *England The Photographic Atlas* reveal. British fields including those of great antiquity derived from assarting [g] – a farmer's piecemeal efforts to bring more "waste" [g] woodland, fen or heath into cultivation – tend to have irregular outlines but are roughly square, while the enclosures typically ignored the old

15

furlongs of the open fields to produce straight-sided fields mostly large enough for efficient cultivation with a width-to-length ratio no greater than 1:2. It would seem that, perhaps based on our enthusiasm for mixed farming, the best interests of stock-keeping have influenced both the shape and size of our fields as well as the need for stock-proof boundaries.

In 1652 Walter Blith saw wholesale field enclosure as an essential precursor to his ideas for agricultural improvement. No doubt he would have wished "The Right Honourable The Lord General Cromwell" to whom he addresses his writings to sweep away the ancient system of open fields over night. In reality it turned out to be a very slow process but eventually it became the most tangible feature of the so-called agricultural revolution of the seventeenth and eighteenth centuries.

The landscape of about three thousand parishes, mainly those across a broad diagonal strip from Hampshire to Lincolnshire, was completely changed as their massive open fields were divided by thorn hedges into rectilinear blocks. However much we may shake our heads at the apparently "crazy" system embedded in the layout of the common fields and however much we may see the laying out of the rectangular fields following enclosure as a necessary precursor to agricultural development, we should never forget the cost in human happiness and dignity in the later stages of the movement. The way of life of the rural poor in village after village vanished overnight, as the most traumatic event since the Black Death reached their community, their feelings summarised in poignant verse:

> The law condemns both man and woman
>   who steals a goose from off the common,
> But lets the greater robber loose
>   who steals the common from the goose.

The latest but surely not the last change in arable farming practice has removed many of those hedges to once more create huge sweeps of open land set out for mechanical cropping.

The details of this remarkable story of the making of lowland Europe's scenery I leave to such experts as the late Professor W. G. Hoskins and more recent authorities such as David Hall, Oliver Rackham and Christopher Taylor, all of whose writings have helped me to scratch the surface of this fascinating subject. With the notable exception of the origin of the open-field system

16

their years of rigorous research have provided many of the answers as to the motives, methods and consequences of our ancestors laying out their farms the way they did. Leaving aside the hugely significant social and economic factors and barefaced avarice to focus solely on the impact that enclosure had on arable farming, several things become clear. Of these, two seem to me to be of particular importance. Enclosure segregated livestock and crops; from then on, stock set foot on arable fields only if and when it suited the cropping programme, for example to graze on a short-term ley, to eat roots in winter or to manure folds. Enclosure created distinct fields whose boundaries effectively "packaged" crops. From then on, within the rotation, each year each crop had a location and each location had a name. Each field was a defined, discrete area of land whose history and characteristics were known and could be taken into account when locating crops and carrying out both preparatory and standing crop husbandry, knowledge that proved to be extremely valuable in maximising yield.

We now have a good idea of the scale of the manual work involved in creating these fields, particularly the soil-shifting and bank-, hedge- and wall-building. There is an irony here, as the more we learn the more awesome the achievement seems to be until our very understanding almost beggars belief. Having said that, a word of caution is in order; not every hedge-bank owes its origin to the sweat of the landworker's brow. The high banks framing deep-set country lanes in hilly districts were typically produced by erosion as rainwater washed away the mud churned up by farm carts. The often significant banks running across a hillside that mark a sharp change of level between arable fields may owe something to the turn of the mouldboard plough but much more to soil creep – a phrase describing the slow migration of soil down even gently sloping ploughland. A combination of wall or hedge and the long grass of the field margin trap these soil particles until over time a drop which can be well over a metre develops between fields.

In Britain and Northern Europe the boundaries that define field shapes and sizes produce some very contrasting landscapes. Perhaps the most striking difference is between those described by the French-derived terms "bocage" and "champion" (hedged and hedgeless) – a contrast brought home to the British in 1944 when the deep-set lanes and high-banked hedges of the

17

Normandy bocage became a series of tank-traps facing the invading Allied army.

Field patterns tend to fall into three classes: the geometric, the informal, and, as ever, some in-between. One might almost describe them as the shaped and the shapeless. Known as "regular", "semi-regular" and "irregular", they turn out to be diagnostic guides, telling those who can read them which of our various ancestors were the last to set out the basic layout of the landscape in question. I say "last" because over large areas of Britain fieldscapes have been redrawn several times or at least modified by the demands of an ever-changing agriculture, not least very recently by the removal of hedges. Diligent searching can sometimes reveal rather small, regular-shaped fields with more or less straight sides and right-angled corners lying around the heart of a settlement whereas the surrounding fields have irregular boundaries. Typically the inner fields were set out on previously cleared land, whereas the outer fields are the result of "assarting". On a larger scale this contrast between the regular and the irregular creates the strong regional characters so magnificently shown in *England The Photographic Atlas*. It is clear at a glance that field shape and size contribute hugely to the difference between the respective landscapes of Lincolnshire and Sussex or Northamptonshire and Kent.

FIELD BOUNDARIES

Field boundaries that defined our past farming practices are by far the strongest man-made image in the agricultural landscape. They more than any other feature store our farming history and create regional character. Their longevity has made them a rich source of information for social historians.

My interest in field boundaries is, of course, based on their role in the story of cultivation. Those that remain in use come in many forms; there are ditches, either with or without banks, walls of various styles, and hedges and shelter-belts. In 1985 the Countryside Commission surveyed these various types of field boundary in England and Wales for both their length – measured in kilometres per square kilometre of land – and their distribution. After what must have been a Herculean task the data showed that hedges, with a total length of over six hundred thousand kilometres, are by far our most common field boundary.

It seems there are most hedges in the North-East and fewest in the South-East; it was much the same story for stone walls and yet again the South-East had fewest banks but this time it was the South-West that dominated, as anyone who has tried to negotiate the Cornish lanes will have guessed. Of course a lot of these regional differences must be influenced at least as much by field size as by local custom.

Such boundaries may seem exclusively related to stock-keeping, but arable farming has also had an influence. Ditches were an essential part of most drainage systems. They have to be dug to a gentle fall if they are to carry the water quickly away without causing erosion. Their need to run downhill, and the location of a suitable outfall, often defines the long axis of a field. The drainage waterways of some of our flat lowland areas such as the East Anglian Fens and the Somerset Levels are the strongest pattern-makers in otherwise rather featureless landscapes.

Hedges, one might assume, were established to contain animals. Just so, but go and stand on the other side; from that point of view they border arable land to keep stock out of crops. Therein is the clue: regardless of the historical period these strong boundaries were essential to mixed farming.

In exposed sites, hedges as well as shelter-belts provide protection and markedly influence a field's microclimate. For crops this is a matter not so much of temperature as of shelter from wind and storm, as A. D. C. Le Sueur pointed out in his still relevant book first published in 1951: "The small fields of West Cornwall that produce the very earliest crops of flowers and vegetables shelter behind high hedges of such exotics as Escallonia and Elaeagnus." The Experimental Horticultural Station at Rosewarne in Cornwall, sadly now closed, did valuable research into shelter and quantified its very significant benefits. Far to the east, the orchards and hop gardens of Kent are screened by plantings that might be described as either the tallest working hedges in the country or the narrowest of shelter-belts.

Hedges are themselves cultivated. For the past two hundred years new ones will have been planted, although earlier examples may be the result of woody plants colonising protected field boundaries, the only bit of land left to them.

Once hedges are established their cutting becomes one of the farm's seasonal tasks. The way this was done varied from place to place and time to time, but it is fair to say that the classic treatment was "plashing" or "laying" as it has become known, a major undertaking traditionally tackled only every 8 to 10 years. Arthur Young, writing in 1804, claims that Hertfordshire farmers excelled in the craft and devotes five pages and seven illustrations to a step-by-step description of their method. This involves the part severance of stems of several years' growth, trimming their side-shoots then pulling them down and securing them as a stock-proof boundary. The stems respond as their auxins [g] tell them they must: by producing upright growing shoots along their length which serve to reinforce the barrier. It is costly work and has been replaced by tractor-mounted cutting. Done with skill on a regular basis, mechanical hedge-cutting gives a useful, good-looking result; done badly and it is about the ugliest manifestation of mechanised farming.

Hedges can be surprisingly old. As landscape features some are thought to go back more than a thousand years, and the plants that form them can be as ancient. Some shrubs are perpetuated as coppice, which seems able to render specimens of some species almost immortal, and others keep going as a clone by producing suckers. Even the hedgerow herbs from bluebells to dog's mercury can be the descendants of individuals that arrived as refugees from nearby woodland which probably vanished centuries ago.

PATTERNS IN THE SOIL

Terraces, often surviving from ancient cultivation practices, are a very special set of features and still make a strong impact on the landscape. To grow their crops civilisations round the world have terraced hillsides, more or less round the contour. Most terraces such as those of South America and the Mediterranean lands were constructed to prevent soil erosion, aid irrigation and in the most extreme cases to hold just enough soil to establish a tree or a few cereal plants.

Ground levelling still goes on, in some cases on a massive scale using terracing blades fitted to huge tractors and in others to grade the land into the best shape for some of the most valuable horticultural crops. Constructing retaining walls is usually far beyond the economics of today's commercial cropping, so it is not surprising that we rarely get a chance to see cultivation terraces constructed. The Eden Project in Cornwall used massive machines, to move some 1.8 million tonnes of material to terrace a 16-hectare claypit. Visitors marvel at the results, but it has made those of us who experienced it first-hand respect our ancestors' achievements in rock-carting, soil-shifting and wall-building – handwork and animal power that together sculpted whole hillsides in South America, Asia, and around the Mediterranean Basin.

The cultivation of one crop in particular demands almost absolute precision: wetland rice. Traditional rice-growing needed flooded fields for the first half of the crop's life after which the land was allowed to dry out prior to harvest. The rice paddies of South-East Asia are one of the wonders of the pre-industrial world and must surely be the largest example of the old adage, "Form follows function", and that splendid German word for "a landscape strongly influenced by human effort to make it more useful": *"Kulturlandschaft"*! In English we use the direct translation "cultural landscape". The human effort that formed it across the whole of Europe from the Highlands of Scotland to the tip of Sicily was, and still is, predominantly that of some 150 generations of agronomists.

Britain has few massive agronomic earthworks or retaining walls, but our past farmers left their mark on the land in the form of more subtle humps and hollows, three-dimensional patterns in the soil that remind me of giant earth sculptures. Those by far the most common are known as "ridge and furrow", others as "lynchets" and some books manage to confuse the two! Both survive where arable lands were turned over to grazing, preserving the tillage patterns of earlier regimes of land tenure.

Lynchets are the less common but the more dramatic. Hoskins describes them as "remarkable patterns of ancient cultivation terraces". They are etched into the gently rolling hillsides of several parts of the country, including my adopted county of Wiltshire and neighbouring Dorset; one of the most spectacular and easily accessible sites is cut into the hillsides just to the north of Mere while another prime example appears as a series of giant steps edging the Ridgeway above the village of Bishopstone. For those who do their sightseeing from their cars, several series are visible from the minor road between Devizes and Pewsey. Terrace width depends on the steepness of the hillside; the risers are often over four metres high, their slope determined by the angle of repose of the local soil.

For the layman it is easy to confuse lynchets with the ramparts of the "Iron Age hill-forts" of Wessex, but these are of agricultural not military origin. The usual explanation for their construction argues that over hundreds of years medieval farmers ploughed these hillsides in strips usually along the contour. Their early mouldboard ploughs were always set to throw the soil downhill, digging into the slope at the top-side of the developing terrace and depositing extra soil along the down-side. Over time this modest movement of the surface soil could, it is argued, have produced steps down the hillside. The majority of these impressive structures are said by many writers to have medieval origins, having been started whenever the pressure for crop land became extreme enough to force the cultivators off the valley floor.

So much for explanations found in most texts. The more my colleague Peter McLoughlin and I looked at these impressive earthworks the more such explanations appeared to a down-to-earth engineer and an even more earthy horticulturist to be both impractical and lacking in common sense. It seemed hard to believe that such structures could have been formed without some initial deliberate effort at terracing aided no doubt by the kind of soil creep discussed above. To my great relief our doubts are brilliantly expounded in the appendix at the back of the third edition of *The Open Fields* by C. S. and C. S. Orwin. There seems more to making a lynchet than even the most stoic medieval ploughman could manage. Once started, the terraces continued to be cultivated along the same lines, although presumably getting slightly wider year by year. Most returned to permanent pasture but even today a few still carry crops of cereals, the combine harvesters following the field layout set more than a thousand years ago.

The place Peter took me to see ridge and furrow at its best was Edge Hill and the surrounding district, where Oxfordshire, Warwickshire and Northamptonshire meet, however almost any railway journey across the English Midlands will produce views of ridge and furrow. In medieval times this "champaign" landscape was predominately arable; with its near-level vales and gently rolling hills it was at the heart of the open-field system in England. This is roughly the area that Oliver Rackham terms "planned countryside". You might even call it "twice-planned", as it fell victim first to the still little-understood force that cast it into the wide sweeps of the open fields, and then to the enclosures that reinstated a field pattern. To its east and west lay further large areas of open fields, but here the ploughmen rarely chose to form these remarkable corrugations and away from the Midland Plane open-field farming was interspersed with great tracts of "ancient countryside", whose irregular fields and narrow lanes are still with us, having generally avoided the first upheaval and hence also the second.

It is very clear that the practice of ridge and furrow deliberately used the action of the mouldboard plough to create undulations on arable fields, indeed far from producing terraces in some cases the pattern these ploughmen left behind tends to run obliquely up and down slopes, while both contemporary maps and aerial photographs show the ridges within adjacent blocks of land at right-angles to each other. Ridge and furrow seems to have become a very loose term used to describe several different shapes in the landscape. However when used precisely it refers to the undulations resulting from the medieval practice of a ploughman repeatedly setting out his work in the same series of narrow "plough-lands". Working outwards from each centre-line the action of the mouldboard resulted in the soil slowly migrating to form a central ridge and a deep permanent furrow down each side.

As Hoskins puts it, "The ancient pattern of medieval and Saxon open fields is fossilised so to speak under grass when sheep and cattle pastures were created between the fifteenth and seventeenth centuries." And, one might add, if it has avoided the conversion to arable cropping so profitable in the second half of the twentieth century.

The open fields Hoskins refers to are those huge stretches of ploughland that surrounded villages in many parts of Europe during the Middle Ages. Within this general term sat the "common fields". They were the arable lands of a village held under feudal law and managed locally, typically through manorial authority, as single cropping units, albeit they were made up of scores of strips in the hands of dozens of individual farmers. Under such law occupiers owed service to their lord, which typically included periods of work on the demesne lands. It was the same picture in lowland Scotland, with huge areas of open fields divided into strips under the "runrig" system of land management. Here the strips or "rigs" of the "inbye" or land nearest to the houses were intensively cropped while the larger "outbay" was mainly down to grazing.

The "strip" was a basic unit of medieval land occupation, sometimes quoted as having had a "typical" width of 22 yards and a furrow length (a furlong), of 220 yards, hence an area of one acre. Confusingly, a number of these strips lying side by side were also referred to as a furlong, making this the second order of land area within the largest unit, the "field".

More critical studies show great variation in both the width and length of strips, probably because of a mixture of local custom and the lie of the land. To take one example, the 1613 map of Horsley in Northumberland, halfway between Corbridge and Newcastle, shows only around 20 per cent the strips approximating to a furlong in length. The great majority of the remainder are significantly shorter and only a very few are longer. Across the country, regardless of their exact length, strips were typically many times longer than they were broad, in contrast to earlier squarer fields. This change was probably linked to the shift from cultivating both ways (cross-ploughing) to ploughing only up and down the field's long axis.

There is far less random variation in the width between furrows. Indeed it could be argued that ridge-and-furrow cultivation was based on a "unit" of 5.5 yards, a figure we shall meet again on pages 250 and 271. This was the distance between ridge crests of the "narrow" ridge and furrow such as some we have near my village in Wiltshire. Many in the Midland counties are twice that width at 11 yards across. The Horsley map reveals that, at least in that village, "a strip" could be as narrow as one ridge 5.5 yards wide. We know this because in part of one field 14 farmers worked the 23 strips shown, so some must have cultivated only one and, when measured, all show a uniform width of 5.5 yards. Surviving ridge widths, as seen so clearly from the air, tend to be uniform over the ploughland of a village, perhaps because of local soil conditions. Maps, however, typically show wide and narrow strips, suggesting that some strips carried more than one ridge.

Subsequent activities have usually left us with only a fraction of the whole picture fossilised beneath pasture. Nevertheless there remains enough evidence on the ground to show something of this remarkable story.

Some historians seem particularly attracted by ridge-and-furrow patterns that carry the telltale signature of a rather stretched reverse "S". This shape is said to have helped ploughmen steer their oxen round narrow headlands as they turned to plough the next furrow. However these reversed-S shapes are by no means universal and an ox team's turning circle cannot be the explanation for the very many examples of curved ridge and furrow that strike off at right-angles from each headland. I suggest that many of the curved furrows are simply a ploughman's compromise when he wished to follow two mutually exclusive traditions: setting out at right-angles from a headland and yet ploughing the shortest distance to the opposite side of the field.

If the ploughman sets out at approximately ninety degrees to the headland in a field whose sides are not parallel he must swing his plough team back on track if he is to achieve a direct crossing. The same set of conditions and constraints apply as he returns across the field. Such manoeuvres produce a curved furrow track. The curve would be slight on a field one furlong across, even when the two sides are out of parallel by as much as thirty degrees.

Why did they produce ridge and furrow? Not I think because they could not work out a way of preventing it from happening! These undulations have been linked to the demarcation of land "ownership" or tenure. No doubt ridge-spans, or their multiples, conveniently marked out the width of a strip, making it easier to find your own patch in an otherwise featureless open field. In the absence of ridge and furrow, confusion through the loss of strip markers was common, according to Rowland Parker in his remarkable book *The Common Stream*, which chronicles medieval life in the Cambridgeshire village of Foxton. His reading of the court rolls of the Chatteris Manor shows that their disappearance was not always accidental, certainly not in the case of William Cassandre, who was charged with moving a boundary mark in spite of it having been "placed by agreement of the court". William was clearly not an ideal neighbour and nor was Peter Clark, who apparently made no amends for a 4-foot (1.25m) encroachment "despite many previous orders". The widths of egress that came before this manorial court seem trivial, ranging from 1 to 4 feet (0.3 to 1.25m), but as a percentage of one of these long, narrow strips was not insignificant. John Rayner, however, must have been *the* neighbour from Hell. His transgressions between 1543 and 1576 included the removal of several strip markers and no less than twelve trespasses with the plough.

Though ridge and furrow helped to prevent such sharp practices, I would join with most writers with close links to the land who consider the logical explanation for it to have been linked to soil moisture. Medieval British farmers had no well-developed system of irrigation or of subterranean land drainage, so both dry and wet years could lead to extremely serious crop reductions. Moulding the fields into ridges and furrows following the undulating lie of the land drained off surface water. It also helps explain why extensive areas of ridge and furrow do not have all the ridges running the same way but form a patchwork of blocks of land.

Of course ridges dry out much faster than furrows, which gave the farmers two choices. If they sowed the whole area with the same crop the furrows did well in a dry year, the ridges in a wet one. The other approach was to sow a ridge crop and a furrow crop. This may seem a far-fetched idea, but it was still being suggested in the early part of the twentieth century, i.e. winter wheat on the tops, spring in the furrows.

We may think the first option a poor answer with half the field performing below par most years, but it is just the way pre-industrial and subsistence farming operates. Waterlogged soil is lethal to most crops and in the days before land drainage seventeenth- and eighteenth-century husbandry texts recommend creating ridges before planting fruit trees and hops. *A Treatise of Agriculture,* written in 1769 for Scottish farmers, recommends sowing turnip, carrot and parsnip only along the crest of ridges. At this time these were novel field crops in Scotland and the book's author turns to the Auld Alliance for support from the writings of M. Le Bretagne based on his experiences in France. Throughout the nineteenth century, turnip seed-drills continued to be designed with a curved roller to straddle shallow ridges set about 0.5m apart, and sow a single row of seed on their crests.

Anyone who doubts the significance of such slight changes in topography to plants should make a spring visit to a ridge-and-furrow field on low-lying clay soil. Buttercups and daises occupy respectively furrows and ridges just as if planted there.

Many such low-lying ridge-and-furrow sites are water meadows, their furrows being the ends of a system of channels linking back to a stream that allowed a farmer to flood the area. The practice was well established by the early years of the seventeenth century when, appropriately enough, the Honourable Henrie Hastings persuaded his tenants in the manor of Puddletown in Dorset to come together to carry out the necessary work.

In spring the water temperature was slightly higher than that of the soil, which both encouraged the all-important "early bite" and protected the young grass from late frosts. Spring grass allowed the farm to carry a larger flock of sheep that in turn provided more manure for the arable crops. In all this was a great example of the integration that is at the heart of well-managed mixed farming.

Cultivation, particularly using today's powerful equipment, can of course destroy these undulations. But it can also reveal traces of the past both in the winter and in the growing season. Bare earth following tillage can reveal traces of the past by showing building debris or the contrasting colour of the field's topsoil against the lines and patches of the typically lighter-coloured subsoil material brought to the surface by site works such as field boundary ditches and banks, hundreds or even thousands of years ago. In summer the picture usually develops as crop marks as a result of the plants growing less well on the subsoil. These are best seen from the air in dry years.

Although it is possible to describe field patterns and sizes as being typical of particular periods in particular parts of the country, and to identify times when major changes took place, it is as well to take note of Nigel Harvey's wise words in his book *The Industrial Archaeology of Farming*. He reminds us that: "Whatever the overall pattern, farmers have always altered the size of their fields to suit their needs, dividing large into small or amalgamating small into large."

It is hard for us to imagine the appearance of a countryside dominated by the open fields of medieval Europe. Typically the arable lands beyond the immediate environs of a village were divided into only three fields. But the very word "field" gives the wrong image; such areas were very different from today's arable broad acres or our neatly demarcated paddocks. Given that the medieval manors that lay at the heart of this system of farming were scattered across the whole country, with its contrasting landscapes, their productive hinterlands must have been equally various. Few if any would have been surrounded with a continuous belt of arable land, defined by clear geometric boundaries set in a rolling countryside. These open "fields" were intersected by streams and sometimes by wetland or heavy clay outcrops left as marsh or spinney. Within them rough grass common ways provided some grazing and gave access to the furlongs of ridge and furrow, while the bulks and headlands added finer patterns. Indeed, some idea of the complexity of these open fields can be gained from the many words used to describe their various features. In addition to those already mentioned they include the following:

bightle	butt	cench	close
flat	gore	infield	lount
parcel	ridge	rood	shift
stitch	went	wong	croft
bulk	bylend	champion	overland
garth	headland	land	shot
quillet	rigg	selion	
virgate	wick	yardland	

All are noted in the glossary; however, judging by the diverse definitions given by various writers, their precise meaning, always supposing they once had one, has been lost in the mists of time. We might also be cautious in fostering an image of country-wide uniform cropping around every village. As I frequently point out, variation in climate and soils so affects both productivity and risk that there has long been clear variation between regions, but when this became established is not clear.

To the villagers, the fields must have appeared fragmented by land tenure even though adjacent strips carried the same crop, so that every farmer's wheat was set side by side, strip by strip across one of these sprawling fields. Another of these three vast fields would have been without any crop at all, a uniform fallow. Like so many technical terms fallow has changed its meaning when in general parlance. Right up to the eighteenth century it referred to land that was "allowed to rest and at the same time is ploughed", indeed the root of the word fallow is "falwe", Middle English for ploughed land. This practice became known as "bare fallow" to distinguish it from the land that was allowed to rest without having any seed sown upon it and without being touched by the plough, which was known as a "lea", a "lee", a "ley" or a "lay". As so often happens, the meaning of this term changed, to describe short-duration grassland. There is another change, too: nowadays leas are sown, not produced by "tumble down". (The percentage of the uncropped land in medieval times that fell into each of these two categories is not clear, so pedants please note that in this book fallow refers to both conditions of rested land unless otherwise stated!) From at least the time of the Roman conquest, for some seventeen hundred years, taking the land out of production was regarded as a vital part of the arable crop cycle. Just why this period of fallow was seen as essential is not clear to me. Over the centuries some writers have praised it as a way of "cleaning" the land of weeds without being hindered by crop plants and for a small area, typically in the lord's domain, it was a way of adding nutrients in the form of excreta from "folded" livestock. Others believed that fallow land "recovered", allowing its soil to build up a supply of available nutrients. Research supports this idea to some extent but it may well be that the greatest value of fallowing was not felt in Northern Europe but linked to its origins in the dry lands of the Mediterranean region. Even today dry land farming continues to use fallows to accumulate soil moisture between crops.

One group rejected the whole idea of resting the land, in fact so keen were they on intensive cropping that they sank massive investments into irrigation systems to negate the annual dry season and so be able to take several crops per year every year. These people were the early Muslim conquerors of North Africa and Spain. During the latter part of our "Dark Ages" their wide selection of crops and cultivation skills forged ahead supported by the scholarship of the "textbooks" that explained them, yet their story is seldom given the credit it deserves. It is not hard to find quotes from the simple wisdom of Piers Plowman, but few in Britain have heard of the immeasurably more scholarly utterances of Ibn al-Awam or Nasir-i Khusraw writing some two hundred years earlier about the by then long-established husbandry techniques of the Muslim world.

Few if any of us who saw the changes produced by arable farming in the twentieth century imagined that we would see uncropped fields once more incorporated into farming practice. Not many people imagined that the "scientific agriculture" of the developed world would produce a local surplus of crops such that there were no profitable alternatives and that governments in Europe would pay farmers to take some fifteen per cent of their arable land out of production. Annual fallow in the form of set-aside has returned as part of our rural landscape after an absence of some five hundred years.

The early enclosures of the open fields seem to have taken place through private agreement slowly over the centuries from around 1500, yet in spite of the best efforts of the influential supporters of this new way of farming, more than half of our agriculture was still located on open fields in 1700. From the 1750s onwards enclosure followed the passing of private Acts of Parliament and was handled by specially appointed commissioners for each parish. The professionalism of these officers and their surveyors did more than allow the development of new farming systems; it patterned large areas of our landscape with the straight lines and right-angles still evident today. Unlike most earlier hedges that are thought to have been established from local selfsets, the young hedges that embossed those patterns were products of a branch of agronomy, the nursery trade. The favoured plant was hawthorn, also known as whitethorn or May. Millions of transplants were produced in specialist nurseries, many clustered round Melbourne some ten miles south of the city of Derby. After foresters these nurserymen must surely have been the first specialist propagators in the country. The owners of these new fields were very conscious of the value of land and were determined not to give more than was necessary to achieve a stock-proof hedge. Pruning and laying became standard routines in the husbandry calendar.

For long enough for people to think that it had always been like it the English lowland agrarian scenery stabilised following the enclosures into the patterns that best suited mixed farming, stock and crops, with some parts of the country showing a bias towards one calling or the other. By chance the shape and size of the fields proved appropriate to the developing mechanisation of crop production until a series of events in the twentieth century changed that, and to many who have the luxury of admiring the countryside but do not have to make a living from it, the changes were dreadful.

The forces at work that drove these changes were two world wars, advances in engineering, agricultural research and a demand for new crops. Both wars produced a demand for home-grown food and whereas the first resulted in little permanent change to the appearance of the countryside the second started a series of indelible changes that continued for some thirty-five years. Cultivation pushed outwards into the so-called marginal lands so that hillsides and fens, woodland and heath all became ploughland, and what would have taken thousands of man-hours to clear could be done in a few days with one person on a machine. The native flora and fauna both disappeared as the countryside took on a new and to many a strange and unwelcome appearance. These changes were not restricted to bringing new land into cultivation. Long-standing arable fields were amalgamated by removing hedges, piping ditches and streams and flattening stone walls. It seemed to many that in one generation the cultivators were removing both the last traces of our wildlife and their predecessor's handiwork to produce a bland, characterless landscape. What would, could or should such organisations as the National Trust, the Country Landowners Association or the Council for the Preservation of Rural England do about it? In truth the answer was not very much. To be fair, studies were undertaken, including two excellent pieces of work commissioned by the Countryside Commission. The first was known as the *New Agricultural Landscapes Study*, which was followed by Ralph Cobham and his colleagues' analysis of a series of demonstration farms. Together these studies not only flagged up the changes that were taking place but also made pioneering, practical suggestions for creating a degree of harmony between aesthetically pleasing landscapes, nature conservation and economically viable farming. More recently such issues have become part of a major change in government policy, as funding is transferred from supporting crop production to paying for "nature conservation and scenery" through the Farm Stewardship Scheme.

Seen from a distance, crops vary in both texture and colour, often from season to season, emphasising the patchwork of the fields even for those who haven't a clue what any of the crops are. One of the biggest changes to our rural idyll has come from the introduction of new crops. If you have a colour-sensitive, artist's eye the increase in barley in some areas over wheat will have registered in the dominance of light green over dark and an earlier change in late summer to a different shade of ruddy gold as the ears ripen. Every new crop makes its impact on the landscape both in the growing season and at harvest. The shiny green of sugarbeet fields arrived in Britain in the 1920s, at about the same time as the grey-green turning nearly chocolate-brown of the field bean crop almost vanished along with the farm horses it fed. Such beans had been grown in Europe since the dawn of agriculture and before that around the Mediterranean basin, so there is something reassuring in their return as cattle feed. The sugar beet was developed by the French around 1800 from white Silesian stock feed beet. But you could say it was "industrialised" by the Germans. They needed a source of home-grown sugar to replace the cane sugar imports lost through the British naval blockade in the Great War.

Minority crops are usually so mixed in with the big players that they seldom produce more than the odd surprise when a strange flower colour pops up in an unexpected place. There are however a few places where these minorities are a regular part of the local scene and some have even become tourist attractions; the fruit tree blossom in Kent and the Vale of Evesham used to be a crowd-puller and the bulb fields of Lincolnshire feature in many coach company brochures.

Inevitably reference to "crop rotation" occurs many times in this book under various guises however this seems an appropriate place to consider it in its own right. A fully developed (but nowadays rarely practised) rotation achieves three goals.

It moves each crop around the arable lands of the holding.

It keeps the hectareage under each crop, or group of crops, roughly the same year on year.

It ensures that each field in turn is subject to the same sequence of crops and that the husbandry and use of each leaves the land in good condition for those that follow.

A rotation may include any kind of annual crop, a short-term ley or a period of fallow. Rotations can be as short as two years or as long as twelve and are often integrated with stock management. The greatest benefits of rotating crops around the arable land of a holding are in disease and weed control together with the once-a-rotation gains from deep cultivation and the after-effects of nitrogen-fixing leguminous crops

For some two thousand years Britain's arable farmers have switched their crops round their fields. In medieval times the rotation, barely changed from the Roman design, turned on the cycle of the fallow, whose ordered movement round the village's two or three arable fields ensured that in its wake autumn-sown wheat was followed eighteen months later by barley or other spring-sown crops.

Resting the land slowly gave way to continuous year-on-year cropping, a system that became formalised in the second rotation to dominate British farming. Known as the Norfolk Four Course it was introduced in the 1730s by Charles, second Viscount ("Turnip") Townshend. Well over two hundred years later the cropping sequence of roots (turnips etc.) followed by barley followed by seeds (clover, peas etc.) followed by wheat was still receiving accolades. One came from no less than the chief scientific adviser to the Ministry of Agriculture Dr H. G. Sanders who considered that it was "doubtful if farming will ever see [another] rotation which will conform as well to the canons of good husbandry as the Norfolk one".

At the start of the nineteenth century Arthur Young noted 4-, 5-, 6-, 8- and 12-year rotations, all still based on cereals, roots and legumes. The longer examples used short-term leys and different members of each crop group [g] within each protracted cycle to reduce the build-up of very host-specific diseases. Nowadays our summer fields produce all kinds of surprises as new "break crops" [g] are tried, not simply to maintain the rudiments of a rotation within the dominance of the cereals but to search for more profitable alternatives in an ever changing agricultural market.

The virtues of crop rotation, including some very marginal ones, have become something of a mantra in school geography. This in spite of many trials showing that there is little intrinsically bad about continuous monocropping on sites free of catastrophic host-specific, soil-born pathogens, and if all the necessary husbandry inputs are provided. The most famous investigation into continuous cropping is to be found within the Broadbalk Experiment at Rothamsted, where wheat has been grown continuously since the 1850s. Plots with and without fertiliser continued to yield their same quantities of grain year on year for over a hundred years, those with no added nutrients typically producing around one tonne per hectare.

Today's break crops include sunflowers, linseed, lupins and, if we follow Europe, it won't be long before the feathery foliage of one of the longest-cultivated plants in the world returns to British agriculture: hemp. (Though the future fields will offer little comfort for anyone seeking a biochemical way out of their worries; they will have been sown with non-drug-producing varieties used for fibre.)

I have left the most dramatic example of a "new" crop to last: *Brassica napus*, or "oil seed rape". In 1970 British farmers grew 10,000 hectares; 25 years later that had shot up to 500,000. This is a crop that goes for the retina, indeed its acid yellow flowers attack the eye twice over, by colour and by the irritation their pollen grains induce. "New" had to go into quotes because I have just been browsing through the *History of Seed Crushing* in Great Britain by Harold Brace which, for those who have not got round to reading it yet, points out that we were growing rape for oil in the mid sixteenth century and by 1593 it was being exported to the Netherlands.

There is one feature that we don't see much of in Britain but may get glimpses of in the far South and West, namely fields covered with transparent plastic sheeting. It is much more common further south in Europe, where it is used to warm the soil and later shelter early crops. Very recently its large-scale use to cover strawberry fields in Herefordshire has caused a rumpus, with people objecting to their green and pleasant view turning into an enormous dazzling reflector as the sun catches the plastic.

It is the boundaries and crops they contain that provide the visual images of the arable countryside, but alongside that these fields can paint just as vivid a word picture. Fields have names, not just the occasional special field but virtually every one of the tens of thousands that make up our countryside. In the dictionary *English Field-Names* compiled by the appropriately named John Field they and their meanings and derivation, often from Old English, are listed. They fill over 265 pages from Abbot Bottom (land whose income contributed to the support of an abbot) to Zulu Land (an ironic name for a field remote from the farmstead). Some names describe size, others distance, direction, soil fertility, cultivation practices, crops, wild plants and folklore. Within the list of denominatives are some two dozen words used to describe arable land.

If the alterations to our lowland scenery brought about by changes to arable agriculture have not passed without comment from those who admire our traditional landscape, the outcry about forestry has been far greater. Over millennia our wildwood was slowly converted into productive woodland by foresters who managed the regeneration of pole-wood by coppicing and the growth, felling and replacement of selected trees. These woodlands were as near as we may ever get to a form of cultivation that is productive but truly sustainable. In most places the foresters worked with one eye on the trees and the other on the game, governed by ancient laws and the power of the owner. When we visit surviving examples of such woods we are struck by how natural the wood seems under this form of management and how rich it is in diverse wildlife.

Glimpses of Elysium these woods may be to some people, but not to the foresters reeling from the timber shortages caused by the mass felling during the First World War that reduced our woodland cover to the lowest in Europe at some seven per cent. The remaining woods were slow to yield and contained the wrong species. Clues as to what to do about the problem had already been planted by many of the great landowners, who had developed a fascination with the north-western North American conifers and put down trial plots on their Scottish and English estates. The trees grew, and they grew fast and straight. The evidence was conclusive: plant conifers in single-species, single-age blocks, treat them like cabbages on new land, and if required drain and add fertiliser. Grow them with care and attention, regard any other species, plant or animal, as a weed and when the trees are the right size harvest the lot. Foresters could hardly be blamed; that's what farmers and market-gardeners had been doing for hundreds of years and no one objected – indeed painters and poets and songwriters celebrated it in their art and the church organised harvest festivals to rejoice in its success.

Then as each year the trees slowly got larger all hell let loose against these strange angular, uniform blocks that had appeared on the rolling hillsides. The British middle class discovered that they had always had a love of woodland but it had to be British woodland made up of a mixture of native species and it should have wild flowers and the leaves must turn russet in the autumn and it must always seem possible that Robin Hood and his merry men were round the next bend. The new conifer plantations offered none of these illusions; even the tracks which since time immemorial had been known as rides were now called fire-breaks, which either ran along the contours or horror of horrors were straight. The anti-conifer lobby had a powerful ally with strong arguments, the conservation movement.

Britain effectively had and still has no other woodland habitat than supposedly productive sites. They divided into two very unequal parts. The smaller were neglected farm spinneys that either were overgrown or were being bulldozed out altogether as a waste of good land. The larger were fast turning into conifer plantations; neither was a sound basis for a biodiverse woodland ecosystem. Much has happened since those days and now this country is a leader in skilfully combining conservation landscape design and varying levels and types of timber production. Forestry led by the once reviled Forestry Commission (Forest Authority) employs both ecologists and landscape architects. Several species of British native broad-leaved trees are being planted to blend both existing and new plantations into their surrounds, while wildlife-friendly management systems such as continuous-cover forestry are being adopted. Our national concern for greater self-sufficiency in timber has a long history, from the oak needed for Tudor fighting ships to the revetments of the First World War trenches. There was even concern that a shortage of pit-props would effect energy production in and just after the Second World War. Fast-growing, straight-trunked conifers seemed the answer with their softwood timber established as the ubiquitous lumber of the temperate world. Today there are plans to return some forests to broad-leaved species by removing millions of conifers over the next ten years. One such site on the heathland at Wareham in Dorset is the very place where Blanche Benzian and her colleagues carried out research in the 1960s into the nutrition of conifer seedlings aimed at producing bigger, better and faster-growing transplants to meet the country's needs. Forty years and no coal mines later, her trees, just entering the prime of middle age, are due for the chop; how fashions change.

No sooner however do we find our woodlands returning to a system of management whose aims seem acceptable to all parties than a new tree crop with the potential to deliver a powerful visual impact appears: coppice for biomass fuel. These closely packed plantations of one or a very few species grow as a mass for around three years. They reach some four metres in height before being cut to the ground. The following year the remaining stumps sprout to restart the cycle. Biomass as it is now being developed has a high water demand, and its strong but fluctuating appearance could have a significant impact on some low-lying areas.

Horticultural arable crops rarely make an impact on the broad brushstrokes of the landscape except in such unusual circumstances as the polythene structures of southern Spain described in Chapter 17. The patterns once formed by market-gardens surrounding many European cities and the small but intensive nurseries of parts of Holland make strong images on old maps, but on the ground they have all but disappeared as they have been either amalgamated into larger holdings or more often built over.

Fruit-growing and similar plantation tree crops such as olive, grape and coffee produce some of the most dramatic man-made landscapes in the world, as several contemporary photographers have recognised. People seem to be comfortable with the idea of vast areas given over to our staple crops, as in the wheat lands of Australia, the American corn belt, and rice in the Mekong Delta. Though, at least to the British eye, fruit grows in homely orchards of a few acres, the truth is very different; plantations of tens and sometimes hundreds of hectares cover whole hillsides and leave their geometric mark on all five inhabited continents from the temperate lands to the tropics. At this huge scale something very interesting happens as the curves and undulations of the landform interact with the parallel lines of the crop to produce that contradiction in terms an accidental art form, and one that dwarfs installation artist Christo's attempts to wrap up the odd valley.

If we can tear ourselves away from all this scenic power and grandeur and return to the British Isles, our thoughts might turn to those homely old farm orchards now becoming recognised as a gene bank for old varieties of several kinds of fruit. They present a watercolour-romantic image of a bygone age, ready each autumn to produce the cider for Rosy. Planted with trees grafted onto strong-growing rootstocks, they were widely spaced in their owners' favourite design, the quincunx, that layout that makes rows seem to radiate out from wherever you stand. Sadly the last twenty-five years has seen most of these traditional orchards grubbed up. The commercial orchards of specialist crops such as the cherries of Kent, plums in the Vale of Evesham and apples in Somerset have fared almost as badly; taken together they now cover less than one per cent of our cropland

and the area is shrinking every year.

The replacements for these early to mid-twentieth-century orchards, and there have been precious few of them, are usually planted much closer together, many with the trees trained along wires to form a kind of hedge but with each branch positioned to give the fruit as much sun as possible.

Finally, and to end on a buoyant note, come the pick-your-own holdings, typically dominated by soft-fruit plantings with strawberry and raspberry well to the fore. Their impact on the countryside is somewhat controversial, for while they offer the buying public the chance to join in the harvest, the associated car parks and roads, weighing sheds, box stores, toilets and even children's play areas send shivers down the spines of most planners, who rightly wonder were all this infrastructure will stop.

A CROPLESS LANDSCAPE

So much for the changes in the appearance of our lowland landscape due to the changes in the kinds of crop grown and the methods used to produce them. Nowadays there is a much more fundamental change being discussed: the cessation of agronomy over significant areas of Britain as the First World's demands for food and industrial crops are met either by production under more favourable climatic conditions or as cash crops in some of the emerging countries of the Third World. We have a fairly good idea of the sequence of changes that abandoned land would go through as the flora of large areas slowly became dominated by woody species. Such almost unimaginable changes would have a dramatic impact on everything from biodiversity to the very basic patterns of the landscape and our ability to see them. The discovery of old field boundary walls "buried" within forestry plantations reminds us of how complete such an erasure would be.

There is at present a lot of talk about how farmers are the custodians of our scenery, and what would happen if farming ceased over large tracts of land and the countryside was managed for "leisure". Leisure is in quotes because no one has any clear idea what that could possibly mean, let alone what its impact might be. Most of this discussion is focused on grassland management including mountainside, moor and heath. As I have tried to show, a great deal of our crop production is concerned with feeding stock, so arable lowland would presumably be drawn into this revolutionary change from productive farming.

It seems to me that if such changes were to take place we would have to decide how much of this land was managed for the perpetuation of our native flora and fauna through habitat conservation or recreation. Sustaining such sites will require husbandry inputs, but the involvement of the new brand of agronomists will have to go further than that. Conservation areas are likely to present a very different picture from what we now think of as British lowland scenery, so their size and location will directly impact on the overall view. If we wish to retain this appearance we will have to develop what we might call scenery management. That policy would have to employ techniques now used by arable farmers and growers.

The study of anatomy [g] remains an important if unglamorous aspect of our understanding of plants. This cross-section of the stem of a young false acacia (Robinia pseudoacacia) *tree is based on a photomicrograph first reproduced in the 1920s.*

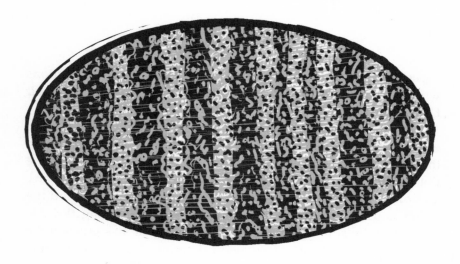

2 GETTING TO KNOW PLANTS

Gilbert White in a letter dated 2 June 1778 praised the "philosophic" study of plants and the investigation of "the laws of vegetation", but added this rider. Botanists "should promote their [plant] cultivation and graft the gardener, the planter and the husbandman, onto the phytologist".

I wholeheartedly agree, but have long contended that the reciprocal argument also holds good. Of course there are people who reason that as plant husbandry is, after all, the archetypal down-to-earth pursuit, there is no harm in a cultivator's understanding of basic biology remaining at best vague and at times even mystical. "Because it works" may seem sufficient answer, but I don't think so. It is my intention to introduce most of the science that's needed to understand the story of man's cultivation of plants as and when it is necessary to the story. The following says little that most readers have not heard long ago, probably in a school science class. Its inclusion is prompted by the observation I share with several colleagues and that giant of American horticulture L. H. Bailey, that both professional cultivators and amateur gardeners are often disadvantaged by their failure to make the connection between plant biology and crop production; as the late Professor Leonard Broadbent used to say, "Horticulture IS applied biology."

Plants, like animals, are made up of various organs that perform specific functions. The organs are built up of cells, each of which contains a nucleus with the full complement of chromosomes for that species. Each chromosome is made up of thousands of genes, which may be thought of as instructions written through the arrangement of the atoms that make up their DNA.

It is now clear that a gene or a combination of genes is behind every aspect of the life of every individual living organism, both the being and the doing (or, if you prefer, the not being and the not doing!) – the being short, being red, being sour, being hard, and on and on as far as your imagination can take you. And the doing is the same: climbing, dropping leaves, opening flowers, turning to the sun, making chemicals. Once one has grasped the fundamental, total role of genes in determining and controlling the form and function of living things it becomes easy to understand why being able to add or subtract genes from the set that literally makes a species or cultivar confers such possibilities.

Man the cultivator has always tried – with no little success – to influence what he grows. We have chosen the wild species from which we have made our crop plants, and for thousands of years we have made these crops by selecting mutants and by hybridisation, words which, we should remember, describe processes of genetic manipulation. Today, by the techniques which we have chosen to bring together under the title "genetic engineering", we are on the threshold of being able to determine a plant's genetic content to an extent previously unimagined.

The impact on cultivation techniques will be huge; the needs and demands of new crop plants is of course as yet unknown, but there is already sound evidence that fertiliser, irrigation and pest- and disease-control programmes will change and the need to control plant shape and form by either chemical means or pruning may disappear; even harvesting is likely to become simpler.

On looking at this list it begins to seem as if such engineered plants will deliver a predictable harvest at a predetermined date with the minimum of waste. My guess is that while they may well have the ability to do such things, the plants will not grow themselves; to achieve such results will still need many of the old skills plus a considerable number of new techniques.

The basic organs that form the morphology [g] of a plant are roots, stems, leaves, flowers and fruits. As we shall see, these are all capable of huge modification, both by natural selection during evolution in the wild and by man's selection when in cultivation. Moving from the externally visible to the hidden internal structure of a plant, the conducting tissue (vascular bundles) is one of the most important tissues. It is made up from two series of tube-like cells: the xylem transports water and dissolved minerals, the phloem the sugars produced during photosynthesis [g]. Some xylem cells are fibrous and tough and after modification become a major component of wood. Cambium cells are closely associated with the conducting tissue. They and the other meristematic [g] cells found in buds and growing points are capable of dividing to produce daughter cells. That is how a plant grows as these new cells develop into the range of tissue types found throughout a plant.

It is in their nutrition and reproduction that plants differ most from animals. The intake of "food", that is the raw materials of growth, comes in the form of dissolved minerals and nitrogen via the roots and as gases through the leaves. The energy to drive the growth processes comes in the first place from light in the processes called photosynthesis. The light energy is trapped by the chlorophyll within the green chloroplasts typically located in leaves; water and carbon dioxide are combined to form sugars. The resultant carbohydrates are either burnt up to drive the chemistry of the life processes or elaborated into the more complex molecules among which the proteins are the most important.

Reproduction can be sexual, in which case there is a fusion of genetic material from both male and female gametes, the male being held in pollen grains, the female in the ovules which develop to become the seed. So far it seems straightforward and familiar; however, in plants these gametes can both be from the same bisexual flower, from separate-sexed flowers on the same monoecious [g] plant or, when cross-pollination [g] occurs, from another plant of the same species. As if that were not strange enough to the mind of a simple animal, we have to contend with vegetative reproduction by which a single plant can divide itself into many independent specimens known collectively as a clone. Clones may seem to be the stuff of science fiction and scary new research, but in the plant kingdom they are old hat. The notorious weed couch-grass very seldom sets seed and whole gardens and allotment sites may be infested with what to a geneticist is one plant.

GROWTH CONTROL

Enzymes and hormones are the two sets of biochemical compounds that control most of what goes on in the internal workings of all living things, including humans and plants. Hormones are often described as chemical messengers; they trigger and stimulate new developments and also many of the changes a plant undergoes during the seasonal cycle. Enzymes are chemical enablers; little can happen within the world of the myriad chemical reactions that constitutes life without their involvement. It is through enzymes that genes exert their influence on the metabolism of living organisms.

Of course, a knowledge of the plant biology sketched out over the last two or three pages has not turned cultivators into plant physiologists, geneticists or even bio-technologists. Nevertheless it has created these disciplines, and their practitioners' search for the answer to Why? has had, in its turn, a dramatic impact on the much older How, When, Where and What of crop production.

The three million British hobby gardeners pursuing their interest in decorative gardening might seem to be unaffected by these insights into plant science but whether they know it or not they are not. Every garden centre that sells seeds, plants, fertilisers and crop protection materials together with their advice notes is packed full of merchandise that has developed from our greater understanding of these sciences. To me one item says it all – our magnificently improved hanging baskets: new kinds of plants, new composts, new fertilisers, new additives and even new liners to save the sphagnum moss.

Scattering seed, pulling weeds and scaring birds could well have been protoagricultural activities before the introduction of either crop translocation or land tillage.

3 THE ORIGINS OF CULTIVATION

IN THE BEGINNING

> The largest single step in the ascent of man is the change from
> nomad to village agriculture.
> – J. Bronowski, *The Ascent of Man*

Sometime around eleven thousand years ago, somewhere around
the Fertile Crescent, centred on that area where Iran, Iraq and
Syria come together, someone deliberately threw seed onto the
ground in anticipation that they would grow to yield a harvest.
Put that way it does not seem much, but from that act developed
arable farming, the human activity that feeds the world and upon
which we all depend. Eleven thousand years is no more than
some 7 per cent of our species's time on this earth. In comparison
with the other 93 per cent when we were first grazer-browser-
hunters and then hunter-gatherers it may seem but yesterday,
however such a date for the start of cultivation means that half
our agricultural experience was gained in the Stone Age, before
the advent of metalworking. Another, more human way of
picturing eleven thousand years of cultivation is as three hundred
and fifty generations of farmers. Given what we know of the
history of the part of the world where this took place, it is not
beyond the realms of possibility that, unbeknown to them, some
of today's Middle-Eastern farmers may still continue this
unbroken agrarian family history.

It seems inevitable that there must have been such a moment,
but it was certainly not the beginning of our story. In Winston
Churchill's words it was more like "the end of the beginning"!

As the English translation of that world authority on the origins of farming Jacques Cauvin puts it,

> One must not imagine these first agricultural activities as exactly similar to those of a more advanced agriculture. The familiar image of the farmer leaning on his plough or his hoe and covering the seed in the turned furrows does not seem to correspond to the first agricultural period. The wild cereals, as perhaps the most primitive domesticated forms, grow as well, or often even better, after a simple sowing on the surface of the soil, if need be after the clearing of the most bulky natural vegetation by burning or tearing it out.

To understand just how these first farmers might have arrived at Cauvin's image we need to take several steps back to build up the picture of "the beginning of the beginning"!

Under some circumstances in nature, large areas can become dominated by a few or sometimes only a single species. Such quirks of ecology, sometimes termed "pure stands", are found in both woodland and grassland habitats, hence monocultures are not a human invention but an extension of the situation found at our ancestors' best gathering grounds. Two species of wild wheat grow from Israel north through Lebanon and Syria then west through eastern Turkey to Iraq and Iran. Much of their natural habitat has been disturbed by man but dense, almost pure stands of one, einkorn, still persist on some mountainsides, as Professor J. R. Harlan found back in 1966.

There is nothing unusual about omnivores focusing on such locations if they offer a specific food source and concentrating their food "gathering" on it whilst it remains "in season". Our televisions show us pictures of grizzly bears feasting on salmon and apes gorging on wild figs. These creatures know where such concentrations of a specific kind of food are to be found, they know when it becomes available and they make the most of it whilst it lasts and, significantly, they may defend it against others.

We may debate the degree to which any other species has a sense of the future, but there's no argument that many collect and store food. For much of our 150,000 years as *Homo sapiens* our ancestors gathered plant food, employing what we may assume to have been a very opportunistic approach. We do not know when our species started to collect and hoard food but it was then that we became true hunter-gatherers with a thought for the morrow as well as the pleasure of an immediate feast. When more than you could immediately eat became an asset to survival rather than a waste we had moved, albeit subconsciously, a very significant way along the road towards the concept of crop dependency.

As omnivores we benefit from plants in our diet to supply vitamins, some minerals and roughage even when there is an abundance of meat. It has been suggested that a stage could have been reached among some groups when regular gathering led to some degree of dependence on specific species in specific locations within the local flora. Some writers suggest that such sites might have yielded around twenty per cent of the group's food.

One must be very careful not to misinterpret or oversimplify the writings of individual archaeologists in an area that attracts so many theories and provides so little hard evidence. The best overview I have read of these diverse opinions is Professor Barbara Bender's book *Farming in Prehistory: From Hunter-Gatherer to Food-Producer*. Although it was written over thirty years ago I think it fair to say that in spite of all the new findings the central question remains: why, after so many millennia of dependency on gathering from the wild, did humans start to cultivate plants?

From among the many ideas discussed in the literature the sequential approach of Marek Zvelebil of the University of Sheffield to the "evolution" of cultivation strikes an immediate chord with me. As a botanist Professor J. G. Hawkes, writing in 1969 in *The Domestication and Exploitation of Plants and Animals*, expresses similar ideas by reminding his readers that as annuals the wild cereals of the Middle East depend on seasonal drought to suppress perennial herbs, thereby allowing their seedlings a competition-free start. Clearly the first cultivators could have made use of such patches of clear land as ready made seedbeds.

Some archaeologists describe the most advanced form of the organised gathering of known stands of food plants as proto-agriculture, and argue that each year people would set out from their permanent dwellings to harvest such easy pickings. In this hypothesis the next "logical" development is to make an effort to manage these wild plant sites. Even the use of fire and the felling of trees can extend a suitable habitat and change its floristic composition. It would seem reasonable to imagine gatherers defending such areas against predation from, for example, birds and other grazing animals. Indeed I see no reason why many of the actions we now think of as part of the routine of husbandry, such as pruning, weeding, fertilising and some forms of invertebrate pest control could not have been observed, understood and even practised on naturally occurring stands of native plants in this period before agriculture. Over seventy years ago J. H. Steward reported that the Native Americans of Owens Valley in southeastern California had dug ditches and dammed streams to increase the yield of wild food plants long before tilling, planting and cultivation were known to them. Lynda Dick Bissonnette in *Women and Plants* records that in the same part of the world the Yokoch-Mono people both weeded and dug round wild sedge plants to improve the quality of their rhizomes used in basket-making.

Occasionally such "plant-friendly" activities can happen without human intervention; others are incidental, resulting from actions carried out for other purposes. What is important is that the results were seen by the foragers and, if this hypothesis is correct, deliberately repeated on and around the plants they were intending to collect. Such actions might well have resulted in not only improved growth within the stand of the desired plant but its spread. Recognising that we could influence the spread of a plant and thereby gain a greater harvest may rank as one of mankind's greatest discoveries. That being the case, it is ironic that "spread" has become the plant quality most feared by many of today's suburban gardeners. From their point of view the spread of weeds and rampant flowers signals trouble.

These proto-agricultural activities would surely not have developed unless people had recognised the plant's response to them; that was the real discovery. We may never know which activities came first, or if there was a significant time interval between them. We now understand that these apparently separate tasks are all interdependent; together they form the complete package that is needed when plants are brought into cultivation if they are to yield a worthwhile harvest.

This was the time when those all-important improved forms, the first cultivars, appeared very occasionally among stands of wild food-plants. It has been argued that these human interventions are likely to have had an impact on the genetic make-up of the population. Although the activities may have been unwitting and incidental to the method of harvest, they could have been essential to the success of the future efforts to cultivate these plants. It seems that the yield of genetically unaltered wild plants would not have produced a sufficiently greater harvest to make the effort used in their cultivation worth while. Indeed some field researchers claim that wild stands of einkorn wheat can produce around one tonne per hectare, which works out to kilogram of grain per ten square metres. Working on such a wild stand, one archaeologist using only his bare hands managed to harvest one person's daily requirement in half an hour. Clearly the first efforts in cultivation faced formidable challenges to achieve higher yields if measured against such data. If however the prime reason for embarking on cultivation was crop relocation rather than yield improvement, then other considerations become relevant. Relocation can make sense in terms of convenience, of security and/or of providing appropriate growing conditions if climate change renders the old sites less satisfactory to the growth and dominance of the desired species.

The archaeological evidence for the start of plant domestication comes from the plants themselves. The remains of the seeds used as food increase in size in a way that we can only explain by human activity. This means deliberate or unwitting selection over many generations, and the only feasible way of that happening would be if these subjects were being husbanded in some way. Professor Hillman makes a clear separation between "domestication" and "farming", his argument being that the former, based on wild plant genetic improvement, preceded field-scale production.

This concept brings me to what is to me the defining act and the true birth of agronomy: translocation – the activity that marked the end of the beginning of man's road to dependence on cultivation. It was the moment when someone determined that at least part of their food supply was going to come from a spot of their own choosing. As with the other basic acts of cultivation, translocation and its potential benefit was probably first "demonstrated" by accident: the dropping of seeds gathered from the wild as they were either carried home or processed ready for the pot. Although translocation is the standard term in the literature, it can be easily misunderstood. Surely no one considers that the first cultivators either deliberately stripped natural sites of their wild food plant populations or that they ceased to harvest such areas. Translocation, in this context, should be considered as the spread of such species by seeding sites previously unoccupied by the desired food plant. Eventually these new selected locations came to dominate the food supply. In the latter stages of the story the increase in the incidence of seeds of local wild plants that thrive in cultivated fields is equally indicative. It seems the first arable farmers invented weeds as well as crops.

To those of us who live in moist, temperate lands with rather heavy soils, translocation conjures up pictures of necessary hard work to prepare a site for transplanting or seed sowing. A lot of that effort is directed towards removing the site's vegetation and, as ecologists would have it, creating a favourable microsite [g] for each seed to grow. However, the first cultivators in the Fertile Crescent lived where conditions could have allowed them to get away with simply scattering seed, indeed (the first?) indiscriminate broadcasting of grain would have revealed those sites where there was no absolute need for tillage. In this area with its distinct wet and dry seasons and a naturally open soil, annuals including the ancestors of the cereals dominated the flora. Much further south, it is this cycle that produces Namaqualand's fantastic display of annuals. These germinate at the start of the rains, produce a profusion of flower and seed, and then shrivel up with the onset of the drought, leaving large patches of bare earth. Their seeds fall onto this natural weed-free seedbed, from which they could start the cycle afresh with the return of the rains. If as seems likely the first translocators failed to harvest all the seeds, annual reseeding might not have been necessary and could have been left to nature. It sounds like the Garden of Eden! Maybe translocation was not such hard work after all.

Professor Hillman has proposed a very plausible motivation for translocation. Eleven thousand years ago the growth of vegetation on the site was controlled by the availability of water. Professor Hillman has suggested that the increased duration of the annual drought, based on a known dry period, may have reduced the yield in the traditional wild harvest locations. Such changes could face a previously well-nourished settled community of hunter-gatherers with only two options. One was to do what so many others had done under similar circumstances, namely move and abandon their village, but maybe they liked the settled life and did not relish the prospect of rebuilding their lives elsewhere. The other option was to somehow "transfer" the failing wild food plants from their droughted natural habitats to the remaining seasonally moist sites fed by ground water. This elegant suggestion of drought as the goad to crop translocation encompasses the now widely held hypothesis that cultivation arose from a settled way of life and did not initiate it.

Following the Hillman line of reasoning, cultivation started with that one simple objective: to transfer wild food plants from deteriorating conditions to better. But if the sowers had applied some of the proto-agricultural activities they had observed and maybe practised on wild populations, and if these same food plants now responded favourably, then crop husbandry had truly arrived. By opting to transfer their favourite food plants these villagers could rightly have claimed a place among the world's great innovators.

Of course, it would be totally wrong to think that once that fateful act happened gathering from the wild stopped forthwith. Not so, I say with absolute certainty as I wipe the blackberry juice off the keyboard! Professor Hillman describes the replacement of gathering by cultivation as a step-by-step process in which the gathering of wild staples decreased as the dependence on crops increased. At Abu Hureyra this took some two thousand years. Over and above this the gathering of the many other species of food plants continued long after the bulk of the diet came from a small number of crop species. Hew Prendergast and Helen Sanderson of the Royal Botanic Gardens, Kew, have shown that we are still at it. They have put together a fascinating list of today's British gatherers, including those who pick elderflowers for cordials, nettles for cheese-wrapping, heather for air filters and wild garlic as a culinary herb. The twist to this story is that these gatherers are not seeking self-sufficiency; the wild harvests are sold to the appropriate manufacturers. Could that person in front of you at the checkout buying French Golden Delicious be a hunter-gatherer on a day off?

It is at this stage that mankind takes what is usually seen as the last great step in the story, tillage. This is, both literally and figuratively, the ground-breaking work. This was soil disturbance not to harvest but to cultivate, to make a more successful seedbed or friable soil to receive roots and tubers. Even superficial tillage can result in successful sowing and transplanting in soils that would offer a very poor seedbed if left undisturbed. Once established, crops growing on these somewhat heavier soils may well do very well. In calculations of the energy balance between working to obtain food and its nutritional value, tillage dominates energy expenditure. On this basis it seems reasonable to suggest that while the simple translocation of unimproved wild cereals could have been worthwhile, tillage would not pay until the improved forms referred to by Professor Hillman appeared.

We will join the discussion on first tillage tools later. Suffice to say at this point that they must have been simple but able to disturb a considerable area of soil. Just how large an area really depends on what was regarded as a worthwhile harvest. For example, a "field" of around 25m by 25m might yield some 60kg of grain, which would go a very long way towards providing the carbohydrate needs of a family of four for a month. We may not regard that as a great contribution to the challenge of feeding this family the year round, but we might view things differently if it saved us from searching the countryside for 100kg of edible fresh roots. Professor Hillman postulates that in the early period of cultivation a combination of fresh and stored crops would have supplied food for a little under six months, leaving the people dependent on gathering from the wild for sustenance for the rest of the year.

I think the archaeologists who consider that these early efforts at crop production would have needed specialised tool-kits for plant tending and soil working have got it about right. As Marek Zvelebil suggested in a paper in the *Proceedings of the Prehistoric Society*, bladed tools fashioned from antler, bone, stone and wood could scrape or cut into the soil surface, remove weeds and create a thin layer of tilth. Using these seems to me to offer a much better chance of growing a crop than relying solely on a digging stick. Tillage may not have been the first act in our discovery of cultivation but once introduced it has remained at the core of agronomy ever since. Around it have grown the husbandry techniques that fill the pages of this book.

Marking early arable farming settlements onto soil maps shows us that their occupants developed yet another skill: the ability to recognise and detect the best sites for crop production, soils that combined good plant growth with ease of tillage and crop management.

The hunt for the best land had started. For the next eleven thousand years it has been the strong rather than the meek who have inherited the good earth

So if developments progressed slowly through these stages, it would seem that agriculture/horticulture had no eureka moment. It was not an invention like the wheel but most likely a series of discoveries based on both observing and manipulating wild plants. These proto-agronomists learnt by observing how wild plants responded to their environment; they were the world's first field·ecologists.

We do not know if the first growers added extra nutrients in any form. It is much more likely that on occasions they scattered seed over land that by chance had received dollops of potential plant fertiliser in the form of human and other animal faeces and urine and ash from fires. Someone made the connection between patches of exceptional growth and what had gone on before.

While there is no evidence of irrigation until millennia after the first efforts to cultivate plants, nevertheless in time the artificial watering of plants became the most sophisticated aspect of prehistoric agriculture.

Today's experts tend to call pest and disease control "crop protection", a phrase well understood by experimental archaeologists, who point out that as a vital food source both wild and cultivated "crops" would have been watched over throughout their development and most closely guarded against all comers as they reached maturity.

There is every likelihood that these first translocators were women, left as ever by the menfolk to the tedium and hard work of gathering plant material for the pot while they had the excitement of the hunt. It seems completely appropriate that women extended these early acts of husbandry by taking the radical yet quintessentially maternal step of preparing and caring for each new generation of the crop. And this brings me to what I believe may be the key to the success of our first cultivators. Might it not be that as women they did the very best thing: they treated their crop plants as if, like animals, they too were living beings. Of course they were, and they needed and responded to a combination of the activities I have tried to separate out but which can all be summarised in the phrase "tender loving care".

Such an attitude has stood the test of time. It is only in the very recent past that scientific crop management has produced equal results to those achieved through "TLC". It is an approach that's by no means dead; it is still practised by all those amateur gardeners who cherish their plants and heap intuitive attention on them throughout their lives. What was once the basis of a family's survival now adds success to the pleasure of a relaxing hobby.

As we have seen, agriculture can be recognised by its use of those improved "cultivars", their large-scale translocation and arrangement into "field crops". There seems to be good evidence to suggest that, even when these domesticated crop plants were used, very primitive field cultivation gave at best only marginal advantages over gathering, if the wild stands of cereals were producing the 1 tonne per hectare (7.8 hundredweights per acre) mentioned earlier. One estimate suggests that early cereal harvests may have added only around two to four times the quantity of seed sown, and of course the next sowing required its share before the coming year's food supply could be estimated. Early yields in Britain suggest that things were very slow to change; it has been estimated that British farmers still only gathered 1.5 tonnes per hectare in 1700. According to Arthur Young, it was only 5 per cent more in 1800, while data from the tithe surveys show that figure had hardly changed by 1830. Today it is between 7 and 8 tonnes. There is one set of figures significantly at variance with those quoted at the beginning of this sequence and they deserve to be taken very seriously, namely those that are the result of the very imaginative work of Peter Reynolds as director of the Butser Ancient Farm project on the Hampshire Downs. He and his team set out to reconstruct an Iron Age farm and cultivate period-correct crops using period-correct tools and methods. Here year after year, under the most carefully managed conditions, fields of einkorn wheat have given 1.4 tonnes per hectare and emmer wheat has exceeded 2 tonnes per hectare.

The evidence is that sowing rates have stayed fairly constant at around 200kg per hectare. If these very low early yield estimates are accurate, cultivation must have spread driven not by the promise of easy pickings but by necessity or predictability of supply. Some anthropologists seem not to go along with such material triggers but prefer to speak of a "cultural readiness" that lay behind the Neolithic Revolution of which the birth of agriculture is a part. Whatever that means, it is certainly not the lure of an easy life. Perhaps the idea that crop-raising is at heart more a way of life than an industry has a very long history.

MIGRATION

This then is the hypothesis for the start of cultivation in one specific part of the world. Not all locations were blessed with plants of the same genetic potential. For example Marek Zvelebil in his review paper is persuasive in gathering evidence to suggest that the early stages of a not dissimilar process may have taken place during the Mesolithic period over large swaths of Northern Europe. However he is very doubtful if any of the local plants made it to the last stage. The first field crops seem to have all been imports from the south.

We can be more precise about the origin of these migrants that became the foundation crops that formed the basis of farming throughout Europe. There can be very little doubt that they developed from wild populations growing in the Levant. After domestication their offspring are thought to have started to spread through Anatolia some ten thousand years ago, reaching first the Balkans; from there one branch crossed the Adriatic to the Mediterranean lands of Europe and another spread into Central Europe via the Danube valley and the Hungarian Plain and onwards to the north. The east and west branches of this coming of farming to Europe met in what is now Northern France and there is some debate as to which branch had the greater influence on British origins.

Few if any experts now believe that the ideas and understanding behind each phase of cultivation was thought out afresh by communities across Europe. Once on the move, farming seems to have reached out over some three thousand kilometres in three millennia, giving rise to the handy but not literal tag of a speed of one kilometre a year. We may assume this was a very uneven temporal and spatial advance, with perhaps whole communities shunning agriculture altogether and others pursuing only the domestication of animals to became graziers rather than tillers.

Spread, then, wins the argument over rediscovery, but we are left with two fundamental questions: how and why? Was it by imitation or immigration? There is still debate over whether this onward progress came about by successive communities observing and copying their southerly neighbours, or by experienced farmers or new brides migrating into lands to their north. Given the sparseness of settlements and this rate of adoption, a decade of sly observation and fireside gossip could elapse before following in your neighbour's footsteps. So it seems possible that cultivation was just another technique spread by contact with more adventurous groups, and archaeology is rich in evidence of such contacts by both land and sea. I. J. Thorpe addresses these issues in *The Origins of Agriculture in Europe*, but wisely leaves the debate open until there is more evidence. Peter Bogucki writing in *Europe's First Farmers* is convinced however that cultivation spread, at least across Central Europe, by the migration of colonists, their progress traceable by their "hallmark" architecture and pottery. He finds it more difficult to suggest why these people, equipped with the very skills that allow settlement, should have continued to have such a wanderlust. Indeed wanderlust may not be an appropriate term even for their forebears because, as E. S. Higgs points out in *The Early History of Agriculture*, hunter-gatherers were almost certainly not directionless wanderers but moved within a territory with which they were familiar. For many years it was thought that Europe's first arable farmers were also to a degree nomadic in as much as they practised a form of "slash and burn" shifting agriculture to maintain fertility. But, as the editors of *Early European Agriculture* cogently argue, both the archaeological evidence and today's agricultural research seem to support the contention that, just as in the Middle East, they established permanent settlements dependent on the long-term use of suitable local land. Those engaged on the British Academy's Research Project on the Early History of Agriculture considered that, to be energy-cost-efficient, arable fields had to be within a kilometre of the dwelling. These researchers' Europe-wide studies of such sites indicate that the majority have some 50 per cent or 114 hectares of land suitable for cultivation within that perimeter.

To what extent these first European farmers practised any form of rotation or rested the land by fallowing is not known, but even allowing for those practices, that area is enough to support a sizeable population. Indeed I would say that before the advent of draught animals and the ard, with only stone, bone and wooden digging tools, manpower would be the factor limiting production. Locating fertile soil is not as obvious as finding water or a ready supply of flint. Perhaps at the start there was no conscious identification of good sites so that converts to this new way of life simply tried to farm wherever they were, but only those on the best locations made a go of it. Or perhaps a description of suitable soils (or their telltale flora) travelled north as part of the oral "instructions" on how to cultivate. If this was the case then groups living on unsuitable soils either decided it was not for them or else moved. What becomes clear when we superimpose the position of settlement sites on today's soil maps is that once arable farming became established in the Neolithic period, the location of suitable soils determined the settlement pattern across much of lowland Europe. The search was on for light loams that worked easily to make a seedbed, were fast-draining and from which it was easy to remove weeds. Such soils are less fertile than some heavier loams, but that would have been a worthwhile trade-off for their ease of management.

As a cultivator, my thoughts keep returning to the magnitude of the task facing either an individual or a group at the very outset of this adventure. For surely there was no parish council decreeing that "We will all become farmers next year." So was the first "crop" in a settlement no more than one person's effort, perhaps a lone woman's small-scale tryout? She would have needed to cultivate around 5m² for a day's food, which would hardly have turned heads, but a 25kg sackful from 250m² (16m by 16m) might get the elders thinking and persuade her family of five to slowly increase this to the 1ha they would need for a year-round supply. The crops, basic tools and techniques were long established, so the European hunter-gatherers of the Late Mesolithic did not have to invent cultivation, but they did "need" a reason for adopting it. Aside from enslavement or enforcement, the following have been suggested as possible incentives:

Overcoming food shortages linked to over-hunting and over-gathering and/or increased population.

An easier way of getting food.

A dependable food supply based on yield and storability.

The only way of establishing a local supply of non-indigenous high-quality foods.

More nebulous reasons such as changes in fashion, and the need for a food surplus to demonstrate wealth and power, also have their supporters, as does the readiness of the society to accept change. I think that's where my lone woman's efforts comes in; after all my generation knows the power of "Min. of Ag." demonstrations to influence some of the most reactionary of countrymen. Even in much later periods of history we are uncertain of the forward march of cultivation. It is unclear which skills were lost following invasions, which were retained and what new methods, techniques and equipment were introduced by the conquerors. The spread of the plough across Northern Europe presents one such conundrum.

The first crop cultivation in the Americas appears to have had its origins some considerable time after people settled in those continents, in which case agriculture-dependent civilisations must have been "invented" at the very least twice, once in the Old World and afresh in the New. Indeed it seems very likely that at least two more claimants can be added to the list, as farming in the Indus Valley and in China are thought to have been independent discoveries.

Just as around the world cultivation was discovered several times, so on a local scale the domestication of some indigenous species appears to have occurred more than once. Surely this should not come as a surprise. After all, once the idea of cultivation is abroad, using your ample supply of local wild seed is a much more direct way of getting started than waiting for a small sample from another settlement. Just the same thing goes on today every time someone sows wild collected seeds of a herb such as sage or thyme rather than taking cuttings from a cultivar.

Some researchers who have worked on the origins of cultivation among some early communities in the Americas favour a different theory as to how these people came to transplant crop plants. They write of "dump heap" plants, those weeds and useful plants whose seeds or ramets [g] grow after being discarded on the rubbish heap. They point out that anyone observant enough to survive in a primitive culture could hardly have missed the fact that vegetation, particularly annuals, grew exceptionally large on middens and rubbish heaps. Of course, such places are often rich in nutrients from decomposed organic remains and with an open structure. Indeed there is no need to work hard trying to justify this part of the argument; it happens to every amateur gardener who sets out to make a compost heap but fails to tend it. It is possible that these heaps were our first allotments, a demonstration of what could be done and even the best kind of "soil" to do it in.

It is not hard to imagine the original specimens that were growing wild round and about the homestead being wiped out by over-collection, while very vigorous self-sets appeared on dump heaps. From this evidence people might have made the next and crucial step towards man the gardener if not yet the farmer. They planted replacements and introductions from further afield around the dwelling. Of course such efforts are meaningless for the staples in the diet but perfectly sufficient for those herbs with a strong flavour or even medicinal, hallucinogenic or religious properties. These are just the kinds of plants that are needed in small quantities, and it is very convenient to have them immediately to hand when needed; even today our TV gurus frequently remind us to plant herbs close to the kitchen door!

Making these plants contenders for the first to be cultivated hinges once again on the act of relocation, but there are differences. Now the move is serendipitous; our would-be cultivators had only to observe, learn and repeat the following season. Maybe, along with the nurturing of these dump-heap self-sets, they scattered a few seeds or transplanted some "roots" dug up from the wild. Here the kinds of plants were not those that were needed in large numbers to provide bulk in the diet, so there was no need to clear sufficient land to produce large crops. They were just trying to establish a few useful native plants nearer than half a day's trek away. By the time Europeans reached the Americas many hundreds of years of cultivation lay behind the techniques they found. Perhaps by the very nature of the staples the locals grew it appeared to the settlers in North America that they were gardening rather than farming. Although the yield per unit area may not have been much different from the early cereal fields of Europe, the techniques practised certainly were. Plants of maize, beans and squashes all require a fair amount of room to develop enough to give a good yield. Local custom set maize and beans on small mounds and allowed the vigorous vine-like growths of the squashes to spread between them. Above all the harvest clearly depended on the fate, and hence the husbanding, of individual plants and that to a farmer in any age spells gardening!

Is it then too wild a claim that American cultivation started with the care of a relatively few specimens each capable of giving a useful harvest, whereas millennia earlier in the Middle East this new-fangled idea of growing plants took the opposite approach, a form of simple field production in which large numbers of seeds were scattered to lose their identity within the primitive crop? With one possible exception there seems no evidence for a very long time of the care of individual plants in what we might call the start of horticulture; that exception is fruit trees.

Fruit

Wild fruits in our early prehistory may well have had an important dietary role, but all round the world they seem to have been brought into cultivation for their desirable flavour that so beguiled Eve. The first cultivation of fruit trees and shrubs poses its own questions. We know for certain from several strands of archaeological evidence that prehistoric peoples gathered and ate fruits and nuts local to wherever they dwelt. Even today villagers in the Third World are understandably loath to cut down "their" wild fruit trees. Indeed they endeavour to protect them from the ravages of other species intent on the same harvest. The challenge comes with the deliberate planting of such desirable subjects, because unlike the annual field crops fruits are a long-term commitment, taking anything from five to ten years to come into bearing. To plant them indicates a settled way of life and a confidence in the future. That wait is asking a lot of the first cultivators, so much so that I would favour the early translocation of tree fruits to within the village from chance seedlings. I suspect that germinating pips or stones spat out or thrown away gave settlements fruit trees via the dump heap. Fruit is eaten on the hoof and the inedible bits thrown down wherever the consumer happens to be. This still goes on with mangoes in Africa and, nearer to home, there are more apple-tree seedlings in the hedgerows around our village school than anywhere else in the parish.

By whatever means fruit-bearing species came under our control, it is clear that, while some, such as the date-palm, became significant additions to the diet, others were appreciated as no more than sweet-tasting treats. From 3000 BC onwards murals and written records leave us in no doubt of the importance of plantations, orchards, vineyards and their products, indeed they carry a prominence equal to that of arable field crops. By then Middle Eastern peoples were enjoying figs, apricots, almonds, walnuts, dates, olives and grapes, several of which must have been carried long distances from where they grow wild. Cultivating fruit trees requires its own set of skills; learning them was probably the key to our understanding of pruning, training, vegetative propagation and transplanting, no small contribution to the advance of agronomy.

AGRICULTURE'S IMPACT ON MAN'S SOCIAL DEVELOPMENT

Agriculture has had a massive impact on man's social and cultural development, but anthropologists point out that it cannot claim to be the creator of either civilisation or a sedentary lifestyle. Long before the advent of cultivation people were living in well-constructed shelters, using a range of efficient utensils and tools, cooking a wide range of foods and enjoying the benefits of a significant social organisation. In Britain archaeologists have recently excavated a ten-thousand-year-old Mesolithic dwelling in Northumberland that seems to have been "home" for just short of a century, some five thousand years before cultivation reached us. Far be it from me to wish to play down the pivotal role of my own profession, but it must be admitted that there are many examples of caves having been adorned with fine art dating back tens of thousands of years before cultivation, a clear demonstration of the cultural development of their particular troglodytes.

It must also be pointed out that not all simple forms of cultivation are truly static. Most school geography courses introduce children to "slash and burn" as an example of shifting cultivation. This system of crop production often, but not always, takes place over sufficiently large areas to require the village to be relocated at the start of each cycle of cropping. Such enforced mobility is hardly conducive to great architecture.

Anthropologists with a bent for economics and social structures have put forward a compelling refinement to the "cultivation-equals-culture" argument. It is that farming the land leads to a desire to own the land, and it is that sense of ownership which glues a community to a site. Farming seems to be an innately capitalist activity which probably accounts for the difficulty experienced in organising cooperative ventures, not to mention the dismal failure of Soviet-style collective farms. Apparently our attachment to the land we work holds good, even when it is owned by non-farming landlords.

The history of the world has been one of the rise and fall of civilisations such that many areas in Europe, the Middle East, North Africa, China and North, Central and South America, although playing an important role in the early days of cultivation, do not show a continuous progression of husbandry skills. In contrast they display a series of peaks and troughs as cultures blossomed and were then struck down by incoming groups with little or no history of land cultivation. The evidence shows that they in turn settled down and learned crop husbandry. Agricultural, horticultural, orchard and plantation skills all depend on stable land ownership, and if cultivators are to progress beyond subsistence cropping they need a market or a patron for their products.

6000–5000 BP

We get our first good insight into cultivation techniques more than 5000 years after their origin, so that poorly understood early period stretches over a little more than half the time we have grown plants. What is clear is that virtually all the essential aspects of the craft were discovered and refined during that period. Indeed by the time we have good records, husbandry systems were in place and cultivation skills well advanced, but as yet we don't know precisely when, where and by whom. J. Bronowski describes the Jericho of 8000 BP as "an agricultural settlement" which according to its excavator, Kathleen Kenyon, supported a population of around three thousand. The Egyptologist Professor Walter Emery makes the point in a more general but very telling way: he has commented that practically all the skills so evident in Egypt's first golden age existed by 5200 BP. Our present insight derives mainly from pictures and writings left behind by the then most advanced cultures of the Middle East and the Levant. The clues are scattered across many sites within this broad region but taken together they show us a highly developed craft. Everything from irrigation systems to domesticated draught animals is in use. Impressive as we may find these developments, they are no more than we should expect if we compare cultivation with many other crafts and arts from architecture to dressmaking, jewellery to sculpture. All require both conceptual thought and the tools and dexterity to bring the plans to fruition and all were flourishing by this time.

In spite of the changing fortunes and frequent internecine wars of the many local cultures within the area we now refer to as the Middle East, in the villages the craft of cultivation went on, and has gone on, slowly evolving until today. Starting some six thousand years ago with such Sumerian cities as Lagash and Ur, it has supported each urban centre in turn as its dwellers developed the myriad aspects of the arts and culture we think of as civilisation. Indeed it is thanks to their graphic arts that we get some of our most immediate images of crop production, while the administrator's written records allow us to estimate crop areas and yields; funeral offerings sometimes include models portraying farm work and in rare cases the actual tools and equipment used.

The earliest traces of, or references to, "orchards" in Persia and the lands to its south are associated with established urban cultures, yet the fruit trees they grew – apples, pears, cherries and grapes – were not local but grow wild in Caucasia far to the north. It is thought they were carried as dried food reserves by early migrants. Even the peach (*Prunus persica*) comes not from Persia but from North China, an early traveller down the Silk Road. Given the level of sophistication shown through surviving works of art in ancient Persian cities such as Susa and Persepolis we should, I suppose, not be surprised at King Cyrus's formal gardens, his *pairidaeza* of the sixth century BC. Written records list plants collected from across his empire, and the physical remains of the garden design and its irrigation system combine to remind us that decorative horticulture had already become part of the collective culture that defines a civilisation. There is even evidence to suggest that Persian royalty were themselves hobby gardeners, taking an active part in the cultivation of their ornamental plants. Although these are the oldest surviving remains, pleasure gardens had probably been enjoyed by the wealthy for many centuries before this. Sadly archaeologists have found little if any material evidence for that most famous of ancient pleasure gardens, the Hanging Gardens of Babylon, but most consider that the story of King Nebuchadnezzar II's great horticultural endeavour has a basis in fact.

Many amateur gardeners I meet seem surprised to learn of the level of sophistication of horticulture in Queen Victoria's reign, let alone in the Bronze Age in the Middle East – this in spite of their willing acceptance of the evidence of these peoples' culture, particularly as expressed through the execution of other of their arts and crafts. Given how essential cultivation was to every civilisation, it is hard to fathom why we should be surprised that they grafted fruit trees, irrigated fields or pruned vines. Maybe today's garden club members don't like to admit that these ancient husbanders were probably more skilled than they are. For thousands of years cultivation remained a craft whose processes appeared artless and brutal to the sophisticated urban rich who so enjoyed its products; it is only with the development of all the associated sciences and the emergence of agribusiness, including horticulture and forestry, that growing plants has become widely recognised as a skill-based industry. Maybe it is easier to appreciate what cultivation involves if we think of it as a combination of knowledge, dexterity and equipment.

To the traditional artisan knowledge has always meant knowing what to do and when and how to do it. It was rarely concerned with asking why. Translating this knowledge into useful work required dexterity, hand-to-eye coordination and the use of hand-tools, skills gained from years of practice during childhood. The equipment was little more than an aid to this dexterity. The nineteenth- and early twentieth-century developments were mainly in equipment and materials; it is only in the last fifty or so years that we have gained sufficient understanding of "why" to be able to revolutionise the time-honoured methods of crop production.

As with so many aspects of life, crop cultivation in the time of the Athenian Greek civilisation can be thought of as rounding off this progress through the ancient civilisations of the Mediterranean basin and the start of the birth of its European chapter. By the time Homer wrote the Odyssey, his imaginary orchard of four acres at Alcinous grew "the pear and the pomegranate, the apple, the sweet fig and the luxuriant olive".

Thanks to the scholars working for the Loeb Classical Library, we are able to read a translation of the works of a man who lived at that extraordinary time. I guess that most of us plant people who recall the name Theophrastus will do so as the chap described in some introductory lecture as "the father of botany".

Well, be that as it may, it is clear from these translations that he was an outstanding agronomist who writes with a critical eye on both past and contemporary husbandry methods. He is however not content to report; he has very strong views of his own and criticises what he considers to be bad or illogical practices. He searches for rational explanations. He looks on cultivation as a scientist, two thousand years before those who founded crop science in our own era. We will be hearing more from him when we reach various specific areas of the subject, but one quote will give a flavour of his approach. Here he is on the subject of the contrasting results of propagating fruit trees from seed and cuttings (to us the difference between producing a clone and hybrids [g] from heterozygous [g] parents):

> While all the trees which are propagated thus or by some kind of slip seem to be alike in their fruits to the original tree, those raised from the fruit, where this method of growing is also possible, are nearly all inferior, while some quite lose the character of their kind.

At the height of its power in the first century AD the Roman world left us perhaps the best insight into its understanding of plant cultivation. It comes through the authorship of Lucius Iunius Moderatus Columella, in what has been described as the first textbook on farming. So it may have been, but time and again current practices are cross-referenced with the writings of earlier authorities. As Columella writes in his preface, "There is furthermore a great throng of Greeks ... influences that stretch back beyond the power of Rome into Greek literature." Throughout his writings he is equally open to the ideas of his own countrymen and their methods of crop production, but not without question. Is, for example, Tremelius correct in blaming the Italian soil and climate for lower yields than those claimed by "the Punic writers from Africa"? Clearly he doubts it.

Like Theophrastus before him, Columella appears to think like a scientist; but his enquiring, scholarly writings carry the extra authority that comes from being an estate-owner managing his own farms. He certainly dislikes unfounded explanations, as this précis of the preface to his great work *Rei Rusticae* shows:

> Again and again I hear leading men of our state condemning now the unfruitfulness of the soil, now the inclemency of the climate as harmful to crops; as if on well-founded reasoning, they consider the soil was worn out and exhausted by the overproduction of earlier days and can no longer furnish sustenance to mortals with

its old-time benevolence. Such reasons, I am convinced, are far from the truth.

His confident, often critical writings deserve space in any history of cultivation. Indeed the Western world did not get anything better for another one and a half thousand years! Of course, he was a man of his time and some of his advice is closely linked with the prevailing belief that astronomy and astrology both had a powerful influence on plant growth, so that farmers must have spent their time with one eye on the fields and the other on the heavens. It was not only the Ides of March that you had to be beware of, but the waxing and waning of every moon. These celestial hazards apart, he gives us pages of excellent advice on the cultivation of everything from cereals to vineyards, to which apple cultivars do best on different soils and how to propagate by grafting and cuttings. It is not just the factual nuts and bolts of growing that are important but also the insight he gives into the understanding of plant cultivation. Again it is thanks to the Loeb Classical Library that we can read his books in English. It is a rewarding if somewhat eccentric pursuit I would recommend to anyone who is interested in the history of cultivation.

My lasting impression from studying these two classical writers is not only of how much they and their contemporaries knew about crop production but of their level of cultivar selection. If Pliny is to be believed, by the first century AD they grew almost 40 kinds of pear, over 20 kinds of apples and 9 kinds of plums; that's a much greater choice than today's supermarket offers! These writings, and the excavations at such sites as Pompeii, bring home the scale of the massive discontinuity in Europe that followed the fall of Rome. We did not have to start afresh, but it is a reasonable bet that, some 1300 years later, the market-gardens that supplied the early days of Covent Garden Market would have seemed very familiar to Columella. In many ways we have only overtaken Greco-Roman husbandry in the last two hundred and fifty years.

To be fair, that is a very glib statement because while modern industry uses near-universal techniques for such factory procedures as the production of TV, sets it is not the case in crop cultivation. Here, in common with most craft work, the sophisticated may exist alongside the primitive, making it difficult to talk of a specific level having been reached at any one time. In the Roman world the rich villa-owner farmed very differently from his peasant neighbour. Clearly that differential still persists across vast areas of the developing world, where a modern tractor and plough can share the scene with an ox-drawn ard.

Conquest, war and civil turmoil have sometimes swept across a farming landscape with seemingly little impact, but the destruction of one culture by another is a different matter. The conquerors may add new ways or they may only destroy the old. Often the long view of history reveals there to have been a bit of each. The irrigated arable fields of successive South American cultures ceased with the Conquistadors yet the potato survived. To the north the agrarian tribes of Amerindians lost their lands but gave the European settlers maize and pumpkin and a way of cultivating them. In India and China nomadic horsemen overwhelmed settled civilisations yet agrarian skills survived and were re-established. Across the Islamic world, in North Africa and beyond, the skills of the cultivator not only weathered the collapse of the Roman world but expanded thanks to the flowering of skills and scholarship in the early years of Muslim rule. To quote from Andrew Watson's introduction to his book *Agricultural Innovation in the Early Islamic World,*

> The agricultural achievement of the early centuries of Islam was in fact the work of different peoples whose contributions combined in different ways. Many from the Arabian Peninsula had a very long tradition of intensive, irrigated agriculture.

That tradition reached Europe through the Arab conquest of the Iberian peninsula, where the conquerors introduced new field crops, fruit and nut plantations and the many skills required to nurture such superb pleasure gardens as those within their great mosque in Cordoba and the Alhambra palace. In the eleventh century they established botanic gardens in Toledo and Seville. A hundred years later Granada and Cordoba had been added to these centres of agricultural learning and Yahya Ibn al-Awam was writing *Kitab al Felaha* (The Book of Agriculture), described by historian Sir John Glubb as a lengthy and extremely technical masterpiece. Translations reveal a mixture of the kind of folklore we read in English authors writing more than half a millennium later together with a deep and accurate understanding of the fundamentals of the cultivation of a wide range of crops including no less than 26 kinds of fruits. Readers may find that the following selection of his chapter-headings have a familiar ring about them! The soil; Soil improvement; Suiting plants to different kinds of soil; Water; Irrigation of trees and plants; Manures and composts; Application of manure; Pest and weed destruction; Cultivation of fruit trees; Planting of fruit trees and vegetables; Tree grafting; Pruning of trees; Sowing seasons and quantities to be used.

Fragments of large-scale irrigation works may make the greatest impression on today's visitors to the few surviving gardens, but it is clear that they were only one of many husbandry techniques employed. For well over seven hundred years these skills carried Moorish cultivation far above and beyond the growing of the ancient foundation crops that sustained Northern Europeans throughout their "Dark Ages".

British beginnings

Peter Woodman's contribution to *Europe's First Farmers* on the transition to farming in Ireland and Britain would seem to offer exactly the information upon which to base our understanding of the introduction of crop cultivation. Alas it does not, not for lack of scholarship nor for lack of clarity, but rather, it appears, for lack of sound evidence. Up until now the best that can be said is that both stock-keeping and arable farming were established in these islands by 5000 BP, but had probably arrived only a few centuries before. This is thought to be between 1000 and 1500 years *after* it reached some of our neighbours in North-West Europe; however why its progress stopped just short of the English Channel remains a mystery. Nor do we know how soon after the domestication of cattle they were first used as draught animals to pull an ard, but it is tempting to think that we late-comers may have avoided centuries or even millennia of the drudgery of the digging hoe. If we did our arable farming could quickly have reached field scale production.

Archaeologists regard this time as the start of great changes in the culture. What is now Wessex saw the building of Stonehenge and has produced clear evidence of metal smelting by early farmers, known after their distinctive pottery as the Beaker People. Their innovations came some 5000 years after the area was settled following the end of the last ice age; so our land, or rather some small part of it, has been cultivated for just half the time it has been under continuous human habitation.

No one I know of suggests that Britain's earliest farmers invented the practice of growing plants; the craft of cultivation was introduced from the south. So indeed were contemporary tillage tools, if not at first the ard discussed in Chapter 10 then almost certainly the digging hoe. As with the tools so with the crops, to judge by the early remains of barley, thought to be our most important Neolithic and Bronze Age cereal, and lesser traces of emmer wheat and flax, members of that same group of foundation crops that had supported farming from its outset more than 5000 years earlier and 2500 miles distant. One of the first tangible traces of tillage come from a site only a few miles from where I am writing this. It glories in the strangely contemporary name of South Street Long Barrow. It is a case of starting from scratch: the evidence consists of shallow marks in the subsoil preserved beneath a burial site dated at 3000 BC. Archaeologists have several other slightly less direct ways of establishing the where and when of the arrival of crop production. Traces of crop seeds within dwelling sites, crop plant pollen preserved in organic deposits and changes in weed and snail populations all indicate that the arable farmer, or maybe gardener, had arrived.

Over the last fifty years more and more evidence has been found of the very considerable extent of prehistoric arable farming in Britain. At Heathrow, "framework archaeology" has uncovered traces of human habitation from hunter-gatherer sites in the Mesolithic giving way to arable field systems that became slowly more ordered as they evolved through the Neolithic, until by the Middle Bronze Age large areas of land were enclosed by banks and ditches. Heathrow is only one of many sites that tell the same story, adding up to the many thousands of hectares of what the Ordnance Survey marks as "Celtic Fields", one of the most impressive survivors being embossed on the rolling landscape of Fyfield Down in Wiltshire. As we will see later, it was standard practice to plough these fields several times to prepare a suitable seedbed for a cereal crop. The botanists have even given them their own form of broad bean, *Vicia faba* "Celtica". Ever increasing areas of lowland Britain seem to have been in the hands of skilled cultivators for up to two thousand years before the Romans arrived. As I remark in Chapter 7, even after that traumatic event many British farming practices appear to have continued basically unaltered. Indeed, one report speaks of a field system whose continuous use can be traced from the late Iron Age, through the Roman period and beyond, when it was cultivated by an extensive Anglo-Saxon settlement. It is the same story at West Heslerton in East Yorkshire, where Dr Dominic Powlesland's meticulous archaeological survey of a massive area of farmland and its associated village documents just such a continuity of land use, long lost beneath later cultivation. Perhaps we should not be surprised that it took more than either the coming or the withdrawal of the Roman legions or the arrival of the Anglo-Saxons to faze a group of Yorkshire farmers. Such conservatism may suggest a somewhat less than dynamic farming community, and it is true that throughout this long time most were subsistence peasant cultivators. However that conservatism contains an element of stoicism that saw these holdings feed the population year in, year out regardless of the political turmoil going on around them.

In his recently published work *Crop Husbandry Regimes*, Marijke van der Veen gives extremely detailed information on the various forms of plant debris excavated from Iron Age sites in the North-East of England. It spreads the picture to a part of the country previously considered of little importance in prehistoric arable farming. Far from that being so, both small-scale subsistence farming and larger production units have now been identified, many in areas shunned by today's ploughmen. The familiar crops appear on site after site: emmer and spelt wheats, barley and, on some, flax and the latecomers' rye and bread wheat. And, as any gardener would expect, along with the crops remains archaeologists found massive numbers of weed seeds. The carefully sampled and recorded cropping by Peter Reynolds and his team at Butser may start to provide us with an idea of the scale of the task facing early "self sufficiency" farming families and give us some idea of the area of arable land needed per person.

Such it would appear was the steady progress of cultivation in Iron Age Britain. Then, some three thousand years after its arrival from the south it received its second visitation from the same direction: the Roman conquest. *Agricultura Romana* may not have been so great an upheaval as *pax Romana*, but within a very short time we find new field and orchard crops and fresh ways of growing them while both productive and decorative horticulture were imported "ready-made" from Rome. Typically these additions are found where our sophisticated imperial masters established their order and built their villas in the countryside. Their farms added rye, oats and flax. Villa gardens introduced new plants for both use and pleasure. New vegetables and herbs included cabbage, peas, celery, white mustard, turnips, carrots, parsnips, cucumbers, coriander, fennel and dill. The remains of a wide range of fruits such as cherries, medlars, mulberries, peaches, walnuts and quinces are found scattered around the remains of their houses. It is not proof positive that they were grown in Britain, but it is likely that many fruit trees and bushes were imported to enrich the gardens and dining-rooms of wealthy villa-owners.

In spite of all this development of husbandry skills for domestic cropping there seems to have been no agricultural revolution in the wider landscape. Farm equipment, including plough design, improved. Farmyard manure was saved and spread but there seems to have been little field redesign beyond some being joined together and the occasional straightening out of the boundaries of the tiny prehistoric paddocks said to cover only 0.1 to 0.5ha. John Wacher in *Roman Britain* tells us that "Even villas continued to use the old type Celtic fields", which "remained much as before" and that contemporary agriculturists recommended that a field should be no bigger than a ploughman and team could cultivate in a day.

With a farming community capable of producing enough food to feed itself, the increasing urban population, the resident Roman army and, as was reported at the time, exporting a surplus of some 800 cargoes of grain from London, it might well have been a case of, "If it ain't broke don't fix it." It is obvious that small fields did not mean small-scale production and it is been estimated that some Cotswold villas had as much as 300ha down to cereals. It must have produced a quite remarkable patchwork across that rolling countryside. Sites of orchard-scale fruit-growing, including vineyards, are known, including one in Lincolnshire where the land was prepared by backfilling trenches with a mixture of organic rich soil, bones and drainage materials. Such a method and such ingredients are almost identical to ones given as standard sixteen centuries later in Victorian texts.

The end of the Roman period plunged Britain into an age every bit as dark in our understanding of its farming as in what we know of its urban matters. The very small number of writings on cultivation found scattered throughout the literature from Europe's Dark Ages frequently refer back to Roman authors such as Columella. The marginalia of illuminated manuscripts occasionally depict farm-work and provide an evocative insight into how tasks were tackled and the human and animal toil involved. At their most informative they can indeed be "worth a thousand words". While both writings and sketches show that a few literate individuals retained an interest in cultivation, they produce no evidence of technical progress. Indeed, husbandry techniques regressed after the fall of Rome and in some areas did not reach the standards of the ancient world again until a thousand years later during the European Renaissance.

Historians seem to agree on two points: that the production of staples must have gone on at much the same level to support the sizeable population, estimated by some to have stood at something over one million, but that the newcomers from across the North Sea brought few new husbandry techniques with them. So we may reasonably assume that the basic crops that survived continued to be grown in much the same way for long into the Anglo-Saxon era, an opinion strengthened by Michael Wood when he points out that Roman Villa estate management techniques appear to have been quickly adopted by their new occupants, the Anglo-Saxon aristocracy. Indeed Stephen Pollington's comment that "by the 8th century a distinctively Anglo-Saxon crop assemblage is in: einkorn, rye, barley and oats are the main cereal crops" gives the Saxons four hundred years to achieve these changes; hardly an agricultural revolution.

If farming managed to go on in spite of the political drama taking place all round it, the same cannot be said for horticulture. The Roman *hortus* that had brought a mass of sophisticated gardening techniques to these shores, and whose reproduction we can see in some "restored" villa gardens, was lost. It is doubtful if even our most Romanised residents continued to grow anything like the same range of fruit and vegetables, let alone flowers, that could have been found surrounding literally thousands of homes for the previous three to four hundred years.

When and from whom we regained our cultivation skills is unclear. There is sound evidence of "Roman" crops being gardened in mainland Europe during our Dark Ages, particularly by the monks. One location provides us with two written, but very different, pieces of hard evidence showing that religious communities did indeed keep horticultural skills alive during those turbulent days. The place is the monastery of St Gall in Switzerland and the evidence comes from a drawing and a book. The drawing is the AD 820 master-plan of the abbey. Not only does it name fruits and vegetables but gives a good indication of the size of orchards and the layout of the cropping beds.

The book, from the same century, is *The Little Garden* written by Brother Walafred Strabo in the form of a poem. Eleanour Sinclair Rhode, that most erudite garden historian and practical nursery owner, enthused over it, although a review no matter how favourable 1200 years after the event is somewhat academic. Perhaps it was the following down-to-earth, timeless description of Brother Walafred's struggle to eradicate stinging nettles that endeared him to her.

> Deep down the roots were matted and linked and riveted like basket-work or the wattled hurdles of the fold. I prepare to attack, armed with the Tooth of Saturn [a mattock?], tear up the clods and rend them from the clinging network of nettle roots.

If the good monk's battle with nettles is immediately recognisable to today's gardeners so surely must be his recommendation to use "*well rotted* manure", advice that must make that still almost obligatory qualification one of the oldest in the gardening lexicon.

The existence of an Anglo-Saxon term for peach tree, *persoc tréu*, suggests that esculent [g] gardening even of exotic fruits hung on in a few places in these islands. To quote Stephen Pollington again, "Gardens set aside specifically for the cultivation of herbs are known from the seventh century onwards in England, at monastic sites such as Ely and Thorney." But that is a gap of two centuries after the Romans left!

There is a final point to make before we leave our agricultural origins. You might think that nothing remains from these early days, that neither the field patterns nor the equipment nor the materials survive unchanged, only the cycle of the seasons persists. But you would be wrong; those first crops, wheat, barley, oats and field beans, still dominate our arable landscape.

Six hundred years after the departure of the Romans the conquering Normans occupied a country still lagging behind

Southern Europe in many of the more sophisticated cultivation techniques, not least those practised under Islam. The huge changes in both farm layouts and husbandry practices that marked the early medieval era are dealt with in Chapter 7. But new crops indicate that changes took place even in this most rigid of farming systems. Rape for oil was established in the fourteenth century and a little later flax and hemp, brought over from mainland Europe, supported rope- and sail-making industries in Wessex. These introductions mark the beginning of the ebb and flow of arable crops. The fibre crops, for example, went out of cultivation with the demise of the trades they supplied and centuries later turnips, introduced as stock feed around 1750, almost vanished with changes to sheep management. Potatoes became a field crop in about 1800 and finally in the twentieth century came sugarbeet, the re-emergence of rape and, very recently, maize for silage. Remarkably, these four are the only significant additions to those seminal crops in today's arable landscape.

CROP ORIGINS AND MIGRATIONS
The first crops

It is impossible to say just how many of the 300,000 kinds of vascular plants that make up the world flora man has used during our wanderings across the globe. We have developed less than 0.5 per cent as crops and recently Schoonhoven estimated that 95 per cent of our food comes from no more than 30 species. And yet studies show that the local people select more than 90 per cent of the woody plants of the Amazon for specific uses.

There is a big difference between use and cultivation. Most authorities consider it reasonable to assume that the gatherers collected a wide range of plant species for the pot, but in contrast very few became the staples of agriculture. We know very little of the weeding-out process in between. However, Anthony Huxley in *Plant and Planet* cites two archaeological sites in Iran where the remains of several no longer grown species of legume seem to have been cultivated for their protein-rich seeds That difference between use and cultivation helps explain why a dictionary such as George Usher's *Plants Used by Man* runs to some 12,000 entries. Nearer to home we can take a look in Sir John Hill's *Family Herbal* of 1812 and discover a total of 500 British plants "remarkable for their virtues". From such massive numbers other authors have extracted the food plants. Dr Lewis Sturtevant's *Edible Plants of the World* describes over 1300, which he implies is a very conservative selection. Including that most contentious group of "useful" plants, the species with psychoactive properties, adds significantly more to the list as, while the developed world struggles with the impact of the handful grown as often illegal crops, experts have studied more than 90 others in use around the world.

The authors mentioned above set out to list all the plants that played a part in the lives of long-gone pre-industrial communities. Some of these exploited plants were cultivated, but others, probably the majority, were gathered from the wild. Indeed many, particularly those with medicinal value, were probably in an intermediate class, part of the local flora but nevertheless with a few specimens flourishing as garden plants "for the wise woman's convenience". The Queen's Garden at the Royal Botanic Gardens, Kew, holds just such a collection of some forty medicinal herbs selected from seventeenth-century literature. A lot are clearly garden plants, including many from Southern Europe. Others could easily have been gathered locally from the wild, but not now I fancy off Kew Green. Among the imports is globe artichoke:

> Some write that if the yoong buds of Artichokes be first steeped in wine and eaten, it provoketh urine, and stirreth up the lust of the bodie. I finde moreover, that the roote is good against the rank smel of the arme holes, if when the pith is taken away the same roote be boiled in wine and drunk.

Meanwhile, our native flora provides primroses:

> The rootes of Primrose stamped and strained, and the juice sniffed into the nose with a quill, or such like, purgeth the braine, and qualifieth the paine of the migrime ...

Today the range of plants in regular use has shrunk, together with our knowledge of how to use many of the missing entries. Our attitude towards eating plants has changed. Nowadays many people's first thought is towards the risk of poisoning, whereas in the past vast numbers of plants were used for each of the major culinary roles, for example Sholto Douglas in *Alternative Foods: A World Guide to Lesser Known Edible Plants* lists over 40 saladings, 50 pot herbs and an amazing 200 species producing non-alcoholic beverages.

Just as there can be some understandable confusion between "wild" and "cultivated", we should differentiate also between natural species and the cultivars they have given rise to. For hundreds of years virtually all our cultivated plants have been man-made by the selection of, to us, beneficial mutations and chance or deliberate hybridisation. Our shops, fields, parks, sports fields and gardens are almost entirely populated by unnatural plants. Year round my local greengrocer (fortunately we still have one) sells only two wild species, brazil nuts and mistletoe. It is much the same in the florists' department, where only the desert cactus and a very few foliage plants are as nature left them. Just how, where and when these changes happen is outside the scope of this book but there are many writers who deal admirably with such questions. Some such as Mangelsdorf focus on one crop; others including Vavilov, Tudge, H. G. Baker, and Langer and Hill review a wider range of food plants; yet others such as Harwood and Fisher also deal with decorative subjects.

Crops can be discovered several times as they come to the notice of successive groups of farmers. Sunflowers are a crop that's currently in vogue around the world. But it is not a new crop, nor was it when the seventeenth-century settlers from Europe worked out its cultural requirements and sowed sunflower fields in the Americas. Come to that, neither was it when the Spanish grew it two hundred years before. The first sunflower cultivators were Amerindians five hundred years before that.

After reading Sholto Douglas we should perhaps not be too surprised to find some 400 distinct crops in the *Collins Field Guide to the Crops of Britain and Europe*. At the other end of the scale is the approach taken by the writers of such agricultural textbooks as Lockhart and Wiseman's *Crop Husbandry*. They describe the cultivation of some twenty major crops that so dominate arable farming in Britain today that taken together they occupy over ninety-five per cent of the land.

Why this handful of now dominant crop plants rose to such prominence is not clear; certainly it is not because they showed outstanding early promise if such miserable examples as wild cabbage, carrot, beet, maize, and tomato are anything to go by. Indeed some wild ancestors such as those of beans and cassava were even poisonous, yet they were among the chosen few. Having a useful harvest is a very different matter from cultivating the plant that bears it. One thing modern horticulture and agriculture have taught us is how relatively easy it is to learn to grow most plants as a crop if there's the incentive. Who a generation ago would have thought of fields of evening primrose (for oil) or glasshouses full of pots of ivy as houseplants?

Evidence from around the world shows that the first plants to be cultivated, the so-called foundation crops, were not new foods; they were components of the local flora and had long been important items in the gatherers' diet. When ethnobotanists talk of the "domestication" of crop plants they refer to the genetic changes that combine to turn a wild plant into a crop plant. Those changes are not only about larger yields but more about a plant conforming to the needs of the cultivator. For example it is essential that seeds don't fall before or during harvest due to seed-heads shattering or pods bursting. Such disintegration happens in wild grasses but not in cultivated cereals.

Professor Hillman is confident that these changes took place thanks to the activities of very early pioneer cultivators, most probably at the stage of proto-agriculture; indeed there is sound observational evidence to show that, even in the absence of deliberate selection, the genetic base of a population of a species can change rapidly under the influence of man's activities.

Hillman argues that organised farming as we think of it, where whole villages are dependent on the harvests of the surrounding arable fields, did not become the norm for most communities for hundreds or even thousands of years after the start of small-scale domestication. Looked at in that way, the seed of improved crop plants was available before the development of organised arable farming. Indeed that's the way he considers it had to be, because dependence on the large-scale but primitive cultivation of wild species cannot make sense as the yields will not compensate for the effort required to produce them.

Foundation crops

Archaeologists who have studied sites occupied around the time when the local inhabitants were first embarking on crop cultivation are at times confronted with the evidence of remains of four very different kinds of food plants. Typically, and even well after the establishment of farming, researchers find copious remains of wild plants gathered in their season and consumed as a normal part of the diet. It is likely that their leaves, stems and roots added bulk to the contents of the cooking pot as well as being in themselves valuable components of the diet. It seems that for a long time these fresh offerings continued to be foraged from the wild but eventually a few became our vegetables, the province of that second group of cultivators the gardeners.

Along with these specimens of the local flora, excavations unearth two groups of domesticated plants. The most important for the story of farming and as a food supply are the foundation crops. Over time these became the basis of arable farming. Authorities identify eight such seminal crops from the Fertile Crescent; all are to us outsiders. Originating as wild plants in the Levant, most travelled across Europe with the spread of civilisation. Not surprisingly the first six are food plants; two types of wheat (emmer and einkorn), barley and the legume pulses lentil, chickpea, bitter vetch and pea. The last of the list, flax, is now mostly thought of as a fibre plant although at the outset it almost certainly had a dual role, providing both food and fibre.

The remains of these foundation crops are found time and again in excavations of the appropriate period throughout the Middle East. In most cases it is the seeds or fruits that are unearthed, being associated with either post-harvest storage or food preparation, or else with the cooking process.

From this evidence it seems that in every case it was the seeds of the foundation crops that were eaten, giving rise to probably the first cereal-and-pulse-based diets. Seeds offer two huge advantages over other plant parts such as stems, roots and leaves: they can be stored dry indefinitely following a single annual harvest, and they are far and away a more concentrated source of nutrition. Seeds alone make anything approaching a vegan diet possible and a mix of those gathered from the foundation crops supplied a reasonable balance between carbohydrates and proteins. Of course we are not certain how large a part plants played in these peoples' diets and it is clear that that varied from place to place and over time, even from season to season. We should remember that *Homo sapiens* is equipped as an omnivore and that a very wide range of animals, both wild and later domesticated, were consumed at different times and in different parts of the world.

The third group of food plants are the herbs, many of them perennials, that are used in small quantities for their powerful flavours or medicinal proprieties. As I said before, they may have played a significant part in very early attempts at cultivation. Many of these plants have remained almost unaltered over the thousands of years since they were taken into cultivation by these first cottage gardeners.

The final group is the fruit-bearing trees, vines and bushes. I have already looked at the unique challenges of bringing such permanent but slow-to-crop plants into cultivation. As yet we do not know when the odd tree scattered round the village became the orchards so clearly depicted in Egyptian murals.

The first improvements and hybrids

It is obvious that our cultivated plants, or at least their ancestors, must have started as wild components of a local flora somewhere in the world. From those beginnings many crop plants have developed to such an extent that we can no longer be certain of their specific origins and it is not possible to point to any one exact wild progenitor. Such plants are known as "cultigens", hybrid mixes that probably contain genes from several wild species. An excellent example of this is the most important group of food plants in the world, or one of them: the wheats. Taken together they are now the world's most extensively cultivated crop yet in the form we know them none exist in nature. They are hybrids, and the most important member of the group, bread wheat, contains the genes of at least four grass species, but if that were not remarkable enough these ancestors belong to two separate genera. Surely this remarkable sequence of matings and the associated doubling of chromosomes that facilitated fertility must rank as the most fortunate act to have occurred by chance in the fields of the early farmers. It is thought that the first crosses occurred early in the development of farming in the Fertile Crescent but the final hybridisation that produced bread wheat came when these forms met and bred with a weed grass in the area around northeastern Turkey, Armenia and Georgia some ten thousand years ago. Hybrids that combine the genes of such distant relatives are rare and are now achieved by so-called genetic engineering; how lucky we are that no Sumerian protesters pulled up that first seedling destined to become the mother of so much of the grain in the world's bread basket. The story of the evolution of bread wheat is paralleled in the Americas by that of corn (maize). There has been a tremendous amount of research by such workers as Leonard Blake and Hugh Cutler based at Missouri Botanic Garden, St Louis, that has helped plot the early development of this crop by Native American farmers.

To many people a wild species appears to be made up of a population of identical individuals, offering little or no room for the selection of those with desirable traits. However, our ever expanding understanding of genetics has taught us that this is not so. In every wild population there is in fact a wide, albeit usually hidden, variation in the expression of many of the characters that go to make up an individual. The gene base of a species is larger than that held in any one individual.

Such "natural" selection depends on the success of individuals or their offspring that have the most suitable "hand of cards" for the prevailing conditions regardless of whether these conditions occur in a wild habitat or a farmer's field. Although this may seem like a long and tedious process, it has been found that many genetically inherited characters are quickly and easily influenced by the basic acts of cultivation. This has been shown, much to the concern of ecologists, when a species, at risk in the wild, is taken into cultivation. It takes only a comparatively few generations for significant changes to accrue.

So we know that the origins of genetic diversity are already present in every wild population, but with plants that is only the start of the story. Most plant species can hybridise with at least some of their close relatives, that is with others in the same genus. Thus, unlike animals, plants have the potential for producing a wide range of often fertile bi-specific hybrids [g]. A small number of these hybrids have been found among wild populations, many more when two closely related species are grown in close proximity as often happens, to everyone's embarrassment, in botanic gardens! Nevertheless most require the direct intervention of man, either to affect the transfer of pollen or as the much more elaborate manoeuvres involved in today's techniques of plant-breeding.

We shall probably never know the details of our involvement in the first genetic improvements that changed wild plants into the improved forms that eventually became today's high-yielding cultivars. We know from the retrieval of the remains of ancient seeds that these changes started only a few hundred years after our ancestors' first endeavours as cultivators. These, from our point of view, improved forms probably arose as naturally occurring selections, the offspring of a small number of plants within the population of thousands that made up the crop. In some cases their success would have depended on their being better adapted to the conditions cultivation imposed on them. Others were probably found by sharp-eyed cultivators and deliberately nurtured for their desirable traits. As we have seen, increase in seed size and non-shattering seed heads in cereals probably came high on that list. Indeed the increase in seed size that resulted in the harvest organ assuming a greater proportion of the total dry weight of the crop plant may well have been the greatest single factor contributing to the yield improvement gained over wild stands in the first millennia of farming.

At first sight the most remarkable thing about the emergence of these genetic changes is the ability of the villagers to pick out the slight improvements. The second is that they had the discipline and foresight to save and sow the improved form rather than enjoy the pleasure of a more easily filled cooking pot. It may be however that this skill and willpower was at least helped by the basic "rules" of Darwinian evolution. Some advantageous changes have been described as "unconscious selection". The theory of natural selection suggests that, inevitably, generation after generation, year after year, "improved forms" (our definition) would have come to dominate the population if they were also the best at exploiting the new circumstances created by the transition from the wild habitat to a primitive arable field. In so doing they would slowly have become the main content of both the sown field and, hence, the cooking pot.

This all seems like useful steady progress, but developing and keeping valuable subspecific characteristics is full of difficulties. With some plants, saving a quantity of the harvest to sow for the following crop is relatively trouble-free and without too many nasty surprises. With other crops the new generation can bear little resemblance to the plant you gathered it from, particularly if that plant is growing near to other forms with which it can hybridise. Like the blades on Boadicea's chariot wheels, hybridisation cuts both ways. It can produce inferior offspring as well as improvements.

Before the days of a highly professional and regulated seed trade the difference between getting a uniform "stand" of seedlings rather than a mixture of various shapes sizes and colours was often linked to the way the plant is pollinated. Many plants cannot fertilise themselves, but such outbreeding species will receive and accept pollen from any of their broad kin that are within range. This results in a diverse mixture of individuals rather than a recognisable "race" or cultivar being perpetuated. It is as if all the genes from far and wide went back into the melting-pot every generation. In contrast, inbreeding or self-pollinating plants such as peas and beans are the predictable, dependable chaps that, apart from the rare appearance of a mutation, reproduce faithful replicas of their parent. Slowly, by roguing [g] the seed crop and preventing unwanted cross-pollination [g], even outbreeding [g] crops developed recognisable "varieties".

CULTIVATED PLANTS AND SUPERNATURAL BELIEFS
The basic acts of cultivation, and some method of applying them, all appear to have been discovered before recorded history. These activities include land tillage, sowing, weeding, spacing, nutrition and irrigation; measures were also taken against the curse of pests and diseases, even if there were no effective controls.

So in broad terms people knew what had to be done, and yet they generally got very low yields when measured by today's standards. In almost every society, regardless of race or religion, it seems that running alongside that basic understanding of the work required to grow a crop was a fear of the mysterious, apparently supernatural, natural world. It seemed that some power within nature might at any time snatch the harvest, leaving famine in its wake. It is as if people could not bring themselves to trust the prosaic routine work of the cultivator. A good harvest demanded the addition of some extra discipline, act or ritual.

Some of this ceremony and magic attempted to influence

environmental conditions, particularly the weather, which otherwise might bring storms, floods or droughts in the growing season and rain at harvest. Some however were clearly linked to what were then the hidden mysteries of plant biology. The advent of pests and diseases, seed dormancy, viability and storage; germination, cell division, flower initiation, pollination and fertilisation, fruit development and ripening – all these and many more took place, or failed to take place, apparently independent of anything the grower could do. Such attitudes persisted for thousands of years; some have been recorded by anthropologists, particularly Bronislaw Malinowski working in the early years of the twentieth century in Melanesia. He catalogued the incredibly close interrelationship between magic rites and each husbandry activity from land clearance and basic tillage to planting, weeding and harvest.

So while I feel certain that a good harvest motivated their physical efforts in the field, it seems that growers have never been averse to soliciting a little help from afar. From as far back as the archaeological evidence takes us, man has called upon the supernatural to aid him in his quest for food. The famous cave paintings of Southern Europe, Africa and Australia span a huge period of time, yet almost all appear to depict hunting and the hunted with scant reference to plant-gathering. However there are exceptions such as late rock art in both Northern Italy and Sweden, where people are shown ploughing with oxen. If archaeologist Professor Herbert Kuhn's argument that the advent of cultivation changed art is correct, we should not expect to see graphic representations of crop production. He believes that whereas the hunter depicted the here-and-now, first in the naturalistic style we find at, for example, Lascaux and later by more stylised representations of the hunt, cultivators' concerns have always been dominated by the seasons and the vagaries of the climate. As he puts it, "they seek to commune with the divine powers that no human will can command but who bring warmth, fructifying rain, dew – and storms". He argues that the more man reached out to what is beyond their sight and touch, the more their art become removed from the incidental. They attempted to portray eternal forces through geometrical forms, in circles triangles and squares. Who would have thought that farmers were responsible for abstract art?

Some writers consider that the various female "Earth Mother" or "Venus" figurines discovered at Upper Palaeolithic sites suggest a recognition of our dependence on the total productivity of the Earth. Indeed there seems a general agreement that the gods of vegetation who were believed to be responsible for plants starting into growth each spring were worshipped long before agrarian pursuits superseded hunting and gathering as the mainstay of daily sustenance. It has been suggested that after that transition to a dependence on cereals such vegetation deities became the "corn gods".

All across the world, once man becomes involved in plant cultivation and thereby responsible for an annual harvest sufficient to feed his people he seems to have become very willing to share that responsibility with the supernatural world, if not to hand it over. In *The Golden Bough* Sir James Frazer places Adonis in this role and identifies Osiris the Egyptian god of death as another "of many corn gods" whose spring resurrection rites he considered to be essentially a festival of sowing,

> which properly fell at the time when the husbandman actually committed the seed to the earth. On that occasion an effigy of the corn-god, moulded of earth and corn, was buried with funeral rites in the ground in order that, dying there, he might come to life again with the new crops.

Throughout this massive, authoritative work Frazer emphasises that in many ancient beliefs the links between plants and "their" gods are perceived to be so close that the plant may be venerated and ascribed supernatural powers.

Typically festivals coincide with specific, critical times in the farming calendar, stages in crop growth or cultivation practices. Within the last hundred years various groups around the world have continued to endeavour to nudge nature and their land to yield rich harvests. Typically, and to the horror of Christian missionaries, it was by example that the Good Earth was reminded of its ability to be fecund. As Professor Will Durant put it, most were

> festivals of promiscuity coming in nearly all cases at the season of sowing as a ceremony of suggestion to the earth in spring to abandon her wintry reserve, accept the proffered seed and prepare to deliver herself of a generous litter of food.

No wonder the Reverend H. Rowley was shocked when he found that "not only is full sexual licence permitted but any visitor attending the festival is encouraged to indulge in licentiousness."

By far the most bizarre horticultural advice I have come across claiming supernatural intervention also involves sex! These instructions come to us from long ago down a long chain of translations. English from Spanish from Arabic takes us back to al-Awam. He knew it from *Agricultura Nabatea*, Ibn Wahsiyya's tenth-century translation of Kutsami's book written in Chaldean, a text thought to have been derived from ancient Babylonian writings. I reproduce Peter McLoughlin's translation of these instructions without comment; save to say that grafting must have required even greater dexterity then than now.

To graft,

> Find an extremely beautiful maiden, take her by the hand and place her above the roots of the tree which is going to receive [be grafted]. Cut a branch to make the scion. An incision is opened in the tree at the same time as the maiden undresses and whilst taking off ones own clothes. The scion is placed in the appropriate place whilst making love with the maiden standing up.

The annual cycle of the seasons was celebrated by religious ceremonies at the time of sowing and reaping from very early times. Around 550 BC the young Buddha is said to have witnessed a Brahman ploughing festival the memory of which when he later sought enlightenment helped him to the realisation that joy and happiness could be found on Earth without recourse to the extreme of either asceticism or sensual indulgence. Today Christians have their harvest festivals, although there are reputedly often more tins of baked beans than sheaths of wheat. I doubt that the Hindu festival of Pongal faces the same problem in Southern India. In the USA, Thanksgiving was, and still is, based on the East Coast seasons, behind which the rest of the continent falls into line.

World-wide there are fewer examples of specific husbandry tasks being blessed. However, the *Penguin Dictionary of Ancient History* reminds us that in Rome the "list of the gods a farmer could invoke" included First Plougher, Second Plougher, Harrower, Sower, Top Dresser, Hoer, Raker, etc. Quite a useful supporting cast. The early polytheist religions are rich in gods specifically linked to the major crops of the region. Grecian corn was looked over by the goddess Demeter, who "became" the goddess Ceres in Rome. Her festival, the Cerialia, was celebrated on 19 April. That may seem to us an odd time to chose, since it is neither the start nor the end of her annual story, but in Italy that's when the cereals come into ear, and that's what matters. Today's scholars seem fascinated to note that she had her strongest following among "the plebs", but I like that idea: for those at the bottom of the pecking order a full stomach is definitely something to be grateful for.

Later religions, and particularly their rural followers, have been loath to abandon these links with the land and, as we see elsewhere, the Christian church blesses the plough as well as the harvest. Immature apple crops were "christened" and while various saints' days are cited for this unlikely event I can find no indication of a ceremony; maybe it was left to the saint to do. Not so long ago, before such rites became tourist attractions, superstitious members of the farming community gathered to call upon the help of other-worldly supernatural powers. The links between the land, fertility and plants can be seen in such activities as the West of England wassailing of apple orchards on the eve of Epiphany. In its pre-tourist form this involved the awakening of the tree spirits by banging on improvised drums and firing guns together with much cider drinking and toasting of the trees with:

> Here's to you old apple tree, whence thou may'st bud, and whence thou may'st blow and whence thou may'st bear apples enow!

Cherries had to wait a little longer; they received their blessing in full bloom. Richard Mabey in his superb book *Flora Britannica* says of the spring festivals: "Rites for encouraging growth in the fields clustered around the movable feast of Rogationtide, and Rogation Sunday became officially sanctioned by the church for the blessing of crops." Folklore across the world abounds with thousands of figures similar to our "Green Man", part-tree, part-human, and everywhere there are the agriculturally ever active "Little People".

Throughout the world local people have made endless links between specific plants in their wild flora and the supernatural. Most of these relate to non-crop species, although many were gathered for use as medicines or poisons. A few examples, particularly among trees, carry over into the time when they entered cultivation.

The mysticism surrounding the apple deserves a study of its own. We must however be careful, as the name has been used by translators to cover various desirable but otherwise unrelated fruits found in the ancient literature of the Middle East from the Old Testament to Greek mythology. In spite of such confusion, our apples, kinds of *Malus*, appear throughout Northern European folklore. Idunn's "apples of youth" are not only the gods' source of vital force; they are the real thing, the apples we know and love, or at least their direct ancestors. The most tantalising and frustratingly enigmatic reference I have found notes "the apple orchard's role in early English courting rituals". It would be nice to know a lot more about the cultivation of orchards of this date, let alone these rituals; and what did a suitor do if no one had had the foresight to plant an orchard in his village?

Crop cultivation tends to carry superstitions associated with dates for sowing, planting and starting to harvest. Columella instructs his readers to sow and cultivate by the phases of the moon, while centuries later timings are often based on the ecclesiastical calendar. "On Candlemas Day stick [broad] beans in the clay" insured that that hardiest of vegetables was sown at the beginning of February; you were allowed to hold back if soil conditions were poor, but "by St Chad sowe good or bad". Easter as your guide gave no such fixed date with it running free of the temporal calendar at the all-important spring sowing season.

Although such links faded with the advance of scientific understanding over the last two hundred years, their echo is still with us. Some amateur gardeners still sow crops, particularly potatoes, on Good Friday whenever it falls, or as the old folks said, they planted their "taters" at the foot of the Cross. Many a New-Age "muck and mystery" cultivator is as keen on the mystery as the muck. Books are published every year giving advice on lunar seed-sowing and some of the sentiments of the harvest festival service don't bear too close scientific scrutiny.

CULTIVATION PRACTICES IN THE SIXTEENTH TO NINETEENTH CENTURIES

By the mid sixteenth century when Thomas Tusser wrote his celebrated series of poems under the title *Five Hundred Points of Good Husbandry* British farming was still slowly emerging from centuries of medieval stagnation. Further south, things seem to have got off to an earlier renascence; indeed the Bolognese writer Piero de' Crescenzi wrote his massive twelve-volume *Liber ruralium commodorum* around 1309. Although it was often republished over two hundred years, and hence in circulation in Tusser's day, it was not translated into English and even now we know it mainly from the reproduction of the illustrations it gained in its later editions. Crescenzi wrote on both the farming and gardening of his day, but recent critics point out how much his advice rested on the classical authors we have already met. So it may have done, but that was the approach taken by all the writers of the period and as far as cultivation goes we know of little new for him to have said.

Tusser is by far the best known of the few early British writers on farming that based their comments on their own observations rather than reproduce a stream of quotations from the classical authors. An educated (Eton and Cambridge) "gentleman farmer" he gave clearly sound advice in the majority of his "points" but they strike me as a codification of existing good practice more valuable to novices than to practical farmers with generations of experience behind them.

For the next three hundred years British agriculture was set to progress on the enthusiasm, writings, inventions and experiments of such landed gentry.

A century after Tusser, in the closing stages of the Civil War Walter Blith wrote *The English Improver Improved*. At one level Blith's book provides accurate practical advice on the cultivation of even such minor crops as saffron and woad yet there can be no doubt that he hoped to reach a far more influential readership than the nation's farmers. Indeed before the book proper starts he spends some fifty pages in the form of a series of extended introductions addressed to those with power. He seems to have thought of everyone. Starting with no less than "The Lord Generall" Oliver Cromwell, he goes on to include "The Councill of State" the Nobility, Gentry, the "Houses of Court and Universities" and "The Souldiery of the Nations".

Blith had risen to the rank of captain in the New Model Army and his commitment to the "Common-wealth" and all that it stood for seems the real motivation behind the many hours it must have taken to pen the book's 262 pages. Clearly Blith had no patience with stick-in-the-muds that stood in the way of progress. He saw the authority of parliament as the way of enforcing change. Blith's concern was very much in line with what today's agricultural economists call the National Farm. To him the greatest "improvements" hinged on such basics as enclosure and drainage but on a scale that required state intervention, actions above and beyond the authority of individual farmers.

His broad view reminds us that some of the major advances in cultivation have depended on changes in both the law and the structure of society. That his book survived the Restoration only eight years after its publication, to remain a standard farming text for over a century, indicates its value to practitioners. Were the by then almost treasonable political polemics removed or were they simply overlooked by down-to-earth farmers in search of improved methods?

The eighteenth century saw the beginnings of cultivators gaining an insight into the science of their craft, the first glimmers of what academics might now call the physics, chemistry and biology of agronomy. At the same time the enthusiasm of the landed gentry for agricultural improvements based on such knowledge spurred several to write books – serious, learned, but still very down-to-earth volumes through whose pages we can trace the growth of our understanding of what cultivation does and what goes on around and within plants.

There is even evidence that writings on the practicalities of agronomy preceded academic study. The translators of John Ray's Cambridgeshire *Catalogus Plantarum* of 1660 claim it as the first study of the British flora by "the father of British botany", but it was by no means the first book addressing the growth of plants. As they concede, "Up to the time of Ray, works on plants had been written mainly for utilitarian reasons and the study of botany was merely a by-product of medicine, agriculture and horticulture."

Today's technical progress in plant cultivation as in other things develops from our understanding of the sciences that underlie it. This makes it extremely hard for us to appreciate John Ray's world. On the one hand he was surrounded by evidence of man's intellectual achievements. The writings of Shakespeare were already some fifty years old and the architectural glory of King's College Chapel over a hundred.

On the other hand the farmers in the Cambridgeshire countryside were growing cereals in ways that had changed little in more than fifteen hundred years. None of his fellow academics were interested in plants, as Ray tells us:

> Among so many masters of learning and luminaries of letters I found not a single person who was deeply versed in botany and only one or two who had even the slightest acquaintance with the subject.

Ultimately botany and the other sciences would provide a link between intellectual thought and the craft of cultivation, but it was a slow process that was to take some three hundred years. To help chart that progress I will continue my perusal of some of the books published between the middle of the sixteenth and the start of the nineteenth centuries. One is very small, two very large and the others somewhere in-between. The first to be published was Thomas Hill's *The Gardener's Labyrinth* of 1577, then one of the awkward two that won't fit on the bookshelves, John Evelyn's famous *Sylva* of 1664. That is followed by the smallest, *The Florists Vade-mecum* by Samuel Gilbert, dated 1682. Then comes Philip Miller's giant *The Gardeners Dictionary* in its third edition of 1737.

The first thing that impresses me about all these books is the detailed, reasonable and timeless descriptions of the basic husbandry tasks. If you updated the language and remembered to change the printer's long "s" to a short one you could use large chunks of any of them as a crib when writing an article for the amateur gardening page of the local paper. Take this piece from 1682 on growing double-flowered stocks: "To raise them, get good seeds of right kinds, as of the striped single ones, for the double never yield you any."

Unlike most herbals of that time, Samuel Gilbert's book makes little attempt to link plant growth to astronomical bodies or astrology; he is a down-to-earth craftsman. Miller's instructions for growing chicory seem straight from a gardeners' question time:

> Their seeds should be sown in an open situation and a good rich soil, but not too thick. When the plants have come up, and grown to be about two inches high they must be transplanted into another good open spot of ground at about ten inches distant every way.

Miller has greater ambitions and includes a lot of unlikely entries in his alphabetical listings. He seems to delight in holding forth at length on his communications with the scientists or, as he knows them, the "philosophers" of his day. Light, heat, water, gravity and nitre are among his entries but none has more than a hint that these subjects have a role to play in the growth of crops or, as he calls plant physiology, "the business of plants". Nevertheless things are starting to look up compared with the disinterest poor Ray found only eighty years before.

All these books are technical tomes and devote little if any space to the lives of those who are practising the crafts they so enthusiastically promote. Social historians tell us another story: throughout the whole of this period, land workers throughout Europe lived, to us, mean, unimaginably hard lives: dwelling in hovels, possessing no comforts and few necessities, and surviving on a diet based on cereals together with a few home-grown vegetables and meagre additions of dairy produce with, very occasionally, meat.

Evelyn the forester is every bit as much a cultivator as the others, indeed his *Kalendarium Hortense*, at first bound into the back of the 1664 edition of *Sylva*, was later issued as a separate publication that went through even more editions than the great book itself.

His advice on tree pruning, following some criticism of typical poor workmanship, still rings true:

> In a word by cutting clean, smooth and close, making the stroke upward and with a sharp bill so as the weight of an untractable bough do not splice and carry the bark with it which is both dangerous and unsightly. The proper season for this work is a little after the change in January.

Evelyn was both a contemporary of Ray and a fellow member of the newly formed Royal Society. I hope the two enjoyed meeting and sharing their enthusiasm for "the vegetable kingdom".

By the time we approach the end of the eighteenth century we have a host of titles to chose from. Judging by both the number of editions and the numerous copies that have survived, *Every Man His Own Gardener* by Thomas Mawe and John Abercrombie must have been among the most popular. It appeared at the very time when the market-gardens round the cities of Northern Europe including London were at their peak of production, and American landowners like Thomas Jefferson were developing a deep understanding of land management, from the advantages of contour ploughing to the use of legumes in rotations. It is a safe rather than a revolutionary text, but the detail far exceeds earlier attempts to provide practical guidelines:

> May is now a proper time to sow any of the dwarf kinds of peas. These sorts seldom grow above two or three feet high; some not above 15 or 18 inches but are mostly great bearers, the pods small but numerous and the peas while young eat sweet and good. Sow them in drills two feet or two and a half feet asunder.

Of course taken individually the early books on cultivation don't present a smooth progress from ignorance to knowledge, and as today each reveals almost as much about its author as about its subject. Thus much of William Forsyth's 1818 *Treatise on the Culture and Management of Fruit Trees* is little more than a pseudo-scientific justification for his "discovery" of a way of rejuvenating old trees with the aid of his wound-coating "composition". And that great cultivator Thomas Andrew Knight obviously saw through the mumbo-jumbo, believing Forsyth's "experiments" were being championed for "some motive of private interest with which the public are not acquainted".

Turning to the happier subject of praiseworthy books of the period, McMahon's *American Gardeners' Calendar* heads my list. As an Irish immigrant arriving in Philadelphia in 1796, Bernard McMahon tells us he found horticulture in a sad state. By 1806 his efforts to improve it stretched to over 600 pages of clear instruction blended, as he puts it in the introduction, with efforts "to induce an association of the science of botany with practical horticulture without which the latter can never be so advantageously conducted". The eleventh edition appeared in 1857, by which time it was known as *McMahon's American Gardener*; he richly deserves his commemoration through the genus Mahonia.

There were at least two Britons with similar qualities, both of them Scots. Walter Nicol wrote the extremely clear and informative *Gardeners Kalendar* that appeared in several editions in the early years of the nineteenth century. Unlike so many horticulturists-turned-authors of that era, he describes in his book just what he promises in the foreword:

> Methods of culture both simple and easy (divested of the bustle and intricacy assumed in many works on forcing) and tending to inculcate, throughout, a love for the science, and application, in the young gardener.

Having designed and overseen the construction of many productive walled gardens, Nicol writes from first-hand experience, making it clear that much of their development often ascribed to late Victorian gardening was known over three-quarters of a century earlier.

Robert Thompson, superintendent of the Royal Horticultural Society's garden, was the author of *The Gardener's Assistant, Practical and Scientific.* Writing some years later than Nicol, in 1859, he seems to have been a real searcher after the links between treatment and result, be it in the use of fertilisers or the physical conditions of heat and light in which plants were grown. Thompson seems the sort of chap you would expect to meet today in a research station. It is clear that he delights in the idea of cause and effect in the cultivator's quest for quantity and quality.

My enthusiasm for these two must not make me overlook another book that gave prominence to reporting on the plant science of its day; indeed Charles's McIntosh's *The Book of the Garden* went to press six years before Thompson's. McIntosh was yet another head gardener, albeit in the grand style, being at one time "Curator of the Royal Gardens of His Majesty the King of the Belgians at Claremont and Brussels". *The Book of the Garden* comes in two volumes with a combined total of 1640 pages of small print; around 50 per cent is dedicated to techniques of plant cultivation. The book is obsequiously dedicated, with permission, to none other than Queen Victoria, which may explain a certain lack of spontaneity in style, although this could also have come, as he tells Her Majesty in the dedication, from writing "when often bowed down with fatigue in body and mind". How long would the tome have been, one may wonder, had he come fresh each day to the task?

As a glimpse into these old books reveals, slowly over these three centuries cultivators have come to understand a great deal about what goes on both within and around their crops. It is only during the second half of that span of time that how and why they respond to our husbandry was revealed. The eighteenth century, that age of enlightenment, saw the start of modern man's search for an understanding of the natural world. That quest led us to our present understanding of the sciences and the functioning of the scientific laws that reaches its most elegant expression in the life processes of all living things.

This cartoon brings to life the two graphs showing increasing yields with reducing labour inputs, the twin aspirations of today's agronomists.

4 WORLD CROPS TODAY

If plant cultivation did start with a mixture of a handful of staples and a greater number of flavoursome species scattered around in small numbers, then that is exactly how arable crop production has continued to this day – country by country, climatic zone by climatic zone, culture by culture. In each case we find a few food crops dominating, in land area, in quantity per person consumed per annum, and in financial value. The three grasses, wheat, rice and maize, are by far the most important staples feeding most of the world. There are however millions of people whose major food supply comes from other species: the millets, potatoes, sorghum, yams, taro and even the banana-like plantains. When it comes to plants we are it seems omnivores with attitude. Amazingly the very early food crops of each culture are still well represented today, even if, as we have seen, they have spread to fresh fields. That attitude must be conservatism!

All these key crops fill bellies; some provide something approaching a balanced diet, while others are extremely deficient in some vital requirements. To satisfy these we must turn to the second group of major food crops, most of them derived from wild legumes: peas, chickpeas, groundnuts, lentils, beans and soya. To these we should add the oil-producers such as rape, sunflowers and olives.

Any table of the world's major food crops will show a third category. It is made up of plants whose products are not strictly essential to our diet but nevertheless play a very important role

in the lives of millions. These are the crops that yield the
ingredients for beverages: tea, coffee, cocoa, wine and various
fruit-juices. Together they occupy thousands of square miles in
every continent bar Antarctica.

The accompanying table lists food crops that each occupy
more than 5 million hectares of land. Their sheer scale is hard
to grasp – for example the world's wheat-fields cover an area
nine times that of Great Britain and produce more than 600
million tonnes of grain per year.

MAJOR CROPS - WORLD AREAS OCCUPIED

Crop	Area (millions Ha)
Wheat	215.6
Rice	151
Maize	147
Soybeans	91.4
Barley	57
Cotton	35
Groundnuts	25
Sugar cane	20.4
Potatoes	19
Cassava	18.5
Coffee	10.4
Rubber	8
Olives	8
Citrus (all)	7.6
Grapes	7.5
Cocoa	7
Rye	7
Sugar beet	5.5
Apples	5

A word of caution when reading the table. As a cultivator I
naturally have an interest in the area occupied by crops but we
should remember that yields vary enormously. Those concerned
with the world's food supply and hence global harvests are only
too aware of the huge variation in output per hectare in
different parts of the world. For example Britain's intensive
farming methods produce 7.5 tonnes of wheat per hectare in
contrast to 2.6 tonnes from Canada's prairie system, while water
shortages and other adverse environmental conditions reduce
some African countries' maize yields to little more than 1 per

cent of those achieved in the USA.

Their combined land use amounts to just over 50 per cent of the world's arable land. As the table shows, the top human food crops share world agriculture with some other big hitters. Of the so-called industrial crops, cotton covering over 35 million hectares is by far the biggest of those grown for fibre. Rubber with some 8 million hectares has held its own against the threat of synthetic alternatives. The vegetable oil producers such as oil palm and rape are expanding rapidly while those grown for energy and even plastics are of ever increasing importance. Animal foodstuffs for conversion into meat occupy a large percentage of the world's arable land but a lot, including cereal products, comes from crops otherwise more directly consumed by humans.

Taken together, these "major crops" dominate the world's arable agriculture. Each covers an area way above that which even the combined forces of a plethora of minor crops from vegetables to perfumes and spices can muster. It is they that impact on world trade, and they that get the research funding from both governments and private industry.

Few of us have as clear an idea as perhaps we should of where these crops are grown. Their distribution is partly determined by climate, but local dietary preferences, a country's state of development and its export industries all play a part. Of course ranking nations in order of their contribution to global output, as in the next table, fails to take into account either their vastly different sizes or their output per hectare. Economists tease out home consumption as their interest usually focuses on quantities reaching the world market, a consideration that probably

MAJOR CROPS – COUNTRIES RANKED IN ORDER OF TOTAL WORLD PRODUCTION

Crop	1st	2nd	3rd
Apples	China	USA	Poland
Banana	India	Brazil	China
Citrus	Brazil	China	USA
Olives	Spain	Italy	Greece
Pineapple	Thailand	Philippines	Brazil
Potatoes	China	Russia	India
Soya	USA	Brazil	Argentina
Tomatoes	China	USA	Turkey

influences most people's idea of "which countries grow most of what". Nonetheless, statistics are collected nation by nation and it is left to economic geographers to group them into regional data. National brands encourage consumers to think along national lines, although such images of world pre-eminence are often very wide of the mark – as for example when we think of tomatoes from Guernsey, bananas from the Caribbean and potatoes from almost anywhere but the correct country!

There are however two other types of crop plant that cover huge areas but are usually considered separately because although they are cultivated and harvested they have only tenuous links with arable husbandry. To many people they may not even seem to be cultivated, because both can be managed by very low-input methods. Nevertheless cultivated they are, land is prepared, seed sown, fertiliser applied, and the crop harvested. What more must be done to qualify for recognition as a crop? Go back far enough and these subjects, used for the same ends, were left in the hands of nature, but more and more, country by country, that's a thing of the past. I refer of course to trees and grass, forestry and pasture. Both deserve recognition in this story and both present the same very interesting challenge to today's agronomists.

Slowly over the last few hundred years in Europe and some other densely populated areas of the industrialised world, timber and grass have become more and more intensively managed. The message got about that the greater the inputs in drainage and fertilisers etc. the greater the reward. Concepts such as "improved pasture" and "conifer plantation" spring to mind, enterprises that have all the characteristics of crop production. Graziers and foresters were encouraged to focus on one or a very few plant types, introduced species or their cultivars, capable of rapid growth under the local conditions, all of the same age and treated as a single entity.

The message worked, but today people are reconsidering. Other more ecologically friendly approaches are being tried, systems that are accommodating to local wildlife, both plants and animals. It is possible to have grazing systems that do not require the destruction of the indigenous flora, and continuous-cover forestry can be practised which keeps a woodland habitat intact whilst producing timber.

Looked at from this perspective, cultivation is at a crossroads. Some would have it that the world of low input, low output will be the norm for forestry, agriculture and even horticulture. Others do not consider that an option, but see the road ahead forking, with one branch of this kind and the other even more high-tech than it is today.

Of course the most extreme of organic food enthusiasts will continue to search for that perfect contradiction, cultivation Garden-of-Eden style! Like the witch-hunters of the Inquisition, they will remain not only convinced of their right but equally that condemning the rest of us brings salvation. The more realistic will most certainly monitor technical progress, and at times pressurise governments to ban some aspects of it. At present one can only hope that this collective voice will become as concerned with cultivation's long-term impact on nature as it is with consumer interests.

It is clear that today agriculturists cultivate great numbers of a very few kinds of plants: the major crops that seem to dominate everything from land use to international trade and academic research. What can we conclude from this? Is it that hunter-gatherers were far more eclectic than supermarket shoppers are today, or is it that the number of minor crops is vast but each is insignificant when measured by the parameters used above?

It is probably a bit of each. As we have seen, we certainly don't cultivate crops of everything that used to be gathered from the wild, stinging nettles and cowslips for starters. But on the other hand an average-sized supermarket stocks 20,000 items, maybe 50 per cent plant-based and 50 per cent of these produced from the staples. That still leaves 5000, including spices, flavourings and such oddities as wild rice to share among the botanical also-rans. I would not be at all surprised if your local Tesco were trading in well over a thousand different plant species. I have tended to draw attention to those at either extreme in terms of the bulk used. Of course quite a number are tucked in just behind the big names on the leader board. That very respectable second division includes many of the best-known fruits and some of the commonest vegetables, but most have to have world-wide appeal to hold their position.

It is horticulture that gathers in most of the rest of the field, from watercress to parsley and from strawberries to peppers. While the development of agriculture created large-scale production systems with plants grown and harvested *en masse* and their yield measured by the field, horticulture took a different approach, with each plant or square metre counting and therefore worthy of receiving individual attention. To today's farmer this "tender loving care" approach to cultivation may seem absurd, but it has always been second nature to the gardener. As the Shropshire nurseryman John Rae wrote in 1665, "It is impossible for any man to have plants to prosper unless he love them: for neither the goodness of the soil, nor the advantage of the situation will do it without the master's affection." My sentiments exactly, if I interpret the manifestation of "love" as close and regular observation.

It is only during the last half century that, even in the industrialised world, many vegetables and fruits have become field or plantation crops. Before that they were the mainstay of that now all but vanished holding, the market-garden. The techniques of intensive production with their crop-by-crop variations must surely have been developed independently many times. Gardening, for that's what we are talking about, is known to have become a very sophisticated craft in the widely separated cultures of Central and South America, the Mediterranean region and most particularly China, long before they interacted. I find it hard to accept that the intricate techniques of growing plants "the gardener's way" developed directly out of early agriculture; it seems more likely to have devolved in parallel, with its later refinements coming from the demands and interests of an urban elite.

If my view suggests a slight bias, those without connections with the land should understand how different the respective appeals of agriculture and horticulture seem to be. In the past people did not usually drift between the two, and even today colleges offer courses in both, often operating as two separate entities with neither staff nor students finding much common ground. Even the study of soils and plant biology are taught separately and I can just imagine my friends in either camp saying, "Of course they must be, our approach to the subject is entirely different from the other lot, who really have no idea ..." So although it seems obvious that cultivation is all-embracing, many practitioners in agriculture and horticulture don't see it that way.

Today every one of these minor crops has its specialist growers, often producing on an intense but, to a farmer, small scale. They may lack the broad acres but these growers are using complex levels of applied science and highly sophisticated husbandry blueprints. Behind the scenes they are supported by plant-breeding programmes that have transformed the crop's popular cultivars of only ten or twenty years ago. In many ways the cultivation skills needed to produce this huge diversity of "minor crops" represents the pinnacle of our understanding of plant husbandry – that combination of the application of established routines and the acute powers of observation capable of detecting the telltale signs that warn a grower that a crop is heading for trouble.

A comprehensive textbook on tropical food crops produced on a commercial scale lists over 150, most with more than 10 excellent cultivars to chose from. You might think that the number of different types would be directly linked to the amount of up-to-date research the crop was getting, but in practice today's research stations release comparatively few new cultivars.

Many temperate crops, for both glasshouse and outdoor cultivation, have even more types commercially available. At West Dean College, Sarah Wain grows around 150 cultivars of tomato and even more sorts of peppers each year, the range governed by space not availability. Caroline Boisset in her book on pumpkins and squashes tells us she grows 75 types, the British publication *Seed Search* has sourced 83 kinds of pea, and the French weigh in with a list of some 130 kinds of – yes – French bean.

The greatest diversity however comes not in the form of named cultivars with gushing descriptions filling the seed catalogues but from the accumulation of local landraces by traditional peasant farmers. By hunting through village fields geneticists have tracked down over 2000 forms of rice and, what I find even more surprising, over 400 kinds of lentil – how on earth can they tell them apart? You can't buy packets of seed of each, but every year more and more are being safely tucked away in one of the world's seed banks. Such then is the range of our crops, but there is another diversity that has grown up across the world, the productivity of the land and the amount of effort it takes to achieve it.

PRODUCTIVITY AND EFFORT

Historians, economists, the green movement and above all agronomists themselves all have an interest in learning more about the relationship between the amount of effort put into growing a crop and the yield at harvest time. The historian would like to know just how much things changed in the daily grind of keeping yourself and your dependants alive when people turned from gathering to crop "farming". Of course it is almost impossible to produce a detailed nutritional balance-sheet, because the role of animals as a source of food has a key part in any such calculation. The traditional view was that, as far as food from plants was concerned, farming beat gathering hands down. This has recently been challenged, and there's a good chance we will find out that the first agronomists had to work just as hard, and for even longer hours, weight for weight of harvest, as the gatherers in the next village. It seems entirely possible that concepts such as dependability and availability in the form of repeat harvests from the same convenient location may have played as large a part in spreading the popularity of this new-fangled idea of cultivating plants as a search for an easy life, but one thing is certain: once crop plants were different from their wild ancestors there was no option – we were stuck with agronomy.

At the very least, cultivation means doing something on behalf of the chosen crop before harvesting it. The extent to which this includes land tillage before sowing and supporting the growing crop, and then later fertilising, weeding and irrigating, almost certainly varied from site to site. Whatever and however much of it was done, it would all have been extra to the gatherer, who, certainly before the days of proto-agriculture, did not come on the scene until the harvest was ready. Harvesting the cultivated crop should have been less effort and more rewarding than gathering from the wild, so now we have an outline for a balance sheet to resolve the question of who worked the harder for each bag of food. Was it the gatherer who had just one slow and painstaking job, to gather in a scattered harvest, or was it the cultivator who had to do all the crop husbandry activities plus harvesting, albeit that the gathering was faster, easier and concentrated in a smaller area?

PRODUCTIVITY TODAY

The story of man's development of crop production over the last two thousand years falls into two parts, based on land availability. In every culture where most if not all suitable crop land was in use at an early date, the challenge was, and still is, one of trying to produce more from the same area of land within economic limits.

In those parts of the world where there was new land available for arable farming, increasing the harvest could be achieved by bringing more land into cultivation. This has always been an attractive option, particularly if it took less effort than intensifying production. Over the course of the centuries, land-hungry arable farmers have reduced English woodlands until the land they covered was among the smallest percentage of any country in Europe. In 1664 John Evelyn in the introduction to his famous book *Sylva* set "the disproportionate spreading of tillage" as having had just as great an impact on deforestation as shipbuilding and industry.

I commented earlier that the choice between extensive and intensive approaches to cultivation resulted in very different yields, for example of wheat between Northern Europe and North America. (Incidentally, although Britain just about holds its own for the major farm crops, some of our neighbours achieve higher yields, suggesting that the British are not Europe's most intensive farmers.)

To a local people, their method is the one they know best and makes good sense, but, as we are reminded all too often, vast numbers of people still depend on local yields to have sufficient to eat. To be fair, most famines result from exceptional circumstances such as drought or war, but paltry average yields mean that there are no reserves to meet such tragedies. Once an area enters world trade in farm and horticultural crops, producers have to consider their costs against world prices. With an international price per tonne the winner is the one with the lowest production costs. Of course it is not as simple as that, because transport charges come into the reckoning, particularly for air-freighted perishable produce – not to mention the support from subsidies granted by national governments. Mercifully these are issues far beyond the scope of this book.

Let us get back to something nice and simple like sheer hard graft. What is the relationship between yield and effort when effort, or husbandry as I like to call it, is defined as all the activities that could help to remove the factors that limit plant growth?

I called it hard graft and so it still is throughout the Third World. In comparison, much of the drudgery has gone from arable cropping in the First World, although many people seem not to have grasped the scale of the changes that have taken place in British agriculture since the early twentieth century. Let us imagine a retired farm worker alive today, aged 84 in the year 2000. He would have gone to work as a boy of 14 in 1930 as one of the 5 per cent of the adult male population working on the land. His life on an arable farm would have consisted of handwork and horsepower. By today's reckoning he would have been part of a huge labour force with one worker to approximately 15ha and one horse to every 12ha under cultivation.

The accompanying tables give some idea of the time and effort needed at the start of his career in 1930 to grow wheat (a cereal) and mangel-wurzle (a root crop). Mangel-wurzles, with a cropping density of 75,000 plants per hectare, required almost exactly 4 seconds per plant. With 10,000 square metres per hectare, time spent on wheat worked out at 12.4 seconds per square metre.

Today both horses and hand-labour have been replaced with machines.

1930 – WORK INPUTS DURING CULTIVATION: WINTER WHEAT

Operation	Time per hectare (minutes)
Autumn ploughing	900
Seedbed preparation	480
Seed drilling	140
Pest and disease control	0
Weed control	400
Fertiliser application	140
Total	2,060 = 123,600 seconds

1930 – WORK INPUTS DURING CULTIVATION: MANGEL WURZLES

Operation	Time per hectare (minutes)
Fertilizer (muck spreading)	1,500
Winter ploughing	900
Seedbed preparation	480
Seed drilling	140
Singling seedlings	1,000
Fertilizer (from the bag)	140
Pest and disease control	0
Weed control	900
Total	5,060 = 303,600 seconds

TODAY – WORK INPUTS DURING CULTIVATION: WINTER WHEAT

Operation	Time per hectare (minutes)
Autumn ploughing	84
Seedbed preparation	60
Seed drilling	78
Pest and disease control	40
Weed control	40
Fertiliser application	96
Total	398 = 23,880 seconds

TODAY – WORK INPUTS DURING CULTIVATION: SUGARBEET

Operation	Time per hectare (minutes)
Winter ploughing	84
Seedbed preparation	204
Seed drilling	120
Pest and disease control	54
Weed control	36
Fertiliser	48
Total	546 = 32,760 seconds

The nearest arable farm to where I am writing this employs one person per 500 hectares, so the chances are that our retired landworker's sons, daughters and grandchildren are not on the land. At least as important as the reduction in the time taken to cultivate the now very much improved crops is the removal of the drudgery for man and beast. If any members of his family are still arable landworkers they will be highly skilled machine operators with tens of thousands of pounds' worth of equipment beneath their backsides.

The time taken to grow those two crops (with sugarbeet replacing mangel) now reads as shown in the next pair of tables. An unchanged cropping density of 75,000 sugarbeet plants per hectare works out at less than half a second per plant, not far short of ten times faster than when our friend started as a boy. It is the same story with the wheat: 10,000 square metres per hectare works out at just under 2.4 seconds per square metre.

Although these differences in crop cultivation times are impressive they are dwarfed by the comparisons for harvest and post-harvest handling times.

The search for perfection lay at the heart of the aspirations of the old "Florists Societies" with their quest for symmetry in their chosen flowers. This sketch of picotee carnations is taken from a mid nineteenth-century illustration.

5 THE PERFECT PLANT

DIFFERING POINTS OF VIEW

Every gardener knows what the perfect plant is: it is the one
that wins first prize in the local flower show – or is it? The truth
is that plant perfection is not a fixed quality; it changes with the
objective of the cultivator, which can vary so much between
one person and the next as to create even contradictory
standards. Even supposing perfection were achieved it can
never be more than a transitory state, linked as it must be to the
ever-changing condition of all living things. Today's prize-
winner is tomorrow's compost. The judgement of a plant's
quality, like the judgement of beauty, depends on the outlook
of the beholder. A devotee of Capability Brown's parkland
would judge an English oak very differently from a forester, the
former looking for a billowing canopy [g] of spreading
branches while the latter praises a trunk that is straight, tall,
branch-free and therefore knot-free.

Let's start this search for plant perfection with modern
biologists. Those of the "selfish gene" school might well regard
the production of a large number of the highest quality seeds
as the yardstick to success – not many marks for the sterile
show chrysanthemum here! To a plant physiologist, however,
the perfect plant may be the one that so arranges its leaves that
they can receive a very high percentage of the available
sunlight, and whose internal leaf structure is so formed that
that light would be most effectively used to energise the
production of sugars; providing of course that the plant also

had an equally efficient enzyme system to allow all this to happen! And to the ecologist the perfect plant might be one that fits a niche within a certain habitat so well that it grows and reproduces in a highly successful manner, holding its own against competitors and utilising the niche's advantages while tolerating its disadvantages.

To the botanist writing a flora, perfection is a typical specimen, the product of its natural habitat, whereas the agronomist takes for granted the impact of his cultivation on his assessment of a cultivar's appearance and performance. To the virologist, a variegated *Lonicera japonica* is a sick plant; to a flower-arranger it can be ideal foliage. A dwarf form of *Lolium perenne* is manna from heaven to the football field groundsman but a disastrous runt to the winter fodder producer who mistakenly sows such a cultivar.

Now to our main interest: the cultivators. From the outset they have searched for plants that give the highest yield per unit area. But such an approach to growing fresh produce by commercial horticulturists is often damned by epicures for paying scant regard to taste, both flavour and texture. Discerning consumers find it hard to influence these obviously important qualities and claim that the concept of quality in the market place changed dramatically during the twentieth century. This may be so, but defining quality in fresh produce remains a nightmare; we all have our own ideas on the subject. I am in the camp that is much more interested in freshness and flavour than appearance.

The extent to which cultivation methods can, let alone do, influence flavour is one of many areas of biology where, to the general public, belief is more acceptable than science. This in spite of all but the oldest members of our society having been exposed to an educational system that set out to differentiate faith from fact and myth from real experience.

What makes flavour in fruits and vegetables is a complex story outside the scope of this book, but the headings are clear: texture, acidity, sweetness, and, let's say, the presence or absence of specific, large, "flavour" molecules. Very little of any of these factors other than texture is typically controlled by the form of husbandry and most certainly not by whether the produce is "organically" grown or not. Where husbandry comes into the story is in its influence on the tenderness of crops, for example a wide range of vegetables from beetroot to calabrese are rendered "woody or "stringy" if they have insufficient water and/or too little nitrogen.

Two factors are of far greater significance. In fact they are so important that if you did not know them before you should go and get a highlighter right now! The next sentence can do more for the quality of your culinary life than all the rest of this book. **The condition or developmental stage of the fruit or vegetable when harvested and the method and length of storage between picking and eating determine its flavour.**

I would not dare make such an emphatic claim without some powerful backup. I have the necessary support; it comes from the pages of Professor Werner Schuphan's book *Nutritional Values in Crops and Plants*. Although written some 40 years ago it remains a valuable exposé of the factors which affect produce quality. The research he sites illustrates how such factors and their interactions impinge on the biology of a plant throughout its life and between harvest and our eating of what we optimistically call its fresh produce.

With the exception of produce that must be stored for winter the message from the old-time head gardeners was clear, so clear that if they made it today it might well be called their mission statement. "Pick when it is ready to eat and eat it within the day." For obvious reasons produce was gathered and eaten when it had reached its peak of desirable texture and flavour. This is a condition that may not last long and varies hugely from crop to crop, from the deliberate immaturity of spring turnips, new potatoes and green gooseberries to the full ripeness of melons and tomatoes or the "maturity" of frosted Brussels sprouts.

So lesson one is: **Pick at the right stage.**

After harvest, flavours change and to our palate usually deteriorate. Using the best storage conditions for the particular item can slow this deterioration down, but these are living things and changes in their chemistry are inevitable.

So lesson two is: **Eat fresh produce as soon after harvest as you can.**

Of course anyone engaged in today's world trade in what used to be sold by fruiterers and greengrocers will tell you, "All that's a lost cause, pie in the sky, and the gibbering of an out-of-touch geriatric locked in the depths of a Victorian walled garden." So why am I being offered "vine-ripened tomatoes" at a premium price in my supermarket and advice on how to store their strawberries? The popularity of pick-your-own, the farm-gate shop, the farmer's market and the splendid local smallholder's produce on sale at our village garage all support my point. But remember, none of these outlets are guaranteed to have got it right; you still have to pick and chose.

Quality, of a kind, is no longer just for the wealthy, but for everyone who goes shopping for fruit, flowers and vegetables. Today in the First World it is driven by the combined demand of retailer and shopper for blemish-free, uniform-sized, fresh produce. These requirements set today's husbandry objectives for a range of commercial producers, from pot plant growers to apple farmers.

Even though the idea that natural products should be identical and perfect is faintly absurd, let's take a supermarket approach to quality and look at size, shape, uniformity and surface blemish. They may not have much to do with taste, but as we shall see later they are all matters that can be influenced by the way we cultivate the crop.

Size depends on the available resources that the parent plant can muster. As we have seen, these are derived from the soil and air and processed through the use of light energy. An increase in numbers, whether expressed as "many per plant" or "many plants per area", generally leads to a reduction in size. The more there are, the smaller they get. Sometimes a grower deliberately seeks to produce a large number of small items, as in the case of grapes for raisins or onions for pickling. In the majority of cases the market wants unnaturally large items – apples, plums, potatoes and lettuces bigger than those that nature or laid-back amateur gardeners would produce if left to their own devices. In these cases the professional grower turns first to the standard trick of adding more water or nutrients in an attempt to prevent any hold-up in the supply of raw materials limiting growth. These extra inputs usually move things in the right direction, but they may not go far enough. There is often the need to actually reduce numbers by pruning, thinning, disbudding or, in the case of competing individuals, reducing the number of plants per unit area.

Uniformity to produce that every-one-the-same appearance

110

THE PERFECT PLANT

beloved of supermarkets is an inherently unnatural thing and much more complicated to achieve. There is a natural tendency for considerable variation in the size of specimens, be they flowers, fruits or even leaves. In many flowers, fruits and even potato tubers there is a sequence, from the first formed being the largest to the last being the smallest. Letting this size gradation happen and then grading afterwards is costly and wasteful, as any grower will tell you.

Producers use two contrasting dodges to even things up. One is to remove the first-formed or king flower or fruit. Once that is out of the way the rest develop more evenly. The other way is to keep the king and remove all the rest, which produces a few top-grade specimens, as with disbudded chrysanthemums.

If we are dealing with a crop made up of hundreds of separate plants then it is possible to get uniformity by adjusting their spacing. Too much room and each plant tends to go on and on producing smaller and smaller items, too little and a surprising thing happens: instead of dwarfing the lot, and producing a crop of smaller, weaker specimens the population breaks up into a few large and a lot of very small individuals, with few if any of the desired medium size.

Surface blemish has many causes: mechanical, weather, pests and diseases. All downgrade the harvest and turn otherwise perfectly good produce into rejects. Any reader who went shopping for fruit and vegetables in the Soviet Union will know just how dreadful produce can look if no one is concerned with appearance. Much of the damage was mechanical, and any customer who travelled more than a few kilometres on those roads ended up just as bruised as the produce. That sort of mechanical damage often leads to infection and rotting. On the other hand, other damage of various sorts is truly only skin-deep, and until a few years ago was regarded as both natural and normal. However it is not so today, when demands for a perfect skin lead to a great amount of waste and the use of crop protection materials.

Of course the home gardener has little truck with such skin-deep beauty. However, thrift can be overdone, and gardeners with an enthusiasm for storing their produce may recognise the "rotten apple pie syndrome" whereby week after week they expect their family to "cut out the rot" while the sound fruits remain in store.

111

The supermarket approach to "perfection" is not a million miles away from the traditional exhibitor's requirements, as can be seen any day by comparing the fresh produce in a supermarket with specimens exhibited in the most prestigious shows such as those run by the Royal Horticultural Society. Both get some stick from the epicures for lack of focus on flavour.

The challenge of producing perfection from the inherent diversity of nature traditionally starts by putting greater and greater effort into having a uniform and predictable population of plants. Only then is it worth lavishing more and more care on their cultivation. Nevertheless, no exhibitor would think of facing the flower show judge without having a surplus of specimens from which to make an agonising last-minute selection. In spite of the saying, few things in nature are as uniform as the proverbial peas in a pod. The prudent competitor culls out all but the very best.

Carrying a surplus and discarding those runts that fail to match up to the rulebook's definition of a set of desirable criteria is no great problem to the amateur exhibitor, but it becomes a nightmare for the commercial grower struggling to meet the grades required by the supermarkets. If uniformity seems an impossible goal, how about grading the harvest and sending only the ones that fit the requirements of the retailer? Well of course that's what always happened, but as the tolerance of any variation becomes less and less the number of rejects increases and the question of what to do with these becomes ever more pressing. To throw them away simply because they are the wrong size or shape seems criminal, at least to anyone who has lived through a war, but that's what happens to a lot of produce. The alternatives are to feed them to livestock or preferably to find a processing or industrial use for it, such as juices or sauces.

At least the starting-point for a modern crop is far more uniform than ever before, thanks to the production of genetically identical clones by either vegetative propagation or the skills of plant-breeders who equip growers with extremely uniform batches of seed.

Hard-headed commercial food-producers judge a growing crop at each stage against an ideal capable of producing the heaviest yield of the required harvest organ. They are not seduced by a young plant's lush appearance. They know that the heaviest-yielding glasshouse tomato plants may look ugly at almost every stage in their lives, but they have the wherewithal to crop at a staggering 600 tonnes per hectare.

So far so good, but how does a grower eliminate all the factors that can produce, not a crop failure, but simply the natural variability that occurs between specimens at harvest? One approach is to try and standardise soils and other growing conditions, but fields are not the same all over and two fields on the same farm can vary enormously, which may be why some farmer hundreds of years ago divided them in the way he did. Is the answer ever higher inputs, the use of more pest control sprays, more precise crop densities, artificial pollination, fruit thinning, growth-regulating chemicals, fertiliser and water application? All these tasks cost money, and some maybe objected to by customers as unnatural.

Neither plant scientists nor commercial growers are likely to pay much regard to perfection as laid down by the Royal Horticultural Society in their booklet giving advice to flower show judges. It attributes a points value to the various parts that go to make up a plant's morphology, thereby ranking their contribution towards this assumed quality. However, we should not dismiss the huge contribution that the flower, vegetable and agricultural shows have made to the improvement of both plants and cultural methods. In England thousands of such shows were flourishing by the early years of the twentieth century. Even before that the pioneers had been copied in some far-flung corners of empire, so that some time before the turn of the century a Mr Bellairs was able to write home from what was then British Guiana with the news that "The Cucumbers that won the First Prize at the Horticultural Show held in Georgetown this year were Webb's Perpetual Bearer, none of the other exhibits approached them." Clearly local conditions were not able to deprive one expat of his favourite sandwiches.

Even within the show-tent produce takes many forms. Shows for private gardeners focus on vases of flowers and dishes of vegetables and fruits. Those for commercial growers call for exhibits in market packs, while the Frome Agricultural Show in

Wiltshire has classes for rape seed, wheat, barley and, for me best of all, whole maize plants 2m tall pulled straight from the field. In Nairobi I have seen entries for sacks of charcoal and bundles of Acacia bark for tannin, all in the hunt for perfection.

Genetically modified organisms – GMOs

Until recently plant breeding was exempt from a similar witch-hunt to that which befell the use of "chemicals". This in spite of the development of techniques that produced dramatic results by allowing plant breeders to achieve the essentially "unnatural" act of combining genetic material from rather distantly related species. All that changed in the mid 1980s with the news of "genetic engineering". The idea behind the technique of genetic engineering, or genetic modification as the practitioners would have it known, is simple to state in very broad outline, if not to achieve! Some commentators have portrayed the objective as the fulfilment of the long dreamed-of ability to combine the characteristics of two unrelated species to produce a population of super-beings. Not surprisingly, some people have become concerned; the scientists involved have been seen as modern Frankensteins and the edible kinds of these chimeras dubbed "Frankenstein foods". In fact, to date, plant scientists have had far humbler ambitions than Mary Shelley's anti-hero; they have tried to introduce one or more "useful" genetically inherited characters into long-established crop plants, typically for such humdrum objectives as disease resistance. But efforts have gone as far as "engineering" selected crop plants to provide specific proteins.

What to many people is both amazing and disconcerting is that, because of the universality of the genetic code, the all-important pieces of DNA can be collected from either plant or animal tissue. You do not need to be a geneticist to realise that you can't cross a cabbage with a Christmas tree, indeed the inability to cross-breed is used as a way of classifying one species as distinct from another. The time-honoured technique of "pollen-daubing" will not produce such a hybrid. The genetic engineering of plants is the story of how biologists found another way of transferring genes.

The trick they found was to use two kinds of bacteria as intermediaries. These quite literally act as go-betweens from the donor to the recipient. Imagine two plants (not necessarily related). Plant A has a desirable quality such as disease resistance but is otherwise of little value as a crop. Plant B produces excellent crops but is susceptible to disease. To transfer disease resistance from A to B, living tissue is collected from plant A, which is macerated [g] and has its DNA extracted; then, by using an enzyme, the DNA is broken up into gene sized-fragments. At the same time, cells from one kind of bacterium are broken up and fragments known as plasmids collected. These can be induced to combine with plant A's DNA fragments. These "loaded" recombinant plasmids are induced to enter the cells of the other kind of bacterium (typically the gall-forming *Agrobacterium tumefaciens*). Meanwhile tissue from the desirable plant B has been cultured. Its cells are then infected with the bacteria carrying the recombinant plastids, some of which may contain the all-important gene for disease resistance. The genetic material from the bacterium (which now contains the recombinant plastids, which in turn contain plant A's gene) now integrate with plant B's chromosomal DNA. Plants cultured from these cells from plant B by standard tissue-culture techniques will, in addition to B's original DNA, now carry the gene from plant A for disease resistance, delivered via the bacterium.

In one way the outcome of all this seems very like sexual reproduction. In each case an offspring's' attributes are gained from two individuals: its parents. But there are great differences. In a sexual union the genes are inherited equally from each parent and such a union can take place only between closely related taxa [g]. With genetic engineering one individual donates all but a tiny percentage of the genetic material, and this small fragment of DNA can come from virtually any living organism. The resultant individual is a hybrid which can have previously unimagined qualities. One well-known oddity is the tobacco plant that glows in the dark through having acquired a glow-worm gene. To an evolutionary biologist this simply demonstrates the oneness of life through the commonality of DNA. To many members of the general public it is weird and not a little scary.

Biologists now recognise their gross inaptitude in the way they introduced this subject to the public. At its worst the public was presented with some researchers brushing aside people's obvious worry regarding genetic material as just so much DNA to harvest and use regardless of the donor or recipient species. True and amazing as this may be, it is now clear to all concerned that to talk of injecting your favourite vegetable or fruit with bits of insect or jellyfish is not a good way of winning hearts and minds. I believe that the hostility to "Frankenstein foods" was at least as much a reaction against such images as it was based on a totally justifiable demand for extremely rigorous checks. Every right-minded person recognises the need for exhaustive studies on the biochemistry of the resultant organism to make sure that the genotype formed from the combination is not, for example, incidentally producing unplanned-for compounds, and scientists were in the van of initiating such a protocol.

My hope and guess is that within a decade or two the vast majority of the public will have passed through this stage of blanket rejection. This will only happen in the wake of truly transparent safety studies and if scientists manage to get the public to recognise the difference between a technique and the problems it might cause if misused.

The fanciers

Biologists and commercial growers and their customers are not the only searchers after plant perfection. Two other groups deserve our attention, if only for their dedication to the cause: the eighteenth-century florists and today's giant vegetable growers. Both their stories provide excellent examples of man's search for two very different forms of plant perfection and his ability to achieve a staggering degree of impact on both the genetic make-up and the appearance of plants in order to achieve it.

In both cases the search for perfection as they saw it was more than a little involved with competition and rivalry. Yet it is equally certain that such specialist growers also get a lot of pleasure from pitting themselves against the vicissitudes of the climate and other natural hazards to which their chosen plants are subject. There is a deep sense of triumph in achieving some measure of success even if you are the only person to either witness or appreciate it, but it is much better if that success results in you beating your friends to win first prize. The very special definition of perfection held to be self-evident by these enthusiasts has often proved difficult to transfer, even to the devotees' nearest and dearest.

The cultivation of "florist's flowers" must surely come at the opposite end of the spectrum from any of the great systems of crop production. Yet however tiny its scale its inclusion provides the perfect opportunity to highlight some of the most intensive husbandry efforts ever showered upon a group of plants. Devotees of bonsai may do more to their diminutive victims, but the "florists" could fairly claim, by breeding and husbandry, to have created the plants they loved to exhibit.

Both the animal and plant kingdoms have fallen prey to the obsession of the fancier – from pigeons and canaries to guinea-pigs to rabbits and from sweet peas to chrysanthemums, auriculas and roses. The British seem particularly prone to this form of obsessive hobby; the Royal Horticultural Society lists over twenty specialist societies committed to the cultivation of one group or another of cultivated plant, each with its band of devoted fanciers. A very special form of these tightly focused interest groups grew up in the seventeenth century. They were the fanciers who grew and exhibited what became known as florist's flowers. Before looking more deeply into this extreme interpretation of cultivation it should be pointed out that the phrase "florist's flower" has nothing to do with those flowers commonly sold in florists' shops. It predates such establishments and comes from a time when the florist was the grower.

Their interest was in the shape and form of the flower. Colour seems to have played its part mainly in helping to define and embellish that form by adding patterns onto the petals. From our perspective the heterogeneous collection of species selected for this intense interest seems to have little rhyme or reason. James Maddock in his *Florist's Directory* of 1792 regards only eight plants as qualifying: the auricula, pansy, polyanthus, tulip, primrose, ranunculus, carnation and anemone, and then only certain groups of cultivars are included.

Grouping these plants together as florist's flowers could lead to the idea that enthusiasts took an interest in them all. In reality each had its followers who formed their own clubs and ran their own competitions. All of these first eight are hardy herbaceous perennials but have little else in common, require different conditions and flower at different seasons. Many years after these first, and some would say only, legitimate florist's flowers were listed other kinds were added, including the chrysanthemum and dahlia, but by then flower-growing was developing another area of interest, out in the garden. Herbaceous perennials such as the delphinium, lupin and hemerocallis became fashionable and were introduced in an endless range of cultivars to beds made popular by that doyen of the herbaceous border Gertrude Jekyll. Some enthusiasts devoted whole sections of their garden to collections of the most fashionable cultivars of the most fashionable plants, producing every thing from an iris garden to a rosary [g] and a salicetum [g].

From this distance it is hard to get a clear picture of what was going on in the struggle to perfect those original "florist's flowers" as defined by the rules of this strange hobby. It would seem that it was well appreciated that the first and almost certainly the most important thing was to start with the right genetic potential. Many fanciers indulged in breeding programmes and the literature of the time was full of descriptions of new seedlings showing exquisite form, shape and colour. This promising genetic material had to be persuaded to give of its best on the day of the competition, a local or national flower show. Such a need to perform to a critical deadline added yet another dimension to the skills needed to be a champion grower. It called on the manipulation of environmental factors that would speed up or slow down the physiological processes that control flower development and longevity, although I doubt they would have put in quite those words.

We may think of the florist's flowers as simply selected forms of hardy garden plants, but that was not the way they were grown for exhibition. What makes their cultivation particularly interesting to me is that the devotee's idea of perfection is not about having the largest but is a struggle to produce a predetermined but entirely arbitrary size and form. Points were lost for specimens with dimensions both below and above the agreed criteria.

The quest for such specific concepts of perfection led to some somewhat individualistic approaches to cultivation, both in the materials used and in their methods of application. Mystique played its part and there were even reports of healthy collections rapidly declining when distributed among fellow enthusiasts after the death of their owner. Was there any foundation in the claim that the auricula "George Rudd" only did well in Halifax, the town of its birth, or that Mr Loake of Kettering owed at least part of his success to the local loam? Did that story bolster the standing of fibrous Kettering loam, dug from old pastureland? The stuff holds an almost mystic place in the story of potting composts, its perfection reached through a combination of texture and structure.

The old writings are sprinkled with various fanciers' tips, particularly which soil mixes and fertilisers to use. Much as I respect the skills of these long-departed growers, it is reassuring in the light of today's understanding to see how, rather than there being a specific best formula for each plant, many alternatives are championed. After several pages from the old texts repeating, *ad nauseam*, how vital loam was, it comes as both a shock and a relief to a present-day user of loamless potting composts to read that one early nineteenth-century grower used no loam at all! His mix was two-thirds old hotbed manure, one-sixth peat and one-sixth sand. Advice on manures ranged from "use none" to "cow manure" ("the fare most enjoyed"), composted bracken with added poultry manure, horse dung six weeks old, peat, spent hops, shoddy [g], chopped seaweed, sugar scum, night soil, and blood; there are more but I think I have made my point. The list is not all organic; a more recent suggestion is for a whacking 1oz (28.4g) per square yard of potassium sulphate for gold-laced polyanthus, together with "artificially composted straw" or "old mushroom bed compost obtainable through mail order"!

That last recommendation shows that we have reached more recent times and there could be no better evidence that fancying remained alive and well than a quick glance at Mr H. G. Park's 1947 book *Late Flowering Chrysanthemums for Exhibition*. Stopping and taking are not street crimes, but essential stages in training and pruning future prize-winners, while their watering and fertilising are combined by

> mixing the manures into a thick paste, before use well stir and then use 2 teaspoons to 2 gallons of water every other time when watering; always preceding the manure water with clear water.

(And, we may hope, making sure the teaspoon does not find its way back into the cutlery drawer). This brief visit to this most intensive field of cultivation turns out to be a lesson, not in the need for unique or even very special techniques, but in the fact that plants respond to a very basic set of needs that can be met by many alternative materials and methods. The special factor that I believe successful fanciers, exhibitors and collectors have, other than such aids as the ivory bloom flattener shaped like a button hook I have been told about, is not a secret soil or fertiliser formula but the power of observation, albeit that some would call it tender loving care.

THE GIANT-MAKERS

What on earth can one say about the searchers after monsters – giants by weight, volume or some single dimension such as length or girth? Certainly it is not a pretty sight in the gentility of a flower show to be confronted with a line of the vegetable kingdom's equivalent of Sumo wrestlers. They can fill vast areas of the show bench, or at times overhang it, or, when their weight creates risk to life and limb, be placed on the floor beside it. Growing giant produce is by no means a recent fad. Jane Wells Loudon writing in the middle of the nineteenth century noted that both onions and leeks are sometimes "grown to enormous size". As one Edwardian spouse put it, "cauliflower sized dahlias and chrysanthemums, delphiniums with stems like tree-trunks, onions the size of footballs and marrows a yard long and nothing picked until maximum size and toughness". To be fair, sheer weight is the least attractive side of the story. I have seen very elegant exhibits of perfectly proportioned parsnips, carrots and leeks in which length was the only exaggerated feature – well over half a metre for the latter two and more than one metre for the parsnips. Having decided that to discover why anyone should pursue an interest in such horticultural body-building was a matter for a professional psychologist, I turned to the ways it is achieved. By studying the tricks of this monstrous pursuit we can learn a great deal of just how far we can take the concept of producing two blades of grass, or, more likely, two hundredweights of pumpkin, and see which aspects of plant biology are involved.

As one should expect the fundamental requirement is to have the best possible genetic start to your task. Breeding by hybridisation and selection of the most vigorous individuals in each generation has resulted in some remarkable races in which the potential for both overall size and, more practically, the size of the desired organ, has increased to a point far beyond anything remotely advantageous in nature. Truly these are cases of the most unnatural selection. In 1996 Nathan and Paula Zehu took the world record at the World Pumpkin Confederation meeting with a fruit weighing 482kg, that's near as damn it half a tonne. They estimated they had spent 900 hours nurturing the beast. It is not reported if they are getting out more since their triumph. We can only wait in fear of the day in which an expert in genetic engineering takes up the interest. The ancestors of the large-fruited pumpkin are native North Americans, so it is understandable that the USA should be the home of its champion specimens. Why the British selected leeks and gooseberries for the same treatment has no such logical association. Giant gooseberry competitions are recorded in the *Gooseberry Growers Register* which goes back to 1786. The hobby centred on the industrial towns of the Midlands and North-West, where cloth workers vied with each other in local pub-based competitions. By 1852 the champion berry of the cultivar "London" reached 58g, that's over seven times the weight of a normal fruit. I don't know what an American pumpkin champion wins other than fame; the gooseberry kings received some very down-to-earth prizes; surviving records list a pig, copper kettles, chinaware, teapots and a rocking chair. The cultural techniques are almost as bizarre as their products, yet they are based on the most basic concept of all in cultivation, our old friend "the elimination of the limiting factor".

Monster-growers stop at nothing. Most target massive soil preparation followed by ad-lib provision of nutrients and water. Extra light may be turned on and even the gases vital to growth have been boosted. Some have dabbled with extra carbon dioxide by erecting tents over their victims and fitting them up using a gas cylinder. One I heard about "borrowed" a cylinder of oxygen from his welding shop and injected it into the soil around his giant leeks. You may be right in thinking that that must be every "factor" now unlimited. So it may be, but what about short-circuiting the plant's own photosynthetic biochemistry and injecting sugars straight into the vascular system? Yes, they do that as well; maybe it is time to introduce some form of dope testing into the flower show rulebook.

ANCIENT MUSINGS ON PLANT PERFECTION

The search for plant perfection seems to offer countless alternatives and, like the Caucus race in Wonderland they all produce different winners. But let's finish by going back to the beginning (a very Alice thing to do) and join Theophrastus as he muses on a similar question in 300 BC. His concern is to discover the typical specimen (perfection for the botanist) and he wonders if we can best find the true expression of a species among specimens growing wild influenced only by their natural surroundings, or among those enjoying the advantages of cultivation. Put in human terms, it is rather like asking if we should we judge our species' physique from "the man in the street" or by the body-builder who lives in the gym? The following uses extracts from the translation given in the Loeb Classical Library of his *Enquiry into Plants*. The question Theophrastus poses is:

> Is nature and the natural to be seen in what grows unaided or in what is under cultivation? Are we to study the nature of a plant in those that grow without human aid or in those growing under various forms of cultivation, and which of these two kinds of growth is natural?

It is a question that still bugs today's plant scientists. Can we trust cultivars to respond to our experiments in the same way as a wild species? Ecologists find that even wild specimens behave differently when cultivated in a botanic garden from when growing in the wild. As Theophrastus puts it, "Are we to study the nature of a given kind from its wild or cultivated form?"

He first considers wild plants, which he reasons to be undeniably natural specimens. But he then recognises that cultivated specimens responded to being husbanded precisely because they have the *natural* capacity to do so. To him such specimens are therefore also natural because, as we would say, their response stems from their (natural) genetic make-up.

Being the philosopher he was, he presents both of these options, the first being that:

> Unaided growth is natural, for nature contains the starting points in itself, and what we see in plants that grow unaided by man is of this description in contrast to what is of external causation, especially when it is due to art, for the starting point is different.

In his defence of the counter-argument he starts by claiming that:

> Cultivation is natural for the nature of the plant is also fulfilled when that nature obtains through human art what it happens to lack, such as food of the right kind and in plentiful supply and the removal of impediments and hindrances.

In other words cultivators simply provide that which "is also provided by the regions appropriate to a given plant, the regions in fact where we assert that the natures of plants should be studied." Then comes the recognition that cultivators really do add something when he admits that "the appropriate region only provides external help, such as weather, wind, soil and food, whereas husbandry also introduces different movements and arrangements within the plant itself." Are these "arrangements" of the kind that result from pruning and training or is he, I wonder, referring to what we would understand to be genetic changes leading to the emergence of new cultivars?

One of Stephen Hales's early eighteenth-century botanical investigations into the role of water required the collection of "the liquor plants perspire". Water use and the water cycle remain critical aspects of a crop's interaction with its environment.

124

a

p

b

Fig. 9.

6 LIVING CONDITIONS

SOIL, NUTRIENTS, WATER AND AIR

Before we embark on an investigation of what this quintessential human activity known as cultivation entails in the form of hard work for man, beast and machine, we should first gain some understanding of a plant's relationship with its environment. This will help to establish just what any plant, wild or cultivated, needs to give it a good life or at least a fighting chance of reproducing before it meets its death. Cultivation is after all the manipulation of both plants and their environment.

Ecologists will tell you that the plant or animal specimen you see is a product of nature and nurture, in other words the interaction of its genetic make-up and the conditions under which it has been growing. They show this diagrammatically as a specimen impacted upon by these two forces arriving from right and left. Maybe a more realistic image would be of a plant at the centre of the diagram representing the genome "Nature" being bombarded from all sides by influences from its environment. Of course this model holds good for every living thing, and cultivated plants are no exception.

Useful as this diagram is, I have found that it helps our understanding of what is going on when we cultivate plants, if we separate those components of nurture that come from the natural world from those that are the results of husbandry. For many years I have used the simple three-sided figure shown below to depict the influence of genetic make-up, environment and husbandry on a cultivated plant and to remind us of the importance of all three in achieving a satisfactory crop.

Although the appearance and performance of a specimen typically results from a mix of these three influences it is possible to consider them individually.

The influence exerted by the genome is of course all-pervasive in the differences between species. Take for example the different amount of growth made by African marigolds and alyssum growing in the same flowerbed. This genetic control is equally evident between species in the same genus as in the case of the two grasses *Poa pratensis* and *P. annua*. Variation between cultivars lies at the heart of today's agronomy and is dramatically shown by the contrasting stature and growth-rate of selections of perennial ryegrass grown for hay in comparison with those for sports pitches.

Environmental inputs (nurture) can be either beneficial or harmful; for example, rainfall patterns may produce either drought, waterlogging or ideal levels of soil moisture. Husbandry, unless mismanaged, should both ameliorate the vagaries of nature and "push" the plants towards the grower's desired objective; there are few if any more dramatic examples of this than the prizewinning entries in a hotly contested leek competition.

While it may not be possible to quantify the absolute impact on the appearance and performance of a plant of either its genes, or wild and man-made nurture (the environment and cultivation), it is clear that the relative importance of each influence varies from example to example. Hence cultivation has a far greater impact on pot chrysanthemums in a glasshouse where the grower controls most environmental factors, than it has on shrubs in a car park planting that receive little if any husbandry once established.

Much of today's debate in agronomic circles, from GMOs to organic growing and from direct drilling to food miles, is about achieving the optimum balance between these three influences.

A PLANT'S REQUIREMENTS

So let's first look at how a green plant interacts with its surroundings and what it takes from them. Even in an age when school biology has become a thinly disguised course in genetics and biochemistry, most children will have been shown that a seed needs warmth and water to germinate. If the teacher remembers to point it out, we could at the same time learn that the same goes for a mature plant, together with light and carbon dioxide in the atmosphere and oxygen and specific minerals in the soil.

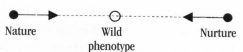

*The position of the wild phenotype along the nature/nurture axis
depends on the relative significance of these two factors*

Given that those basic needs are satisfied, a plant can grow –
leaving aside for now the competition it faces from its neighbours.
Which species survive and even flourish in any particular location
will depend on the fit between a plant's genetic make-up and the
relative abundance of the essential items and conditions in the
area. It is as if a plant can do no other than its genetic best if, at
the optimum temperature, it has all the nutrients, light, water and
carbon dioxide it can use. Of course, like all searchers after
perfection know, such places are almost impossible to find and
almost as hard to make. However, as I've mentioned earlier, some
flower-show enthusiasts and giant vegetable growers take up this
challenge.

There is however another way of looking at how a plant grows
and this is to consider its performance in terms of stress
management. We know that rather than fight it out with those
species that grow very vigorously under naturally fertile
conditions, many plants make a living on some pretty
unfavourable sites such as on high mountains and in semi-
deserts. They can do this because they can tolerate the local
environmental stresses.

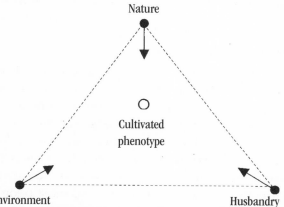

*The position of the cultivated phenotype within the triangle depends
upon the relative significance of the three factors*

These ideas can be transferred to our approach to cultivation. The art of successful cultivation by making a plant unhappy may come as a shock to many garden-lovers. There are however many examples of where crop plants can be more profitable when grown under various forms of environmental stress and where stress is a positive asset to the grower in his endeavours to reach the market's perception of quality. Thus less than theoretically ideal levels of water and or nutrients play their part in producing everything from top-quality malting barley to flavour-rich tomatoes and some fine decorative timbers. Most bizarre must surely be the lack of light used to blanch otherwise tough or rank-tasting vegetables and salads such as seakale, chicory and endive, a technique we shall return to under the heading of protected cropping.

Stress can be the trigger that initiates the next stage in some plants' seasonal cycle, as the following examples illustrate. The flowering of mangoes requires a dry period. What we may regard as very harsh winter conditions are necessary to break the dormancy and get the optimum flush of spring growth in some trees that grow wild in regions blessed with continental winters. In horticulture bulbs and corms are subjected to both heat and cold to break their dormancy prior to forcing for the Christmas trade. Fruit-growers used to induce flower bud development by stressing their trees by either root-pruning or ring-barking; both practices reduce the amount of water going to the top of the plant and can also alter the distribution of photosynthates [g], thereby "persuading" the specimen to invest in reproduction rather than vegetative growth.

ADAPTATION TO ENVIRONMENT

Higher plants have adapted to grow everywhere but in those areas of the Earth's surface that experience the most extreme climate. While it is not perhaps scientifically correct to think of a "normal" or "typical" set of conditions somewhere between the extremes of acid and alkaline, hot and cold, wet and dry, richly fertile and impoverished, such an approach paints a picture we all feel we understand as "good growing conditions" (i.e. free of limiting factors [g]). It is therefore helpful to most people to think of the plants that thrive at the extremes of these conditions as unusual or even strange forms. We see them as having become especially adapted to tolerate, and in a few cases require, such environments.

With the exception of rice's affinity for water, very few of our crop species have such out-of-the-ordinary requirements, which is just as well not only for the cultivators but also for the rest of us who depend on the harvest. Most extreme conditions allow only limited growth even for adapted species, hence the poor biomass per unit area per time potential of high mountains, semi-deserts and the boreal regions.

Fortunately for us we do not have to exactly match a wild ancestor's local climate and soil for its offspring to yield a dependable harvest when they are uprooted, relocated and grown as a crop.

CLIMATE AND THE FITTING OF CROPS TO LOCAL CONDITIONS

> The native place lays the entire foundation for the cultivation of plants. For if we have a considered record of the climate in each region, according to the longitude and latitude of the place, and if we have a record of the soil, we know more data about cultivation that are true, unambiguous and reliable than if the gardeners left us laws of cultivation for each and every plant.
> – Linnaeus, quoted by M. Hickey

Dare I question the words of such a towering figure of the botanical world as Linnaeus? Well yes, not because he is wrong here but because he is only half-right. Long after his death ecologists proposed the following "rules" governing a plant's natural distribution. (A) There must be an initial introduction of the genotype through evolution or an agent of distribution. (B) The species must be able to reproduce successfully under the prevailing environmental conditions. (C) It must be able to survive the competition of the other species occupying the same habitat. Given these conditions the species will spread until it reaches places where these requirements are no longer fulfilled. In some cases, for example when entering a dense woodland, competition (for light) will bar most grassland wildflowers, while the sea surrounding an island is often a very effective physical barrier

In botanic gardens botanists often ask horticulturists to cultivate some rather odd plants: species that trap insects, grow on trees, live in deserts, cloud forests and bogs. For such groups it is necessary to know as much as possible about their natural habitats. But, and it is a big but, most average plants, the so-called mesophytes, are cultivated successfully under conditions surprisingly different from those that surround them in the wild, be it in a farmer's field or on granny's windowsill. Are cultivators breaking the ecologists' rules? Maybe, if they genetically change the plant, producing new cultivars such as the fast-maturing soya beans for northern latitudes, or if they control competition and change the conditions by for example drainage, irrigation or fertilisers, but surely not if the plant turns out to have naturally broad tolerance. Perhaps the cultivator's greatest advantage over nature is that many crops are not required to reproduce *in situ*, indeed many harvests from lettuce to sugarbeet are gathered from immature specimens while subsequent plantings are initiated from imported stock.

Typically crop plants, like their wild ancestors, grow best within one of the major global divisions of climate. For example we have crops for the tropics, the temperate regions, semi-deserts and rainforests. Nevertheless, many give satisfactory yields over some thirty degrees of latitude or in the exceptional case of maize from the equator to fifty degrees north. At first glance such broad tolerances seem to suggest that cultivators may be free from the constraints that are said to define a natural habitat. If so, why should there be any value in my "agri-met" computer program letting me look up so many average meteorological conditions for any part of England? To a layman it may seem detailed to the point of pedantry. It informs me of the average monthly maximum, minimum and mean air and soil temperatures; the average date of the last frost and the number of degree-days above 10°C and below 0°C. The month-by-month maximum, minimum and mean rainfall and sunshine hours are followed by the monthly hours of daylight, solar radiation and illumination. I can read the summer soil moisture deficit and the winter excess, together with the potential and effective transpiration. All of which has allowed someone to calculate the length and period of each location's growing season. As if this were not enough information, one may then correct regional data for the effect of such factors as altitude and aspect. That at least will come as no surprise to anyone living in the South-West of England, as they know the impact that the altitude of Dartmoor and Bodmin Moor has on the region's otherwise mild climate.

It may surprise some people to learn that so much is known about our climate, and you may be thinking that so much data is science gone mad. You would be wrong, though, because meteorologists selected these data for their practical use to agricultural and horticultural scientists. They are the physical components of the climate that together make up a plant's microclimate and can have a huge influence on its growth. Successful arable and fruit farming and commercial horticulture require the location of crops to match the best conditions within the broad latitudinal tolerances mentioned above, particularly those that cannot be economically altered enough to benefit field-scale production. Indeed, meteorological and soil conditions influence the distribution of several crops even within our own small country.

So it seems Linnaeus was right, but the story has a final twist; the "best" conditions under cultivation often differ markedly from those found in the plant's natural habitat. With plants as with people, making the best of one's home is often as much about tolerance as about the ideal! And again like humankind some transported crop-plants have found conditions more to their liking in new lands far away.

Cultivation is to a considerable extent concerned with making attainable adjustments. Put another way, it is about the amelioration of selected items from my computer program's list. To take a simple example let's consider a lettuce in someone's back garden destined for the salad bowl. Two considerations prompt inaction! It is almost certain that the lettuce will grow and it is equally true that it is not possible to fundamentally change the local soil or climate. Nevertheless the keen gardener knows that a bit of fine-tuning will greatly improve his offering at the kitchen door. For a start, lots of additional water, a little nitrogenous fertiliser and keeping slugs and next door's pet rabbit at bay. The result is a combination of the interplay between the lettuce's genes, local conditions, and the owner's best efforts.

The need to make such adjustments varies from site to site and crop to crop, while the degree to which we can realistically and or economically make these alterations varies hugely between items. Only in the most advanced growth cabinets in well-endowed research laboratories are all the conditions under our control, but glasshouses can make large differences. Out of doors we can do comparatively little about heat or light with the possible exception of planting shade trees among some tropical plantation crops. Knowing rainfall patterns and the resulting levels of soil moisture allows for the calculation of irrigation demand and timing. Knowing what to expect allows us to select appropriate sowing dates, anticipate growth patterns and even the likelihood of crops catching some diseases.

It is not much use having the plant if it will not produce the bit you want to harvest in the quantity and quality required, be it root, leaf, stem, flower, fruit or seed. For the grower this is often less demanding than the challenge facing a wild plant that must produce viable seed if it is to perpetuate its local population; his worry ends when the crop reaches the saleable stage. Of course this seems obvious, but you only have to visit almost any plant enthusiast's garden to discover a whole raft of rather sad under-performers. These are not the innate failures of the world's garden flora, but simply the displaced persons of the plant kingdom that can't make a living in their new home. They are forced to struggle against unsuitable conditions to satisfy the collecting urge of the owner. You will see that most types just about grow. But they have the wrong-sized leaves, few flowers and even fewer fruits, or whatever might be the bit you would think was the reason for growing the plant in the first place.

Commercial producers cannot afford such whims; they must find the crops that thrive under the local conditions of soil and climate or at the most need only limited environmental amelioration. An improvement in drainage, the addition of limited amounts of nutrients, a small correction of the soil pH, or extra water in very dry years may suffice. Such demands may seem stringent but, as we shall see later, in practice agronomists are by no means restricted to crops derived from the local flora.

Studying the distribution of a particular crop depends on the scale of the map you use. Most of us were taught about "the corn belt" in the USA or the traditional hop gardens of Kent and no doubt would have got full marks for crayoning in a large blob on an appropriate map. But when we visit these places we find that significant patches within these areas are never used to grow the crop in question because they fail on one or more counts. So a large-scale map shows a much more fragmented pattern determined by the local growers' knowledge of such things as field aspect, the outcropping of a problem soil type, frost pockets and changes in soil pH. Crop sensitivity to soil, real or imagined, is carried to an extreme in traditional areas of European wine production. Here, matters go far beyond yield, as soils and even underlying rock formations are said to influence the flavour of the wine.

Hardly a year goes by without gardeners and farmers declaring the spring season to be exceptionally late or early. This year it is sixteen days early, or so the media tell me! In spite of this precocious start I expect the growing season, influenced by the several factors that combine to determine growth and development, to work to deliver the harvest "on time" as happens most years. Long ago such adjustments allowed the priests to get their harvest celebrations timed to within a week or two, except in those years when the weather turned out to be exceptionally wet for gathering in the cereals.

By coincidence, as I type this from earlier rough notes today's newspaper is concerned with a survey of country life showing that children no longer know when the harvest falls. The explanation given was that urban children are out of touch with nature, but this begs several questions, including: What has nature to do with modern cereal farming? Which harvest would that be? And aren't some crops harvested every week to bring truly fresh produce to our tables? (If not, how come we can buy the same kinds of vegetables and fruit every time we go shopping?)

Canning and freezing may not be husbandry techniques, but they cannot be left out of the story of the provision of green vegetables. These factory-based industrial processes account for a huge tonnage, and although not within the scope of this book they have a huge impact on production. The methods of growing and the precise stage of harvesting contribute to the quality of the final product when it reaches the dining table. The techniques and precision demanded of large-scale growers by the processors has helped advance both the research into so-called blueprint husbandry programmes and their application in the field. When to sow, spray, fertilise, irrigate and harvest are all calculated to produce the desired product. The processor's needs have also been the driving force behind the breeding of many new cultivars, with such specific qualities as uniform and concurrent development of the harvest organ making them ideal for once-over mechanical harvesting.

Having all your flowers out at once and all your fruits ripening together is a risky policy for a plant; one short spell of inclement weather and your genetic future through your offspring is doomed. For thousands of years, right up to a few decades ago, the same traits were also bad for the grower who depended on sequential growth to spread the harvest, give some continuity of supply to home pot or market, and avoid gluts.

At times slight changes in husbandry techniques and crop values will bring about local reductions or extensions to a subject's acreage, but it needs major shifts to trigger a large-scale redistribution. Typically in these cases, national and nowadays frequently international factors come into play such as the comparison between the cost of growing and using locally, compared with growing at a distant low-cost venue and transporting the harvest.

As I have mentioned, to be successful annual crops need a suitable climate only for the duration of their growing season but nowadays even that may not be a fixed length of time as a crop's requirements can be influenced by changes we make to the plant itself through appropriately targeted breeding programmes. Such changes allow us to grow the resulting new cultivars where the climate precludes the older types. Many of the world's most important crops have been subjected to this approach with dramatic results. In the last hundred years earlier-maturing maize cultivars have made it possible to spread the grain crop more than six hundred miles north in North America and in only the last twenty-five years the soya beans that so enjoy the warm but short Canadian summer have been bred to mature before the onset of the fall.

Harvesting a fresh plant is a different story; it is not like the traditional farm harvests which gather in the bits of a plant such as ears of wheat and roots of sugarbeet that come to maturity at the end of its growing season. With fresh produce the harvest organ may be produced part-way through the plant's life cycle. The crop therefore does not need to go through the later stages, which are often the most climate-sensitive.

The most extreme example I can think of are the hypocotyls [g] and cotyledons [g] we know as mustard and cress (bean sprouts are not produced by agronomists). A few years back one would have had to jump from this rather offbeat example to perhaps radish, but now there has emerged a new and extremely fast crop, baby-leaf salad. This, or these, are destined for the supermarket as the contents of those plastic bags filled with the leaves of five or more kinds of seedlings: Swiss chard, lettuce, spinach, rocket, beetroot and lamb's lettuce. Their seeds are precision-drilled in their millions in tractor-width beds and, only some twenty-four days after germination, machine-harvested. The odd thing is that for all the centuries these plants have been grown as vegetables; I bet even the humblest gardeners would have turned their noses up at the idea of taking home the thinnings, but now they are the height of culinary fashion. On the remote chance that one of this new breed of salad-growers reads this, here is a suggestion for his company name: Acetars – the old collective term for salad plants derived from the Latin and still in the English dictionary.

Certainly these young innocents see very little of their full lifespan, while watercress is ready for market after only a few weeks' growth, harvested when the plant is in its full flush of young growth. Others such as young turnips, cabbage, lettuce and leeks are cut down or uprooted about at the point where in nature they would be building up reserves for flowering and seeding. Some are the flower-buds themselves, for example calabrese and cauliflower. Courgettes and cucumbers are very young immature fruits. The so-called root crops would seem to be more in keeping with the seasons but left unharvested would grow for a second year. Such plant material has been part of our diet from before the dawn of agriculture and no doubt each potherb was seized upon as it came into season and was passed over when considered too tough to eat later in the year.

By the same token, flower crops don't have to produce fruits and some fruit crops, like cucumber, should not carry fertile seed. This avoidance of the need to complete the life cycle and secure the next generation obviously depends on some other grower somewhere else growing similar plants through to maturity and selling the rest of us their seed.

A great number of the traditional skills of the older forms of intensive cropping revolved around stretching these fresh harvests over as long a period as possible by adding early and late production to the natural timing of the crop. In the temperate world the long dormant season was always faced with fear and dread, but the worst shortages for both men and beasts

135

came after the winter stores were exhausted and before the first of the new season's bounty brought relief. The "hungry gap" was a spring shortage of food and fodder. The stockmen looked to ways of getting an "early bite" from their pastures. They even went to the extremes of burning the old sward. This is a technique known for perhaps thousands of years to pastoral peoples around the world, though the biology behind the success of burning the old dead grass, which is to do with the release of ethylene gas to act as a growth stimulant, has only been understood for a quarter of a century. From medieval times onwards, the efforts gardeners made to fill the gap may not have been as spectacular, but they were just as enterprising. They were based on finding, or making, favourable locations and playing all sorts of tricks to create an artificial climate. The efforts to create a major climate change belong to the chapter on protected cropping, but this seems the right place to look at selecting or even modifying locations. The climatic factors that really make a difference are soil, air temperature and shelter.

The traditional way to make things warmer in the spring, which is when it matters if you are after early crops, is to use a wall or natural rock-face. It is still rather indirect, as it depends on reflected heat from the sun eventually striking the plot of ground where the crop is growing. South-facing slopes are more effective, and these were, and still are, used for the earliest crops by growers in Cornwall. Some slopes are so steep that the soil washes down and has to be carted back up to the top of the field after each season.

This sort of microclimate produces crops two to three weeks ahead of the surrounding fields. That length of time may not seem much, but it must have meant a lot to people waiting for the first fresh produce of the year, and it certainly means a huge difference to the value of the harvest when it reaches market. New potatoes can loose fifty per cent of their value in four weeks, or put another way the very first are worth twice as much as the bulk of the crop.

If you don't have these slopes you can try to make your own, and that's just what gardeners in the eighteenth- and nineteenth-century walled gardens did. They banked up soil to as much as forty-five degrees against the south-facing wall to receive as much direct early spring solar radiation as possible. Of course this warmed up the soil and it was well understood that the temperature of the soil was as important as the heat of the air because plant growth depends on active roots. We now know that most temperate crops need a minimum soil temperature of around 7°C, with some types of beans and sweetcorn requiring much more.

These artificial slopes work fine, but there are two more bits of physics to take into account, both associated with soil water. This water can act as a very significant thermal sink, bearing in mind that it may represent 20 per cent of a good topsoil's bulk. The second way in which water can reduce soil temperature is by the cooling effect of the latent heat of vaporisation when water evaporates from the soil surface. Clearly good drainage is called for on these early sites, indeed to stop the soil getting saturated the gardeners even went to the trouble of covering them with boards during the worst of the late winter weather. Yet another physical phenomenon, or "trick" as the gardeners would have called it, employed to warm up the soil was to darken the surface with old soot (old because the salts in fresh soot would damage emerging seedlings). Just whether the gardeners understood the physics behind the improved absorption of the sun's energy is open to question but I would bet that my hero Robert Thompson, author of *The Gardener's Assistant*, did.

The ultimate device to get this precious early warmth without resort to cover was to dispense with or at least augment the sun's heat with a method that many would now praise for being both organic and sustainable, the hotbed. As Cowper told us, in verse, back in the eighteenth century,

> The stable yields a stercoraceous heap,
>   Impregnated with quick fermenting salts.

Indeed it is so; hotbeds are formed of fermenting organic material, traditionally horse manure capped with a 25cm layer of topsoil. As the thorough and clear writing Mrs Loudon, widow of J. C. Loudon, tells her readership in *Instructions for Gardening for Ladies*, hotbeds require a lot of material: they "use manure at a rate of twelve to fifteen large barrows full per light." The heat from the rotting material warms the soil to such an extent that the young roots of the seedling crop can be in danger of cooking. Of course, the whole heap cools down after a few weeks but by that time the seedlings are up and the season has progressed enough for them to carry on to maturity without further assistance from the stable.

It is possible to get a good idea of the importance of hotbeds by reading Gilbert White's journals written in the third quarter of the eighteenth century. Hotbeds in all their intricacy of ingredients, construction and management are a recurrent topic in his diaries, as he records the critical role they play in his great enthusiasm for cultivating three cucurbits, namely cucumbers, cantaloupe melons and succade melons. (The last name also appears in early American gardening books but seems to have disappeared in Britain early on; however Charles McIntosh gives it as an alternative to "vegetable marrow" in *The Book of the Garden*; very odd!) Almost daily, White records the progress of his seedlings and how, thanks to hotbeds and their covering mats, he brings them through deep snows and severe frosts from January sowings to fruit in mid April.

Gilbert White was a friend of the scientist and churchman Stephen Hales, who we will meet again later; indeed he was his curate when the latter was rector of Faringdon. Clearly influenced by Hales's investigations, White tested the air beneath the covers over his hotbeds and to his consternation found insufficient oxygen to support a candle flame. Neither man could have known that the oxygen depletion was due to the very microbial respiration that heated the bed, but they did know how to cure the problem. Gilbert White

> laid a leaden-pipe into the frame that has got the tin chimney (according to Dr Hales's proposal) up thro' the back of the bed, in order to convey in a succession of fresh air a nights.

His cherished cucumbers could breathe again.

All these early efforts to beat the hungry gap were home-based, but today our first ports of call must be the roll-on-roll-off ferry terminus and the international airport with its jumbo-jet freight carriers. Over the last forty years in Southern Europe highly perishable temperate-climate crops such as green vegetables and soft fruit have become "early-season" export crops. Road transport distributes them to their northern neighbours but further afield in the subtropics and tropics right around the world on both sides of the Equator many thousands of tonnes of the same fruits and vegetables are loaded into aircraft to complete the provision of year-round supplies to our supermarkets.

This is quite a different story from the earlier spread of crops that became important staples for the local people in their new locations. This new trade has virtually no effect on the diets of the locals – sugarsnap peas and mangetout having as yet to enter East African cuisine.

The need to fit a crop to the most suitable conditions, even if that means rigging them, seems to face us with a conundrum. On the one hand we know that crop plants often originate thousands of miles from where they are now cultivated. And yet on the other they seem so sensitive that there are marked regional differences even within our own small country. Maps showing the distribution of commercial agricultural and horticultural crops come at many scales. The smallest covers the whole world and indicates only such broad sweeps of land use as the American corn-belt. Next there are national maps which in the case of the UK reveal, for example, the preponderance of wheat production in the south-east and grassland stock farming in the north and west. At the largest scale we get county and even parish maps. Climate is the overarching dominant factor behind all such graphic representations; however, as the scale increases, so does the evidence of the importance of soil and aspect to crop distribution. Indeed on many holdings specific crops can be profitably grown only on selected fields. None of this comes as a surprise, but before dismissing it as a statement of the obvious please pause for a moment and consider the standard image of the ancient British farmstead, Iron Age, Roman, Saxon or medieval.

Little if any such crop distribution is discussed by most writers. Knowing self-sufficiency to have been the prime concern of the vast majority of landholders, we today picture each village across the country surrounded by its hinterland of arable fields, each community growing virtually the same staple cereal and legume crops. This is almost certainly an oversimplification of farming at any time but, as suggested earlier, it may well be that the later increase in the importance of cash crops and the break-up of common fields accelerated the migration of crops to their most successful climatic and edaphic locations.

The location and area under production for a whole list of agricultural and horticultural crops have been documented annually for many years by the then Ministry of Agriculture. A cursory glance shows that arable field crops are concentrated in the east of the country but to locate our horticultural crops we need more detail, showing cropping at least at a county level. These data were put into graphic form by J. T. Coppock in *An Agricultural Atlas of England and Wales*. However his maps give us a picture from almost half a century ago when local market gardens had much more influence and produced a wider spread than we have now. It was a favourite exam question to ask students to explain the reasons behind this distribution, good answers typically falling under two main headings: "environmental" and "historic".

Traditionally, local specialities were virtually as pronounced as the labels that used to be put on our manufacturing towns such as "Nottingham for lace" and "Leicester for shoes". One of the oldest must surely be saffron from Saffron Walden in Essex. Liquorice from Pontefract goes back well over a hundred years and then came rhubarb from the area around Leeds and lavender from Norfolk centred on the village of Fring.

The "environmental" group of factors includes soils as well as those items on my agri-met computer program. The need to choose the right soil has been so long understood that Virgil, writing between 36 and 29 BC, spends pages in *The Georgics* reminding his readers of it. He tells them to study "the nature of different soils, the strength and colour of each, and their quotient of fertility" in order to select appropriate crops for each, from black and crumbling land for wheat to more stony hillsides for vines. Closely linked to soil, aspect and local weather patterns is the possibility of avoiding conditions that favour diseases. Taken together these diverse factors produce clear "biologically based" areas, even within a small country. Indeed the environmental group accounts for a general tendency for arable crop production, both agricultural and horticultural, to be located in the south-eastern quarter of England. Within this broad zone some crops were concentrated into specific areas, for example the Weald in Kent for fruit, while others were more generally dispersed. Crop plants often respond to a combination of criteria that show up very clearly on the profit and loss account, but that we find hard to detect in the field. After all, we grow the same sort of plants in our gardens all over the country; just check bedding plants – they are the same in every garden centre wherever you live. To a great extent these garden plants succeed because we fuss over them and we are not that precise in our judgement of their performance. There are limits beyond which tender loving care is simply not enough, the best-known example being soil pH: growing calcifuge rhododendrons in a lime-rich soil is beyond the ability of even the most dedicated enthusiast.

Commercial growers study their harvest records to get a true picture of both yield and income, and they and their bank managers soon know when they have stepped outside a crop's favourable location.

The "historic" heading is where the human element comes to the fore. The cultivation of some crops became a tradition in a region and retained a corner in the market that no outsiders felt confident to challenge. Thus the Vale of Evesham became famous for a whole range of horticultural crops, including the "contradiction" of asparagus on heavy land, but most famous of these "hot spots" was, and still is, the rhubarb-growing district near Leeds in West Yorkshire. Local skills, experience, processing factories and nearness to market were said to contribute to this curious specialisation. I think you could summarise it as "looking over the fence and doing what your neighbour makes most money out of", and that seems to be much the same story in the other cases.

Modern production and marketing have both dissolved and created these pockets. For example, Cheddar strawberries, Devon swedes and plums from Evesham have been reduced in importance, but the field production of vegetables such as onions, celery and carrots has found clear centres of production in East Anglia. Let us for a moment imagine that the horticultural crop map-makers had used another set of data based on crops grown in private fruit and vegetable gardens and allotments. Surely we would then find a much more even distribution with asparagus and onion beds throughout the realm and strawberries and redcurrants equally scattered. Such private gardeners use no magic, but they are prepared to make huge efforts to ameliorate the adverse environmental conditions encountered in their district and, not having to make a living out of their produce, they rarely measure yield.

This sketch, based on the plan of an Oxfordshire village in 1604, shows a fraction of the extraordinary number of individually "owned" strips of land encompassed within its common fields. Strips were as narrow as 5.5 yards (5 metres).

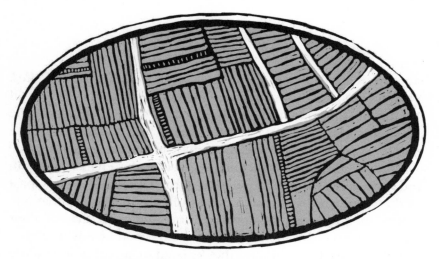

7 CROPPING SYSTEMS AND A WAY OF LIFE

Having set out to demonstrate that, at the plant level, all cultivation is based on the nine basic inputs that fill the second half of this book, i.e. Chapters 8 to 16, it might seem reasonable for me to argue that the world's cultivators have much in common. But I know that both crop production and land-work as summarised by contemporary agricultural geographers and analysts of "agribusiness" are compartmentalised into various "cropping systems". A cropping system could be thought of as the programming of the cultivation techniques employed to produce a particular group of crops. "Cropping systems" is certainly a very broad-brushstroke way of grouping various enterprises, but it at least avoids the even more simplistic national or regional statistics occasionally produced by international bodies such as the United Nations Food and Agricultural Organization. That there are 108 times as many people employed per square kilometre of arable land in the Far East as in North America is impressive, but it in no way compares like with like, either within or between these huge, diverse areas.

Some cropping systems are ancient, others recent; some are large-scale, others small; some are labour-intensive, others not. Without doubt, in the most recently developed of these systems cultivation is an economically attuned, mechanised, technical subject based on scientific understanding and advances.

Such contemporary enterprises seem to exemplify and justify the phrase "land-based industries". Today neither managers nor labour-force talk much about their work being a "way of life". Nevertheless, for thousands of years cultivation was *the* way of life for most of mankind. For the wealthy few, for much of the last millennium, "a way of life" meant the pleasures of the countryside but for the vast majority it meant the miserable life of "Hodge", the general nickname given to the English peasant. Today it is well understood that farm labourers in the past worked long and hard, but it is less often remembered that any misery incurred was as nothing compared with that of their domestic lives spent in dank, dark, one-roomed hovels. Together with their wives and families they existed on a diet of little more than cereals, roots and skimmed milk, with either an early death or the workhouse to look forward to.

The twentieth century saw massive, if long overdue, changes to the lot of the land worker, while the twin forces of work compartmentalisation and advanced husbandry techniques devalued their basic skills. But did these changes so supplant intuitive actions and reduce the commitment of those who work the land and grow plants that little if anything remains of this old idea of a way of life? Indeed, are there still any shared characteristics that span the centuries, link diverse crops and production systems, and somehow unite the world's cultivators?

Perhaps it is not too wildly romantic or reactionary to suggest that dexterity and highly developed powers of observation remain two common characteristics. Many of the operations mentioned in this book are influenced by a combination of prevailing conditions and the state of the plants being attended to. It is the interaction between these two that the skilled cultivator sees and understands. He knows what to do and when to do it (and when not to do it). Much of what goes wrong both in the amateur's garden and on some commercial holdings arises from an inability to read the signs both on the ground and from the condition of the plants. Of course, knowing what to do is no good if you cannot put it into practice, and the cultivator must also have the dexterity to handle plants and use equipment, be it a hand-tool or a machine.

To these skills of hand and eye I would add a sort of overarching but rarely expressed approach to work. Good cultivators, like good livestock-keepers, have always appreciated that they are dealing with living things. Plants are every bit as alive as animals and share the characteristic that the condition we find them in is to a considerable extent a product of their previous circumstances. So good cultivators take for granted that their husbandry should be influenced by what has gone before as well as their plans for the plant's future.

Superficially, many of the older cropping systems seem to have grown from little more than local custom. But we know that all relate to prevailing opportunities and economic conditions. There are cases such as the Enclosures, the Soviet collective farms, the allocation of land to villagers in Africa and the Land Settlement scheme in Britain when "the authority", even in some cases by statute, had a clear idea of how an area of land was henceforth to be managed and cropped. In contrast, most systems have evolved through generations of farmers and growers responding to local conditions, customs and the market. In some cases crops have remained the same for hundreds of years, in others they have changed several times while the system has endured. Some of the following systems are extremely old, others are newcomers. In every case practitioners have identified with them to such an extent that they became the natural labels by which cultivation has come to be classified by geographers, economists and social scientists, and hence governments and the general public.

Classifications have a knack of leaving behind untidy ends, and land use systems are no exception. The larger of the following groupings are based on those used by Dr D. B. Grigg in his book *The Agricultural Systems of the World*. They cover the global canvas reasonably well, but in sketching them I have made no attempt to go into their complexities. Each has many texts devoted to its analysis. My aim is to introduce them to illustrate the many forms that cultivation takes, at different times, in different places and under different social circumstances. Some readers will be more familiar with different group headings such as "nurserymen" and "glasshouse growers"; these I have subsumed into "intensive production" and "protected cultivation".

All cropping systems use and depend upon the same basic actions of cultivation, but what varies is the scale of the operation, its intensity, the equipment used and the way individual crops and areas of land are programmed. There is a general rule that applies to most cropping systems be they menial or high-tech. Where there is ample and therefore cheap land, systems tend to be based on a policy of "low inputs, low outputs." In such cases the inputs include both effort and costs and the yield may be low in either quantity or quality or both. Land shortage, expensive land, small individual holdings and national danger all tend to result in the opposite, that is "high inputs, high outputs" forms of husbandry.

SHIFTING CULTIVATION

The idea strikes us as primitive because it appears not to build on previous effort. Land that has been cleared and brought into cultivation is apparently abandoned and allowed to be recolonised with non-productive indigenous species. In fact it is also quite reasonable to regard these periods of abandonment as fallow during which soil structure and available nutrients return to a desirable level. At its best it has the virtue of being a sustainable system, but it serves to remind us of how hard that is to achieve if one doesn't cheat by gathering up compostable plant material or animal waste from surrounding areas. What is beyond dispute is that this system of cropping needs a much larger area of potentially fertile land than the community requires in any one year. It is also true that such a system works best when land ownership is communal or remains an alien concept. Shifting cultivation may have been a common feature of very early efforts to till the land, and in some cases has persisted successfully until today, but its persistence must have depended on factors such as fertility renewal by seasonal flooding or rapid forest regeneration and the amount of suitable land available. Some slash-and-burn sites, or swiddens as they are known, could no doubt be brought into annual production by appropriate husbandry techniques, and indeed some have.

SUBSISTENCE FARMING

This, we have good evidence to show, is how it all started, at least for those who settled down to village life. Subsistence farming does not exclude the possibility of moving arable crops from site to site within the hinterland of a village, thereby practising a form of shifting fallow between sowings. By the same token, many subsistence farmers sell surplus produce in their local market. Nevertheless, the core activity is to produce food, and often other necessities, for the occupying family. This archetypal, hand-to-mouth way of life is encountered round the world from the croft

146

to the forest garden and shamba [g].

The methods of cultivation are of necessity "organic", with the animals supplying some fertility from manure and urine. However, the practice of seasonally herding the animals to graze on the "waste" [g] beyond the cultivated areas reduces this benefit. Handwork involving the whole family, but with the women taking more than their fair share, is typical of much subsistence farming in the Third World. Primitive equipment restricts land tillage to little more than a surface treatment to achieve a basic seedbed. However, subsistence farming can reach extremely high levels of care, and with crop husbandry more a way of life than a job, crops and even individual plants are often assiduously tended. Hand-weeding, hand-watering, and indeed hand-picking of pests are common practices in some areas. Such attention to detail can lead to high yields, but sadly the reward for all the hard work is a meagre harvest limited by the shortage of nutrients. The need for self-sufficiency underlies such economies and this goes as far as seed-saving to perpetuate crops from one season to the next. Part of each harvest must be set aside and stored as the seed corn for next year, as are some tubers of such plants as sweet potato, dasheen and cassava. Self-sufficiency results in vast numbers of extremely localised selections: the landraces we met in Chapter 4. For many years observers from the First World have noted how indigenous people in many parts of the tropics typically grow a mixture of crops at the same time on the same patch of land. Such plantings are not given to much order and there are few straight lines, so it is not very surprising that these educated agronomists regarded such efforts as lacking the basics of "good practice" as they knew it from home. The rather chaotic picture confronting them revealed an apparent failure to select a single crop type and organise things to suit its cultivation needs. Recently however a lot of time has been spent talking to the local farmers and it has become obvious that this mixing of crops is deliberate and has merit. Multiple cropping intensifies production by endeavouring to take more than one harvest per year from the same plot of land. The most obvious reason for multiple cropping in the Third World is as an insurance against any one type of crop failing, but there are more subtle reasons nearer to our interests in husbandry. There is some evidence that, carefully chosen, the various crops are not so competitive with one another as might have been thought. Furthermore, we now know that such mixtures reduce the incidence and severity of pest and disease damage, make the maximum use of reserves held in the soil and, of course, add to them if at least one of the crops can fix nitrogen.

OPEN FIELDS WITH ROTATION AND FALLOW

The open-field system of farming was, in its developed medieval form, as much about land tenure and the power of the ruling class as about methods of cropping. However even without recounting tales of wicked barons and downtrodden peasants, serfs and villeins it is possible to get an insight into a cropping system that fed huge areas of Northern Europe for almost a thousand years. Land ownership rested with the Crown and, through the king, the religious houses and the lords of the manor. Several classes of "peasant farmer" as we may think of them held or worked land under these overlords, each holding fragmented into strips dispersed around the arable land surrounding the village. As the Cambridge geographer Dr T. P. Bayliss-Smith puts it, for the majority under Norman rule after 1066 it was a subsistence economy "founded on the rights of the peasant to cultivate land in the open fields and graze his animals on the common".

There is still debate among historians around the origins of the open-field system of farming. We know that following the end of the Roman Empire agricultural holdings remained discernible entities typically based on fields clustered round homesteads scattered across the fertile stretches of the landscape, each farmer deciding how best to manage his land.

Historians trace very early evidence of some form of open-field system of farming to the Frankish lands of Northern Europe, from where the idea was adopted by the Emperor Charlemagne around the end of the eighth century. Perhaps as early as the ninth century in both Saxon England and those parts subject to the Danelaw a series of changes started that were to fundamentally alter the rural way of life and make a dramatic change to the appearance of the managed landscape. It would seem that two key factors preceded the rearrangement of the land-holdings; these were the evolution of "the manor" and the authority of its resident, and a migration from scattered farmsteads to form nucleated villages in the proximity of the manors. There is extremely little documentary evidence as to why this move came about, but as Dr Richard Hodges puts it, "The nucleation of villages cannot itself be ascribed to the collective zeal of the peasantry. This was surely the work of a manorial class," encouraged, he points out, by those in power beginning to value land as a resource in both political and economic terms. Knowing the fierce independence of farmers across the world and the heartache that was caused by Soviet collectivisation I agree, indeed I find such changes incomprehensible unless they were caused by the application of some very powerful external force.

It was the farmland around these new villages that became "open" as old field boundaries disappeared and farmers dispersed their land-holding between "strips" and the land became managed through collective action under the patronage and authority of a "lord of the manor". Dr Michael Wood, in *Domesday: A Search for the Roots of England*, writes of the area of Ashdown in Berkshire in the tenth century, where there is documentary evidence from Anglo-Saxon charters – lease documents – of the existence of the open-field system with its classic intermixture of land holdings. The translation reads:

> These nine hides lie among other lands held in share; the open pasture is common, the meadow is common and the ploughland is common ... the lands cannot be described on any side by clear boundary points because to right and left the acres lie in combination one with another.

The "hide" represents one of two concepts of land measurement. That may strike us as odd and certainly makes life difficult for historians, but made good sense in those times. One concept measured land holdings by their productivity, thereby linking area to value. Hence a hide was the area of land necessary to sustain a peasant household, typically set at around 120 acres but varying with fertility – however not apparently by the number in the household. The other concept measured land by the time it took to cultivate it, thereby linking area to resources. It used the acre (a day's work for an ox plough team) and the carucate (a year's work). Both approaches could therefore take account of such factors as soil type, aspect and altitude. One could imagine that on North Wiltshire's poorly drained heavy land the area of a hide could be above average, while conditions could slow down ploughing, resulting in a smaller than usual carucate. In contrast, on the highly fertile light Greensand a few miles to the south the reverse would apply, resulting in a small hide and an above-average carucate.

Surviving manorial maps of the time show an almost incomprehensible number of strips side by side in each great field's sub-units known as "furlongs". Records give us an indication of just how mind-blowingly complex the land holdings were, with each peasant farmer typically having a holding, known as a yardland, made up of between 40 and 80 separate strips of land scattered across the parish. Thanks to the meticulous researches of Rowland Parker we have a snapshot of one such case. In 1673, John Rayner's 40 acres of ploughland in the village of Foxton was made up of 57 separate strips ranging in area from 0.25 to 1.5 acres, each being scattered somewhere within five blocks of land themselves spread across the village's open fields. I find it impossible to see how farmers such as Rayner managed such a system of landholding. Just consider what he might have faced cultivating winter wheat, one of his main crops. With a third of his ploughland down to fallow and half the remainder reserved for spring-sown crops, his modest 13 acres of winter wheat could have occupied 19 sites, some no larger than a modern suburban house plot. Parker wonders how a ploughman ever found the right strip in what must have been a featureless sea of stubble, but find it they did and by 1673 they had been doing so for the best part of seven hundred years. In a large village of around 20 to 30 landholders there might have been well over 1000 strips; indeed the 1613 map of the then modest village of Horsley, referred to earlier, clearly marks some 500 strips covering an area of a little less than 400 acres. Incidentally, following enclosure these strips became some 30 fields, most covering between 5 and 15 acres each. From then on a day's work need no longer start with the challenge of finding your crop.

Of course, the total area under the plough varied with the size of the village. And that changed with prevailing conditions, ranging from the profitability of arable crops versus sheep to the fluctuation in population between times of growth and the ravages of pestilence. At times quite small villages were surrounded by ploughland of over 300ha, while the parish of Whalley in Lancashire is known to have had 1500ha of arable land. Even at the lower end of this range and with the odd patch of wetland and spinney relieving the monotony the visual impact must have been impressive, with the village sitting surrounded by open fields for at least half a mile in every direction.

As we have seen, it would seem that Britain followed mainland Europe, but both the starting date of this mammoth upheaval and the forces that managed it seem lost in the gloom of the Dark Ages, at some time in the late Saxon period. Fortunately the cropping systems are a little better understood. It is said that by the end of the sixth century, well before this great change, most farms in Northern Europe were practising a two-year rotation between fallow and cropping, so in any year half the arable land was "resting". At least that's what some authorities would have us believe, but opinions differ as to the nature of this rest. Some writers emphasise the grazing value of the "weed" growth such land carried, but others point out that by long-standing custom fallow was "bare", by which they mean ploughed regularly to rid it of weeds before bringing it back into cropping. Instructions survive for the timing and style of its first, second and third ploughing, the emphasis being on exposing the soil to the weather to improve its structure. We know this practice of tilling fallow goes back to Roman times and was still practised in the eighteenth century.

Estimates of yield for all cereals are shockingly low compared with our expectations. J. Z. Titow, following his exhaustive analysis of the Grange Accounts of the estates of the bishopric of Winchester for over a century from 1208, calculates that in southern England the average yield of wheat was 6.75cwt per acre (0.8 tonnes per hectare). Indeed in some cases little more than twice the amount sown was reaped, and that after all the hand-labour that went into tilling those fields. These yields are even lower than those reported by Reynolds (page 54), probably owing to disastrous harvests caused by pestilence or bad weather. Records for an Oxfordshire farm from 1311 continue that sad story of hard work for little gain – or grain! Just over 40 per cent of the seed harvested was kept back for sowing a similar area of land the next year. Perhaps a third was more common, but whichever figure we take, some idea of just how things have changed can be gained by recalling that today that figure would be about 3 per cent (in the unlikely event of a farmer using home-grown seed). The assumption that sowing rates were excessive to compensate for the crudity of the husbandry seems not to be valid; what sketchy records we have suggest that they fall just within the upper limit of the range used today. It seems that low yields resulted from what are to us very predictable causes: a combination of low-fecundity cultivars achieving poor plant establishment, low-fertility weedy soils and a high level of pest and pathogen predation. No doubt both the Biblical parable of "some falling on stony ground" and the old adage foretelling the premature fate of many seeds – "one to rot and one to grow, one for the pigeon and one for the crow" – were both based on practical observation.

At some time after the establishment of the open fields, in what is now North-West France, the two fields became three. The change spread slowly north and east to cover much of the Low Countries, Germany, Denmark and Britain. Well, Britain except the West, where the Celts had nothing to do with such a risky new idea. Now this change from two to three fields may not seem like an earth-shattering development, particularly when one realises that it did not mean an increase in the total area of arable land. It did however hugely increase productivity, as now only a third was out of commission at any one time while two thirds were under the cumbersome heavy plough pulled by a team of oxen. Typically the three fields of a community, village or hamlet, were managed as a simple rotation: winter cereal in one cropped field and spring-sown corn, barley, oats or protein-rich pulses in the other. The niceties of land occupation were subordinate to this cropping rotation, but individual farmers cultivated their own strips within these fields.

Such a bizarre mixture of collective action and individualism has several agronomic consequences and begs comparison with the collectivisation of the Soviet policy in the twentieth century. The collective aspects produced an economy of scale and a uniformity of fertility developed during the fallow year. This was followed by further uniformity of tillage based on the demands of a single kind of crop and the use of shared equipment. However, it must have been very rare in Britain to find uniform land and conditions over the whole of one of these massive fields. In addition to such natural variation, the individual efforts and skills of the many farmers must have produced differing results, with each person's dependence on, and reward for, his or her own husbandry efforts probably providing the usual stimulus, a factor so dreadfully lacking in the Soviet system.

Every autumn one of the three vast fields was sown to winter wheat while a few months later another went into spring cereals. Monocultures on this scale are notorious for the build-up and spread of pests and diseases. Some insurance against both these problems and each crop's specific response to the weather came by sowing "maslin", a mixture of two or more types of cereal. The usual mix was wheat and rye, but by 1557 Thomas Tusser in his *Five Hundred Points of Good Husbandry* was pointing out that there was a problem at harvest time, as "Rye tarry wheat till it sheds as it stands." Set against this disadvantage was Fynes Moryson's claim more than half a century later that the bread it made was good for farm workers as it "abode longer in the stomach and is not so soon digested with their labour". Generally used as animal feed, maslin was still a popular strategy on mixed farms well into the eighteenth century. Arable weeds were common and we know that hand-pulling in the standing crops took a great deal of time during the growing season. The many balks [g] and headlands [g] must have been a source of weed seed, but perhaps we should take a more positive point of view and see them as an early example of beetle banks [g]! As I have outlined earlier, eventually the cons were judged to have outweighed the pros and Northern Europe's great experiment in collective agriculture was slowly dismantled by the enclosure agreements of a new breed of farmer.

CROFTING

Crofting has a unique place in the history of self-sufficiency. Over centuries of struggle under the harshest conditions, crofters evolved their own methods of cultivating the land around their "townships". Scottish law recognised the unique status of these last few tenacious tenants of the great highland estates who had somehow managed to remain to become among the last subsistence farmers in Britain. These brave souls continued to win a livelihood from the land and sea after their relatives had left, driven from their ancestral homeland by a series of catastrophes, many brought upon them by those with power and authority. In 1913 the Rt Hon. Lord Pentland of Lyth, one-time secretary for Scotland, put it this way: "The crofter of the present time has through past evictions been confined within narrow limits, sometimes on inferior and exhausted soil." In spite of title and position he seems from the following quotation to be on the crofters' side, perhaps based on the belief in land reform held by the Liberal Party at that time:

> The case of the crofters is but a particular instance of the general rule, by which the smallholder has given place to the large farmer when agriculture for profit was substituted for agriculture for subsistence.

The extremely well academically qualified Dr Fraser Darling, sometime Director of the West Highland Survey, was another and more recent enthusiast for the crofter's life. In his 1945 collection of articles called *Crofting Agriculture* he nevertheless makes the point that judged by the input of skilled labour per unit area crofting is more akin to horticulture.

Some idea of the intensity of effort can be gathered from his description, based on personal experience, of constructing the ironically named "lazy beds" for potatoes. This method of cultivation in Scotland goes back to before 1769, when Adam Dickson in his *Treatise on Agriculture* tells us that potatoes were a comparatively new farm crop. Earlier, "a few only were cultivated by gentlemen for their tables; and these were commonly planted on what are called lazy beds". To form the beds on boggy peat land crofters mark out in a series of long but narrow (1m wide) beds then cover each with a deep dressing of seaweed carted from the beach. The paths between the beds are dug out deep enough to provide a spit depth (250mm) of peat soil over the kelp. Spades were used but traditionalists favoured the caschrom or foot plough. This tool has the appearance of a horizontal blade mounted at right-angles on the end of a long pole. With skill, a forward push followed by a pull back and twist on the pole cuts and levers the sod onto the lazy bed in one action. The paths now function as ditches, which together with the elevation of the beds keep the crop above the surrounding bog. What a contrast to the mechanised potato production discussed later on page 261.

It seems appropriate to recall here that there is clear archaeological evidence showing that man has struggled to cultivate the inhospitable coastal margins of the highlands and islands since Neolithic times; clearly we are a tenacious species.

The crofter's "lazy bed" reminds me of another and even more unusual form of raised bed constructed by other coastal dwellers but living under very different conditions: the thyme beds of the

Seychelles. To start with, thyme is not the herb you would expect to feature strongly in the cuisine of a tropical island; the anomaly of its appearance on Mahae may be due to the strong early French influence. The demand for thyme must have caused a real horticultural challenge. Faced with a poorly drained lateritic soil and an annual rainfall of 260cm, Seychelles early cultivators hit on a novel solution. They constructed shallow raised beds on the sloping tops of the huge granite boulders that outcrop throughout the island, providing the plants with excellent drainage and full sun. A few still exist and bunches of thyme continue to lie alongside the tropical spices in Victoria Town's covered market.

WETLAND RICE

Vast numbers of Asia's rural population are both engaged in and dependent on wetland rice production, yet so intensive is this type of cereal farming that it occupies a relatively small area of the land within the region. With an exceptionally high rural population density of around four people to the hectare it is not surprising to learn that historically about half of the rice grown was consumed within the areas of production. The unique feature of the rice grown in this system is its need to grow in 10–15cm of water for the first three-quarters of its life. To provide the plants with the optimum inundation the paddy fields are constructed as elevated, shallow ponds yet are capable of being drained before harvest by breaching one of the surrounding earth bunds. Although the hillside terraces are rightly regarded as a wonder of early civil engineering, by far the greater part of wetland rice is produced on naturally occurring flat land associated with river systems, in particular the vast deltas of the continent's major waterways. While ample quantities of water are therefore close at hand, there is often need to construct irrigation channels and to lift the water into them. Thus this form of rice production is by far the most important of the ancient cropping systems to supply its crop's water requirements by artificial irrigation.

Although farmed under such unusual soil conditions, virtually all the basic acts of cultivation are involved in producing these rice crops: seedbed preparation, sowing, transplanting (and thereby determining optimum spacing), weeding, and most obviously irrigation. Wetland rice grown in the traditional way is hugely labour-demanding, most particularly because it is a transplanted crop. Half a million seedlings per hectare are planted in 100mm of water; this work is traditionally carried out by women, as is the hand-weeding – what a surprise!

Another unusual if not unique feature is the extremely long period of successful monocropping in these fields. There have been hundreds of rice crops, one following the other with little or no break between, indeed many of the terraced slopes in the Philippines are still highly productive after two thousand years of such a regime. While this is not the only place in this book to flag up some need to treat the concept of rotation as less than holy writ, there remains the need to explain the annual availability of plant nutrients in spite of the addition of precious little fertiliser, particularly nitrogen. Some suggested explanations include the absence of leaching, nutrient-rich river water and accompanying silt, and the decomposition of aquatic nitrogen-fixing micro-organisms.

MIXED FARMING

Archaeological evidence suggests that the division between the stockman and the farmer is a very great deal older than the song from *Oklahoma!*, "Oh, the farmer and the cowman should be friends ..." Mixed farming is the coming together of these two branches of husbandry to their mutual advantage and thus to the benefit of the combined enterprise. In spite of an apparently deep-seated human preference to be either an animal or a crop person, European farms have depended for at least two millennia on running the two farming enterprises in tandem.

Considered as one large unit, the medieval village is clearly a mixed farm with crops and grazing skilfully integrated. The mixed farm under single ownership that we know today emerged from that background as a small number of the most enterprising consolidated, increased and enclosed their land-holding and produced for market. This new class of "yeomen farmers" emerged from both the lessees of the lord's demesne and from among the villagers. Needless to say it was the most enterprising who seized their chance: W. G. Hoskins calls them "capitalist peasants who acquired the lands of their weaker fellows". Advantageous as these changes were to the development of British agriculture, they inevitably resulted in the end of feudal life as large numbers of subsistence peasant farmers became landless workers.

Animals can't live on fresh air, as they used to say; they need large quantities of the appropriate food. The herbivores we have domesticated to become successful farm animals require land to be allocated for their food. Under some extensive systems of ranching the animals simply graze the range, living off the land by eating the indigenous flora. In more intensive mixed farming, three production systems supply stock feed: grazing land, forage crops for winter feed, and arable crops for both winter use and to supply highly nutritious "concentrates".

The last category is always included in the statistics for arable land, and so it should be, with only a little under 800,000ha of UK barley being used as animal feed. Grass, clover or other forage crops are also included if they are grown as short-term leys in an arable rotation. Taken together, these two categories are of major significance, indeed some 40 per cent of our ploughland is devoted to growing meat and dairy products.

The presence of livestock on mixed farms also has an impact on the landscape by helping to conserve field patterns and their locally characteristic boundaries. This is particularly true where the stock joins in the crop rotation, so to speak, by feeding off short-term leys or fields of roots. In such an integrated approach the need to contain animals as they move round the farm leads to a compromise between the creation of machine-efficient arable prairies and the retention of smaller stock-proof fields.

Joan Thirsk in her book *Alternative Agriculture* firmly links leys with arable cropping in the open fields as far back as the fifteenth century. They were in effect part of a long-term rotation and a means of regaining soil fertility after prolonged tillage. I suspect this was mainly by improving soil crumb [g] structure, but nitrogen would have been added from clovers and their relatives and, ploughed in, the sward would have made "green manure" [g]. Today's gardeners are well informed about the value of compost made from plant remains, but animal wastes inevitably dominate the story of organic manures on farmland. Indeed it is easy to overlook the part played by the return of the previous crop's debris, whether as spent animal bedding, ploughed-in-straw and haulm [g] or decomposed roots.

Seaweeds may no longer be regarded as true plants by today's botanists, but their remains deserve a special mention as an outstanding source of organic fertiliser when used in bulk, whether buried, spread as mulch or composted. For centuries "wreck" supplied fertility for the fields and gardens of the thousands of crofters and smallholders who clung to a living around the coasts of the British Isles. As with so many of the topics touched on in this book, further investigation reveals a remarkable mix of folklore, social history, craft skills and sheer hard work. We learn of sixteenth-century local courts prescribing who may harvest which beach, of seventeenth-century debates on whether it is best composted, ploughed in fresh or spread as a mulch. Some believed that specific species of seaweed were best for specific crops. Special tools were developed for winning the weed from the water's edge, from where much of it could only be moved by horse and pannier or man and rope basket; this took place in winter or early spring, to satisfy a requirement of some 30 tons per acre (75 tonnes per hectare). Many held that, weight for weight, seaweed was as beneficial as farmyard manure, and I doubt if we have yet fully understood the unusual ability of decomposed seaweed to influence soil structure and supply nutrients.

Today we tend to think of farm animals as being kept for meat or milk. Historically the most important product was sheep's wool. And, as far as cattle were concerned, their vital role in human food production for the majority of the population was not as meat but as the farm's power source. As time went by they shared this role with horses. That energy was home-grown; fields produced crops to feed the draught animals and the resulting muscle-power cultivated the whole farm. As far as the arable part of the farm was concerned, the manure the stock produced was as important as their pulling power, for what was the use of cultivating unfertile land? Farmyard manure was the vital link between the two parts of a mixed farm, so this seems the proper place to go into it, if you see what I mean. Stock-keeping and cropping had to be in balance. As John Mortimer in tells us in his 1707 book *The Whole Art of Husbandry*, "There ought to be a proportion taken care of between the pasture lands and the crop lands" … Wise words, but farmers were always keen to get as much stock feed "for free" as possible, ideally by their animals grazing the waste or by eating otherwise unusable debris from a previous crop such as barley straw and, more recently, sugarbeet tops.

Herbivores are really walking, self-loading (and unloading)

compost heaps; their digestive tract assisted by their gut bacteria converts part of their food intake to readily available plant nutrients, while other metabolic activities secrete waste nitrogen into their urine. Taken together, these processes yield significant amounts of "fertiliser", but you cannot get something for nothing and herbivorous farm stock do not add nutrients to those contained in their food: they recycle them, some in a readily available form. From the plant nutrition point of view, using animals as intermediaries on the way to the muckheap offers two advantages over allowing vegetation to rot down *in situ*: it is a more efficient way of managing the recycling of nitrogen and above all the muckheap is the place where next season's plant nutrients are concentrated from foodstuffs gathered from afar. In times past this would have been the village "outfields"; today animal food comes from across the world. Set against these advantages it must be said that a badly managed muckheap is also the place where plant nutrients are lost, a great deal by seepage into the immediate surroundings.

Farmyard manure was the prime source of fertiliser for some two thousand years of British farming and horticulture. Probate inventories listed the size and value of the muckheap just as carefully as the wheat in the granary. It is a mixture of the faeces and urine of farm animals together with the straw used in their bedding. It is valuable both as a soil conditioner, contributing to the structure of the land, and as a source of nutrients. The amount of nutrients contained in farmyard manure is to a great extent governed by the amount of urine it contains and it is the job of the straw bedding to sop it up, as the 1908 Board of Agriculture leaflet no. 175 reminds us. It also varies from animal to animal and by the way they are kept. Nevertheless, early horticultural writers seem to exaggerate the need to select precisely the right kind for each crop. "Deer's dung is more proper for tender and smallest plants; cow dung is excellent for most sorts of rare plants whereas horse dung is best for trees and plants of quick digestion." Thomas Hill writing in 1577 takes a different but just as pedantic an approach. He grades manures, giving the highest prize to bird droppings, then ass, followed by goat, ox, cow, swine and last, to my great surprise, horse, "the vilest and worst of all dungs". If growers believed so strongly that each manure had such different qualities it is not surprising that they considered that each crop required specific manure. Of course they were right inasmuch as different plants require different proportions of the various nutrient elements, although this specificity could be exaggerated and still was, three hundred years after Hill's day, by Dr A. B. Griffiths. He gave specific manurial instructions for no less than 58 glasshouse decorative plants and over 100 garden flowers, plus all the vegetables and fruits you are ever likely to grow. No wonder people were glad to follow the advice of Lawrence and Newell from the John Innes Institute (referred to on page 194).

Manure was carted and spread from either the dungheap or the stockyards at the end of the winter. The land for intensive vegetable crops could get as much as 200 tonnes per hectare, cereal and root crops around 25 tonnes, which, for those of us with small gardens, works out at 2.5 kilograms per square metre. Even at these modest rates it was a gut-wrenching task for the men to load and spread, and for the oxen or horses to pull the carts across the ploughland. If the distance was around a quarter of a mile we are told the work required 2 men loading, 3 horses and carts, 2 drivers and 2 or 3 men in the field spreading. I find I am not alone with my bad memories of muck-spreading; one late-nineteenth-century writer reckoned:

> There is no class or kind of farm work that involves more slave-like drudgery than the hauling and spreading of manure ... one of the operations on the farm that is held in awe and dread.

I can't say it gave me nightmares though !

The old textbooks give instructions based not on weight or volume per acre but by "the load". But as Rogers points out, this is not a fixed unit and implies simply "as much as a cart can contain". However, one-horse, two-wheeled tipper carts were almost always used and fully loaded they can carry around a ton of manure. Regardless of the amount per acre required, the number of heaps the drivers placed across the field remained constant; it was their size that altered. The logic behind this was that if heaps were dropped at around six-metre intervals the spreaders, using long-handled muck-forks, could cover the land faster by throwing directly from each heap in turn. The skill was to get an even spread. The task got somewhat easier when horse-drawn mechanical muck-spreaders arrived on British farms in 1905, but it was some fifty years before they were a common sight. Throughout that time muck-spreading remained in the hands of the man with the curved-tined fork.

All that effort achieved less than one person does now sitting on a tractor. It is a tractor fitted with a front-end loader and pulling a muck-spreader. Today's textbooks tell students that a worker so equipped can load, cart for 0.25 of a mile and spread 6 tonnes in an hour, or about the usual dressing for half an acre (0.2ha). Farmyard manure is now seen as much as a valuable soil conditioner as a source of nutrients. As the organic matter breaks down it produces "humus" that binds soil minerals into crumbs that collectively form tilth, that depth of friable soil whose production has been the primary aim of tillage throughout the history of cultivation.

Many of today's intensive animal production units do not produce that mix of bedding and excreta we know as FYM; instead waste is accumulated as slurry, typically a vile-smelling semi-liquid whose disposal is often regarded as a problem despite its high fertiliser content. Spreading it stinks out most of the parish and runoff into watercourses has disastrous consequences for their ecology. At least one very large-scale American pig-producer has come up with a clever solution. They place their units on arable farms, matching pig numbers with acreage so that the slurry produced equates with the farm's fertiliser requirements. To do this you need to know the number of days of pig occupancy per year, and the lifetime average daily volume and fertiliser value of a pig's excreta. You may guess that senior management knows the answer to the first part and gives someone else the job of finding out the rest. But there is no need: Jean-Baptiste Boussingault, that pioneer of agricultural science, whom we shall meet in Chapter 9, did the dirty work back in the first half of the nineteenth century! On corn and soya farms it works out as just under three pigs per hectare of cropland. Obviously both crop farmer and pig-producer gain, but don't go away with the idea that this is the perfectly balanced system that organic, sustainable producers might wish for, since a large amount of feed has to be brought in. This is a strategy devised primarily for the economic disposal of pig effluent. To avoid the smell and pollution, very large, powerful machines inject the slurry into the soil, which is easy to arrange on the American prairies but just one more factor against such a system being adopted in Britain.

There is an easier way of deploying animal waste, and it is one that was used for centuries of mixed farming, namely sheep-folding. As Tusser tells us, "The land is well hearted with help from the fold." The animals were taken daily to feed on the broad acres of pastureland unsuitable for arable crops and every evening the flocks were driven back. Throughout the time when the manorial system held sway the villeins and the smaller semi-servile farmers were compelled to fold their sheep on demesne land from Hoketide (the second Tuesday after Easter Sunday) to 11 November, thereby giving the lord this vital source of plant nutrients for virtually the whole grazing season. Hundreds of years later we still read of flocks being driven daily "up to two or three miles" to spend the night "crowded into folds" at a density of around 1300 animals per acre (3120 per hectare). On reflection, this was not so "easy" a way of manuring the land, at least not for the shepherd, as a 1-acre (0.4ha) fold used some 180 hazel hurdles, and required moving every morning if all the arable fallow was to get its share before the crop went in. Thanks to the feeding and bowel habits of sheep, most of the waste from the herbage they grazed during the day was excreted at night, so they were not so much walking manure-spreaders as manure concentrators.

It seems that the fertility of the thin soils of Wessex could never have supported worthwhile cereal crops before the advent of "artificial" manures without the nightly visits from huge flocks. As a surveyor working on one Dorset manor in 1776 put it, "The sheep are kept primarily to produce manure for the arable lands which is the greatest profit gained by them." This point was echoed some twenty years later when Lord Bath's steward commented that: "The first and principal purpose of keeping sheep is undoubtedly the dung of the sheepfold."

Using the figures collected by Tim Bayliss-Smith for a Wiltshire farm in 1826 as a snapshot, I estimate that their flock of 1400 sheep imported around 20kg of nitrogen per night. That is about half the minimum application per hectare we use today, so in theory the flock, if folded the year round, could satisfactorily manure all the farm's 120ha of ploughland. Arable crop enterprises supplemented the grazing with fodder crops and part of the cereal harvest went to feed the farm animals, including in the case of the Wiltshire farm 16 horses for the 300 acres (120ha) of ploughland. At an average ration of 10 pounds (4kg) of oats per day, based on contemporary yields, that's around 1.5 acres (0.6ha) per horse per year, in this case a total of almost 24 acres (10ha).

Mixed farming became the norm over large areas of Europe, the backbone of the British yeoman farmer's life style. It spread the risk among both the hazards and the gains of crop and stock production. Perhaps its greatest contribution was in providing the logical basis for the introduction of an effective crop rotation.

Arable land on an eighteenth-century mixed farm grew crops for sale and to feed the farm's stock. Viscount Charles Townshend's famous four-year rotation, often referred to as the Norfolk Four Course system, not only helped control weeds and maintain fertility but met both of the farm's requirements. Turnips (stock feed) were followed by barley or oats (stock feed and cash), then by undersowing [g] a clover/grass ley (grazing and winter stock feed) and finally wheat (cash crop). Above all, mixed farming made life a little more secure for John Bull alias Farmer Giles.

PRAIRIE FARMING

Cereals as far as the eye can see – wheat or maze, depending on climate and rainfall; this, agricultural economists have described as typical of vast areas of the farmlands of the USA, Canada, Australia, Argentina and the old Soviet Union. It seems from the evidence of the last half century that prairie farming is a first phase in modern man's efforts to expand arable cropping into new lands: that is, "new" as far as the settlers are concerned. In truth these grasslands were home to earlier scattered communities who found themselves displaced by the newcomers.

What we see today is the successful side of a far from totally successful story that starts with the attempt to turn these vast grasslands into arable fields. Among those who staked their all on this almost superhuman challenge were the poor landless peasants of central Europe attracted half-way across the world by the US Homestead Act of 1862, offering 160 acres (64.75ha) of free land if you farmed it for five years. Some were lucky; they were settled on suitable soil with a suitable climate. Others were not, and the locals knew it. "Wrong side up," commented a Sioux Indian as a North Dakota settler turned his first furrow. So it proved to be for many when rainfall and nutrients were too low for arable crops. In undisturbed grassland the nitrogen is held in the ecosystem in the endless cycle of the sward's growth and decay. In recently ploughed grassland, deprived of either added fertilisers or leguminous crops able to fix nitrogen from the air, this essential plant nutrient element is lost at a startling rate. Some is carted off in the harvest but most is either leached away or converted into nitrogen gas by denitrifying bacteria. After some years the annual loss decreases, but by this time cereal crop yields can have halved from the first heady harvest-home. Eventually, after the heartache, grazing returned to such sites but over vast areas the plough won through. For the successful, the rough-and-ready days of prairie farming lasted less than one hundred years for, as Dr D. B. Grigg suggests, by the middle years of the twentieth century little remained of the system in its original, basic form in either Australia or North and South America.

Prairie farming could not have developed without the appropriate scale of land ownership and a significant level of mechanisation, albeit animal-powered in the early days, both in the field and at harvest, and with an infrastructure that delivers the product to its markets at an economic rate. It is said that its development was a response as much to a shortage as to a perceived objective. There were simply not enough people to farm in the traditional ways. Prairie farming is essentially a low-input, low-output system, in the past often tied to repeated monocropping without any planned rotation. In the early days farmers seemed to show little concern for the future.

Productivity depended on the residual fertility and excellent structure of the grassland soils. Once the sod had been broken, land tillage was kept to a minimum. It consisted of little more than the production of a shallow seedbed followed by sowing, first by broadcasting, then, as the nineteenth century came to an end, drilling. None of the other basic acts of cultivation – weeding, pest and disease control, irrigation and the use of fertilisers – were in evidence. All this may seem like a typical "Old World" view of this brash young farming system, and we should never overlook the challenges these pioneers faced. Life was tough, the work was full of previously unknown risks and domestic conditions were primitive. The aggressive can-do attitudes of these pioneers injected fresh thinking into world agriculture. Prairie farming produced the local surpluses that allowed for the development of world trade in basic animal and human foodstuffs. In the field they showed the way in the use of mechanised equipment followed by the exploitation of the power of the prime-movers, the tractor and the self-propelled combine. In the farm office they recognised that crop production was both an industry and an essential part of what has become known as agribusiness.

Though prairie farming began as a low-input, low-output system, it has become less and less of one since then; however, it remains the logical place to consider the pros and cons of such an approach to cropping. Plants, like animals, have a threshold for many of their requirements below which they simply will not grow. Sadly our televisions bring us image after image of such sites, usually due to drought, but always leading to the same result: famine. Unaided, no farmer can survive such conditions, indeed they are the trigger for slash-and-burn communities to up sticks and move.

Above these base requirements come the advantages of additional inputs provided they are in balance one with the other. As we have already seen, these inputs are more or less critical to both the quantity and quality of the harvest. Intensive growers such as British and Dutch farmers believe in "spending some to make more", yet American farmers who are just as commercially minded are satisfied with yields little more than half of ours. Why? Because the overall profit is as great if they fully exploit their economies of scale and provided they are skilled at determining the critical minimum inputs required to produce the crop.

Low-input, low-output approaches to crop production may find little favour with European producers, but they attract a lot of attention from the sidelines, as reduced inputs clearly are more sustainable than intensive systems of cropping; you can neither run out of, nor be accused of using up, things that you are not using in the first place! Some people link this with the idea that by abstaining you are not damaging the environment so much, either. This is a far more difficult concept to sign up to as a general principle, but it is one that has real merit under extreme conditions. For example, the irresponsible use of some pesticides can lead to toxic levels persisting in the soil; and there is extremely worrying evidence from many places around the dryer parts of the world, for example in Azerbaijan, of the build-up of salt in the soil, to damaging levels, following the prolonged use if irrigation water.

165

PLANTATION CROPPING

This approach to crop production looks to focus capital and skills onto the growing of a specific crop over an area large enough to offer considerable economies of scale. This current meaning of "plantation" comes to us through a slow lexical evolution as much concerned with the settlement of people as the ordering of plants. Within Britain it is most commonly used to describe the large-scale establishment of both timber and fruit trees; in the later case it seems to replace the more homely term "orchard" when the user wishes to convey a more ordered and aggressively commercial approach to fruit-growing. When transferred to more recently developed lands it embraces a wider range of crops, typically monocultures from which little if any of the harvest is used locally. Such "cash crops" usually go to wholesale outlets in markets remote from the local people.

To some extent plantations have become identified in some people's minds with colonial or multinational-company exploitation of local people and their land. Plantations may produce crops for export that have no history of cultivation in the area and whose harvests of fruits or vegetables may even be locally unacceptable. In such cases few if any skilled staff are local. At the very least, this form of agronomy is considered to lack empathy with local needs and the wellbeing of the area. Changing such attitudes is not helped by the historical association of the plantation system of cropping with some of the most notorious slave crops such as sugar and cotton. Against this depressing image of alien intrusion, it is important to recognise that in some parts of the world crops for export play a vital role in bringing in foreign currency.

Many of today's plantations are grown on land first brought into cultivation for just that crop. Its establishment therefore inevitably meant the destruction of the existing natural habitat. Indeed in some cases whole ecosystems have been wiped out by forest or savannah clearance to make way for an economically desirable monoculture. In their early years the new crops were dependent on the natural fertility built up by the local vegetation; in some cases this was soon lost, while in others good management conserved and even enhanced it. Plantations therefore reflect some of the most dramatic powers of today's cultivators but at the same time are stark reminders of the darkest side of man's power over nature. In recent years several clearances have become *causes célèbres*, but for those with long memories the most infamous must surely be the East African Groundnut Scheme. Based on the need for edible oils in the aftermath of the Second World War, and of colossal scale, it deployed the largest equipment ever used, including pairs of second-hand military bulldozers dragging massive chains to root-out bush trees and scrub. Some 150,000 acres (61,000ha) were to be cleared in the first year. Such an extreme approach was of course out of step with both the tempos of Africa and, to their credit, the British colonial service government. As Alan Wood, head of the Overseas Food Corporation's Information Division wrote, it was "in large measure, a story of failure, frustration, heartbreak, bad luck and bad blunders. But the story starts as one of the most inspiring ventures since the Second World War." Such was the fate of the British government's largest venture into Soviet-style, government-administered farming.

The majority of plantation crops are perennial, with economic lives ranging from tens of years in the case of rubber and mango down to a only a few years for sugar-cane, banana and pineapple. Presumably it was repeated monocropping that led cotton, an annual, to be bracketed with the others. In general the system remains the mainstay of the international trade in many crops from tea to mangoes, but small-farmer groups have proved to be an economically viable alternative in, for example, coffee. Such successes are usually dependent on a strong, well-managed marketing organisation.

FIELD PRODUCTION

Horticulturists engaged in vegetable production traditionally regarded their holdings as market-gardens; these are discussed below. Nevertheless, even by 1795 London's demand for fresh vegetables was large enough for the Marquis of Salisbury to investigate the labour demands and cost of the field-scale cultivation of peas, parsnips, carrots, potatoes, cabbage and beetroot on 17 acres (7ha) of his "Experimental Farm" in Hertfordshire. Seedbed preparation and hoeing were expensive, but high yields including 41,000 cabbages selling at 1.5 pence each brought a handsome profit.

During the last seventy years or so, areas of the best arable land on farms across the First World have become the new veg patches of their urban customers. The rate of change from market-gardener to vegetable farmer has varied from country to country. The USA was well to the fore; by the 1950s the average vegetable grower was devoting some 65 acres (26ha) to this kind of crop, and national regions of production were well established. In England some five per cent of our ploughland is devoted to vegetables, the vast majority on the eastern side of the country in a band running from the Humber Estuary to Essex. So successful has field production been that its spread has caused the eclipse, if not the complete disappearance, of the traditional market-garden and its production methods in many parts of the developed world.

In spite of its cavalier approach to the niceties of husbandry as preached by those fabled figures of garden history, the old head-gardeners, field production has brought economies of scale and the chance to use both agricultural machinery and specifically designed equipment. Growing for both the major retail supermarkets and the food processors – canners, freezers and prepared-food manufacturers – requires bulk production from each contracted producer. At the outset it was wrongly believed that the quality of the produce would be inferior, particularly when the harvest consisted of individual items such as cauliflower curds and sticks of celery. In practice the cultivation schedules or "blueprints" have produced excellent results, as we can see from a trip to almost any supermarket. However, such successful blueprints mass-produce only one narrowly defined, uniform crop – defined in this case by the supermarket. There must be countless times when the customer's concept of quality and the supermarket's do not coincide. For example, just why parsnips have to be reinvented to be the size of flavourless large carrots is baffling, and people are lucky indeed if "real" parsnips are available from local market-gardens – in my case those of Bromham just down the road in Wiltshire, where they even bred their own types.

Uniformity is still more impressive than quality. Often some 90 per cent of the crop reaches a uniform, saleable standard. In many ways this form of vegetable production can act as a benchmark for where arable husbandry had reached by at end of the twentieth century. The soil is still being tilled, but not always at the same time of year and certainly not to the same depth. Machines and sprays have successfully replaced the use of hand-tools for the preparation of the land, sowing or transplanting and all the subsequent operations needed throughout the growth of the crop. Labour – the hands that manipulated the tools – has been dramatically reduced. For many crops it took more than ten times the man-hours to produce 100m^2 of vegetables on a market-garden in 1900 than on a vegetable farm today. Now it costs far more to harvest, grade, pack and transport many vegetables than to grow them.

MARKET-GARDENS

Market-gardens have a long and fascinating history. On one hand their story belongs to the social history of the development of urban centres and how fresh produce reached their ever-expanding populations. On the other hand they are at the very heart of the technical development of the craft and science of horticulture. Intensive production at whatever scale has become synonymous with flying in the face of nature. For hundreds of years this intensity was both the only profitable way of producing fresh vegetables, salads and, to a lesser extent fruit, for many of the world's great cities. Around the world, cultivators became expert in meeting urban demands by what, in a scientific age, we have come to call the removal of limiting factors. Perhaps the most dramatic of these was the provision of plant nutrients *ad lib* through the use of absolutely vast amounts of manure from the town and city stables and, it must be said, from their privies and laystalls.

As with so much of the story of the evolution and sophistication of cultivation, the development of the market-garden is directly linked to the type and scale of the culture in which it was practised. These holdings were a city's kitchen garden. For hundreds of years before the establishment of good roads and fast railways, edge-of-town holdings produced virtually all the fresh fruit and vegetables that reached the city markets. Located wherever there was easily worked, well-drained soil around an urban perimeter, they grew crops both in and out of their natural seasons. I have already quoted Andrew Watson from his work on early Islamic agriculture. Again on this subject, he reminds us how sophisticated the husbandry was:

> Lands around cities were almost everywhere given over to market gardens and orchards ... around Palermo as *late* as the fourteenth century much of the Arab heritage in gardening still remained.

169

For centuries such gardens in Spain had grown an impressive range of crops including melons, apricots, apples, almonds, lemons, oranges, pears, plums, aubergines, saffron, peas, beans, chick-peas, fennel, carrots, garlic, lettuce, radishes and turnips; many were Moorish introductions.

Centuries later it was the technically advanced horticulture of the Low Countries that supplied Henry VIII's court with salads; until, as Thomas Fuller put it, "[Market] gardening began to creep out of Holland into England". By 1652 Walter Blith informed potential readers through the title page on *The English Improver Improved* that among a great deal else his book dealt with the cultivation of weld, woad, madder, hops, saffron, liquorice and "divers orchard and garden fruits". All, I think, qualify as horticultural crops.

The story of the origins of the intensive vegetable, fruit and flower growing in post-Renaissance England varies from author to author; most record already well-established areas, as when G. E. Fussell notes evidence of market-gardening near London and in Kent by the 1650s. Nevertheless, most agree that the earliest fresh produce traded in our cities came probably from the gardens of noblemen, clergy and religious communities (hence Co(n)vent Garden) – not exactly the people you would associate with the market stallholders of later years, but apparently happy to turn a penny by sending their staff to dispose of surplus produce. One of the largest apples on offer was the Costard. Those who sold them became known as costermongers, making it the only example I can think of where a plant cultivar gave rise to the name of a trade.

True market-gardening started in the sixteenth century and developed throughout the seventeenth, helped as records show both by the imported horticultural skills of Flemish, Walloon and French Protestant refugees and by the Gardener's Company receiving its charter as early as 1605. Not surprisingly we have many more illustrations of aristocrats' walled productive gardens than we do of commercial holdings. However, apart from the former being exceptionally neat and tidy, the husbandry techniques they depict for the production of "fine" vegetables are common to both, and the scale of the largest was if anything greater than many commercial market-gardens of the time. There is evidence to show that large private productive gardens and the emerging commercial market-gardens were laid out in a similar way. Both were based on "quarters" composed of beds and borders, and while wealthy individuals would protect their crops by surrounding their gardens with walls, the commercial growers used temporary fencing, which according to John Parkinson was constructed of "great high and large mattes made of reedes tyed together and fastened unto strong stakes", a form of protection from wind and frost so effective that "A bricke wall cannot better defend anything under it than this fence will." Then as now, growing in beds reduced the need to walk on the soil, that as the gardeners knew well, prevented compaction and loss of soil structure. Bed size, measured by the rod (30.25 square yards, or 1/160 of an acre; 25.29 square metres), varied with the scale of the crop needed to supply in one case the mansion, in the other the town market. In the private garden, beds ranged from as small as 2 rods but rarely more than 6, whereas in the market-gardens Malcolm Thick has found evidence of a range of sizes from 18 to 50 rods, in other words from 1/8 to 1/3 of an acre. Within the beds, crops from seed were either broadcast or sown in rows, while transplants of all kinds were very precisely ordered, accurately spaced both between plants and between rows to facilitate the very high level of husbandry they received.

By the time Covent Garden emerged as a fresh-produce market in the middle years of the seventeenth century, most of the hardy fruit and vegetables we eat, ranging from such a basic as cabbage to cauliflowers, early carrots, peas and beans, were being grown commercially. Even luxuries such as asparagus and melons were traded in their season. That's a full two hundred years before the so-called heyday of the private productive garden, the Victorian walled kitchen garden. In a letter dated 8 January, 1778 Gilbert White extols the benefits of the improvement in people's diet during his lifetime brought about through the increased availability of fruit and vegetables both from the home garden and as a result of market-gardeners trading in the towns:

> Every middle-aged person may perceive within his own memory how vastly the consumption of vegetables is increased. Green-stalls in cities now support multitudes in a comfortable state, while gardeners get fortunes. Every decent labourer also has his garden, which is half his support, as well as his delight; and common farmers provide plenty of beans, peas and greens, for their hands to eat with their bacon.

In his view,

> It was not til gentlemen took up the study of horticulture themselves that the knowledge of gardening made such hasty advances.

To his great approval, this new-found interest

> promoted the elegant science of ornamenting without despising the super-intendence of the kitchen quarters and fruit walls.
> – *Natural History of Selborne*

In fact these advances were neither hasty nor did they originate in the gardens of the English gentry. They were imports from the growing number of market-gardens that in turn were using techniques developed in France and the Low Countries. Throughout the seventeenth, eighteenth and first half of the nineteenth centuries some areas on the very edge of our cities, described by Professor Alice Coleman as "the ruban fringe", became covered by thousands of market-gardens and, later, small glasshouse nurseries. They supplied the city markets with fresh vegetables, salads and florist's flowers in exchange for the city's mountains of stable manure produced by the thousands of carriage and carthorses. Virtually all European cities had such areas of intense production, with Mountreuil now within the eastern suburbs of Paris being both a prime example and a powerhouse of innovation and progress in horticultural skills. The high walls surrounding its market-gardens were planted with fruit and became famed for the quality of their peaches. The last remaining holdings are still in existence, protected by L'Association des Murs à Pêches de Montreuil; bravo! The radish cultivar "French Breakfast" also survives, a reminder of those times, and incidentally, of just how different the British and continental approach is to the first meal of the day. But it was the very soil itself that tells us just how intensive this form of "French gardening" really was. The man-made soil, mostly decomposed horse manure, that filled the beds and frames was known as "*terreau*" [g]. The "*maraîchers*" prized it so highly that it was valued and sold separately when a holding changed hands. Nowadays *terreau* has a less specialised meaning: it is the French for compost.

These edge-of-town holdings conformed to the nineteenth-century German economist J. H. von Thunen's theory that the use of arable land developed as a series of rings or concentric circles around towns, the innermost ring specialising in horticulture producing perishable, high-value fresh produce. Von Thunen's ring theory seemed sound enough back in 1826 but the twentieth century saw production methods, costs and improved transport shatter its symmetry. Would he, I wonder, now identify pony-paddocks rather than market-gardens as the most profitable form of land use for ring number one?

London had rings of holdings, including an area renowned for its strawberry fields now deep under the East End's Victorian suburbs. *The Neat House Gardens*, a recent book on early market-gardening around London, takes us into that lost world of intensive production often referred to as French gardening. Spanning a period from the mid sixteenth century until the far better-known productive gardening skills of the Victorians, Malcolm Thick's book gives an excellent insight into the practices of intensive crop production over some three hundred years. It reminds us just how far the application of the basic practices of cultivation developed in this period of intensive husbandry by hand and horse.

To achieve success with such difficult but potentially profitable subjects, this new breed of market-gardeners took crop production into a completely new concept. No longer did growers choose the crops that best suited the area and would yield under rough and ready management; they set out to change the conditions to suit the most profitable crops. While their husbandry was still grounded in the basic operations, they added many more features such as temporary or seasonal shelter and protection, training, mulching and earthing-up, and even went to the extremes of hand-pollination and soil-warming through the use of hotbeds. Holdings as small as 6 acres (2.4ha) were able to support a family and their staff, a total of 12 engaged on growing the crops plus several part-timers harvesting, packing and carting the produce. Carting was a daily task, delivering the produce to the city markets several miles away by water, horse and cart, handcart or, very often, balanced on the heads of carrier women, of whom the Welsh and Irish were said to be best. No wonder if as one writer claimed "after several hours labouring in the garden they go to and from the London markets twice a day, though at from four to seven miles distance". It is reasonable to suggest that if these market-gardeners had had today's cultivars and methods of pest and disease control the best of them would have produced yields at least equal to those we get today when we treat the same fruits and vegetables as field crops.

As urbanisation put more and more pressure on land, one after the other these holdings grew their last crop: houses for the new town-dwellers.

As we shall see in the following pages, market-gardening slowly became "commercial horticulture"; some aspects remained very intensive and depended more and more on protected environments, others concentrated on fruit or took vegetable cultivation to a field scale. These trends together with the early stirrings of the influence of science can be detected in the literature. Shaw's *Market and Kitchen Gardening* published in Britain in 1889, although sub-titled "A Handbook of the Practice Adopted by the Best Market Gardeners in the Neighbourhood of London and Other Large Cities in the Production of All Kinds of Vegetable Crops", still contains sections on growing potatoes for exhibition! In contrast, in the USA Cornell University were releasing the results of very well-constructed husbandry trials for commercial crops referred to by L. H. Bailey in *The Forcing Book*, one of his Rural Science Series. At the turn of the century British growers, along with the farmers, were gaining government-funded scientific support through the publication of the Board of Agriculture and Fisheries leaflets. These covered a huge range of concerns, from "Fertilisers for Market Garden Crops" to "Grafting Fruit Trees" and "The Cabbage Moth". Today's readers may be interested to learn that in 1906 this advice came free, indeed that

> Copies may be obtained free of charge and post-free on application to the Secretary, Board of Agriculture and Fisheries, 4, Whitehall Place, London. SW. Letters of application so addressed need not be stamped.

While *The Neat House Gardens* gives us an excellent picture of the early market-gardens, so the 1909 *A French Garden in England* by Helen Nussey and Olive Cockerell brings the story of intensive production into the twentieth century with equal clarity. French gardening was the most intensive form of outdoor cultivation ever devised. According to the preface to C. D. McKay's *The French Garden,* the method was first promoted by Peter Kropotkin in what I think we would now describe as an economic study entitled *Fields, Factories and Workshops.* It was the extremely high productivity that attracts him to the skills of the Paris *maraîchers*:

> They smile when we boast about the rotation system, having permitted us to take from the field one crop every year, or four crops each three years, because their ambition is to have six and nine crops from the very same plot of land during the twelve months. They do not understand our talk about good and bad soils, because they make the soil themselves ...

Apparently the first market-garden run on these lines was established in England in 1905, although it had been the mainstay of high-quality Continental vegetable production for very many years. Surviving photographs suggest that we never really got the message; many English growers did little more than intensify their open-land style of production

So those two young Londoners, Helen and Olive, with just a year's training behind them, deserve recognition as heroic pioneers in setting up this type of holding in Sussex. Theirs is a story of romantic idealism tempered with hard factual information; there's a happy ending – they survived their first year. This was a time before mechanisation when most items used were home-made and landworkers were able to turn their hands to a host of craft skills. Measuring and marking out, constructing and cropping hotbeds, planting, moving, ventilating and repairing bell glasses (cloches), making and erecting straw frost protection mats against walls and over cold frames, using a French-designed *"plantoir"* in preference to an English-made dibber and treading seedbeds before sowing are all part of our heroines' working day. Add to those skills, the more obvious sheer hard handwork of manure-spreading, digging, hoeing and carting irrigation water and you have some idea why I admire them so. Incidentally the bell glasses they brought are advertised in the back of their book at 150 shillings (£7.50) per hundred. By coincidence they sold their melons for one shilling and six pence (7.5p) each, the cost of a single cloche. Today's antique traders ask £120 for a bell cloche, while melons are £1. These bell cloches were imported from their home country of France and used in huge quantities; there is a photograph in another book from the same period captioned "cloches with one cos and four cabbage lettuce under each", followed by the comment "10,000 cloches in all". That was unusual; most such production units were indeed gardens of between a half and two acres (0.2 and 0.8ha), but their total acreage around Paris was big enough with its more than two million bell cloches for the growers to be able to export huge quantities of early produce known as "*primeurs*" to England.

Nussey and Cockerell's choice of a site out in the country but using improved transport to reach their market is typical of how each generation of market-gardens was re-established a little further out from the urban centres. 1862 saw the start of perhaps the most famous crop of a unique area of market-gardening that was most decidedly away from its urban markets. The Tamar Valley horticultural holdings developed on the precipitous slopes leading down to the river that divides Cornwall from Devon, or as the locals would have it Cornwall from England. It grew out of a history of fruit-farming renowned for its local cherry and apple varieties whose tolerance to the Cornish climate helped ensure good, high-quality crops most years.

Visiting London was a very big event for a farmer's son from St Dominic, and twenty-two-year-old James Lawry made the most of it. After the Crystal Palace he stayed on to go to Covent Garden Market, where he discovered that in spite of it being early June there were no outdoor strawberries on sale. James saw a gap in the market that the Tamar Valley growers' early sites could fill at "the astonishing price of 2s 6d per pound [27.5p/kg]". The "strawberry rush" was under way, with the parish of St Dominic alone soon contributing over 250 tonnes to the massive total carried upcountry by rail each season. Strawberries were by no means the only crop produced on these south-facing early fields. The list included most other soft fruits, vegetables, salads and cut flowers, most famously anemones and narcissus, and the most famous of the narcissus cultivars was the "Tamar Double White" a sport discovered in the 1880s by Septimus Oliver Jackson of Clamoak Farm. In its heyday in the early decades of the twentieth century the Tamar Valley had some 400 market-gardens, many of them family holdings of around five acres (2ha) intensively hand-worked.

It is only in the last fifty years that most towns have seen the disappearance of the market-garden that grew "a bit of everything" and sold it direct to the public or into the local greengrocer's shop. There are those that dream that the coming of the "farmers' market" may yet revive the fortunes of these true sons and daughters of the soil.

Geographers and planners also use "market-gardening" to describe production on a larger scale, one that most in the trade would simply refer to as horticultural cropping. Concentrations of holdings large enough to make vegetable and fruit growing the dominant local industry grew up during the nineteenth century in several areas, for example around Sandy in Bedfordshire, in the Vale of Evesham and in the Thames Valley. At the start holdings were small by farming standards and many crops occupied less than an acre (0.4ha). From these modest beginnings much larger holdings selected what were considered to be the most profitable lines and increased their area so that whole fields were down to one crop. Sadly for these market-garden districts, their pioneering efforts were then copied and improved by arable farmers who had all the advantages of soil, site and economies of scale; the carrot barons of the Fens were born! Today most of our home-grown vegetables are produced on a field scale in and around East Anglia or by specialist producers located where they can take advantage of particularly favourable soils or climate. Fruit-growing has followed the same trend, only in this case its migration has continued until it has to a large extent left these shores altogether; its part in small-scale horticultural enterprises I have described below under "Intensive Production".

Early in the twentieth century glasshouse nurseries producing tomatoes, cucumbers and winter lettuce also started to concentrate in a few favoured spots. Not all were closely linked to a single big city but the largest of all certainly was. The river Lea marks the boundary between Essex and Hertfordshire a few miles to the north of London. By 1950 the alluvial soils on the gentle slopes above the Lea supported what was claimed to be the largest concentration of glasshouses in the world; whatever the accuracy of that claim, it is certainly not the case now. Like its market-gardens London's glasshouses are now of greater interest to the industrial archaeologist than to the sightseer. If you want to see a sea of glass you should go to Venlo in Holland – it is as if whole parishes have been covered. This is yet another example of the tendency of protected-cropping enterprises to cluster together.

I cannot leave market gardening without some reference to the current interest in "multiple cropping", a term we have met in connection with subsistence farming in the Third World. For several centuries European and Asian horticulturists have practised multiple cropping in their market gardens and have accumulated a huge amount of knowledge and skill in applying appropriate techniques, some the more complex of which are mentioned in the section on protected cropping.

INTENSIVE PRODUCTION

Concentrating effort and resources on small areas of land in an endeavour to raise fertility and get the highest possible yields per unit area is a very old approach to crop production. The first Europeans to explore the civilisations of China, Japan and parts of South-East Asia found outstanding, long-established examples, as did the Conquistadors on their fateful "discovery" of the Aztec culture in Central Mexico.

Not so many years ago the phrase "intensive production" was used as a quick way of defining commercial horticulture rather than attempting to cite all the crops that fell traditionally within its scope. Today it is not so useful as a definition, as intensification has become a more scattered and diffuse concept.

On one hand, intensity suggests a large input of effort per unit area, which could at times be rewarded with well above average yields. Cropping records for rural labourers' allotments in the nineteenth century suggest that area for area they were getting twice the harvest gathered from the surrounding fields. Intensity can also indicate a degree of control over production that should lead to high quality. Historically both interpretations were correct, but not always on the same holding.

In spite of there being no clear separation between smallholding and market-garden, I intend to elevate the latter to describe the more horticulturally focused and generally technically progressive production units. Smallholdings I associate with effort, almost to the extent of drudgery. They were small, often family-run places, where most of the effort came from man, woman, child and horse, and critically a huge amount of it went into ameliorating local soil and climate. Used to today's farm size, we tend to forget how many such holdings there were. The 1851 census reveals that over half the "farms" in Cornwall, North Wales and the North-West of England were of less than 20ha and only rarely employed hired labour. They seem a natural place for alternative technology and the simple tool or machine.

Brown's patent "Little Marvel" light plough, with optional extra expanding hoe attachment, might have made life a little easier for the family, if not the horse. But the appearance of Gunn's "Success" wheelbarrow – "well balanced and easily handled when loaded" – cannot have thrilled many teenage siblings. Of course Mr Gunn did not invent the wheelbarrow but simply improved its design. Unlike almost every other item in the European tool-shed, the wheelbarrow was not inherited from Rome; it is a Chinese invention from around the second century AD introduced, and maybe even pushed, into Europe via the Great Silk Road at whose end in Byzantium it was discovered by the foot-soldiers of the Second Crusade. Not for the first or last time has the value of a minor trophy of war outlasted the political gains. The wheelbarrow's evolution from general transport to horticultural use is a product of late medieval technology. Anthony Huxley in *An Illustrated History of Gardening* cites a twelfth-century reference as the earliest he could trace, but notes that from then on they appear "in a vast variety of shapes". Before that workers bore produce and materials in wicker baskets or pulled sledges. For most jobs the smallholding lacked the scale of production that could justify any energy source other than manpower. Even if you had some help from beast or engine you still walked. Indeed walking behind horse and tackle was typical of most jobs on British farms right up to the arrival of the tractor. In contrast, advertisements from the USA from around 1900 show farm workers sitting on horse-drawn equipment of every conceivable kind, from seed drills to cultivators and rollers to harrows. They had names like "Sulky Weeder" and there is even a "Sulky Plough", or rather "Sulky Plow", surely the height of decadence!

Life for everyone was understood to be hard on a smallholding; the advertisement for chicken-feed starts "Make Hens Pay", and that for a patent dog medication "If your dog is worth keeping ...", while Saddle Tweed suits and breeches, "just right for the smallholder", were claimed to wear like wire. Ouch! Such holdings were, more often than not, mixed enterprises depending in part on crops but also livestock, especially poultry, rabbits, goats and pigs. Ever since the changes brought by the enclosures some brave souls had struggled on to win a living from minimal areas of land. Some holdings were mini farms; however the 1931 four volumes of *The Practical Smallholder* cover the cultivation of vegetables, fruit, roots, pulses and forage crops, while *The Smallholder Encyclopaedia* from a few years on added cut flowers and copious photographs showing how to dig. All this, together with a lot on the law and land improvement, paints a picture of a struggle for independence on a holding located on inferior land with an economy balanced precariously between self-sufficiency and cash enterprises. There was even a section on "wild fruit", although it is not clear which of these were to be brought into cultivation and which gathered from the hedgerows.

In 1889 the Worshipful Company of Fruiterers offered a prize for the best essay on "Profitable Fruit Growing for Cottagers and Others with Smallholdings"; John Wright's winning submission *Profitable Fruit Growing* runs to over 100 pages. Through a series of examples he sets out to give advice to various categories of reader wishing to grow fruit for sale. It is a revealing list, starting with "A [small] farmer" and going on to a widow, a labourer, a tradesman, and ending with examples for an allotment-holder, a landlord and horticultural societies. All could be described as smallholders of one kind or another and, aside from the first and last, all could, at that date, have been allotment-holders – not of the kind we know today, but villagers, typically farm labourers, renting a half-acre plot to eke out their abysmally low wages with home-grown food and the sale of any surplus. The majority grew mainly staples such as wheat and potatoes, but many included fruit and it is very appropriate that his recommendations all emphasise the value of mixed and intensive production in what he calls fruit gardens. Not content with just orchard production, he enthuses on hedgerow planting of apples and bordering paths with strawberries; real smallholder's tricks those, to get a crop even from the edges and hedges. Sound his advice may have been, but like so many English horticultural writers around the end of the nineteenth century he can't resist having a dig at the French. Can it be other than patriotism that makes him tell us to avoid "these precocious prodigies on French [root] stocks" and plant only "good bush apples trees on the English broad-leaved Paradise stock"?

Smallholdings offered a "way of life" of never-ending employment, but for the successful provided a stepping-stone to farming. Early nineteenth-century writings carry an echo of the noble crofter, offering a new generation of peasants the chance to emerge as yeomen, a sentiment clearly spelt out by William Webb in 1916 in the introduction to his idealistic text *Garden First in Land Development*. In the midst of the Great War he seems confident that: "When the day of peace dawns, we shall cultivate manhood for its own sake, and getting back to the land and more healthful conditions will not be lost sight of."

Both county-council-owned smallholdings and those of the Land Settlement Association Ltd reflected this aim of providing a way for those without much capital to enter agriculture or horticulture. Established in the 1930s to "re-settle unemployed industrial workers", their remit was later extended to include ex-servicemen among their tenants. The LSA holdings were spread over some twelve "estates"; within them each holding of only a few hectares was intended to become a model of mixed intensive crop production.

ORGANIC GROWING

"Nitre is the life of vegetables." This sounds – you may think – like one of those chemists at it again promoting potassium nitrate as a wonder fertiliser. Well, yes and no: the writer is Francis Bacon, the date 1620. However much some might wish Bacon had stuck to pretending to write Shakespeare's plays, he said it, and "What's done is done." True to that sentiment, his words were not forgotten, in fact he was quoted some fifty years later by Robert Boyle, the greatest English chemist of his century, who went on to add that "An enquiry into the nature of saltpetre may be of great use in farming." The rest is history, or was until around the 1970s, when the organic movement found its voice.

Arguably the organic movement is part of a wider mistrust of the contemporary world. It concerns itself with much wider issues than the use of nitre and other inorganic plant nutrients that have been a mainstay of growing almost all the fruit and vegetables eaten by the last three generations of our citizens. The organic movement's wider interest is exemplified by its aim to eliminate the use of most chemicals for the control of weeds, pests and pathogens that I mention in Chapters 13 and 16. These strongly voiced concerns have contributed to several very positive and beneficial developments now taken up by agronomists at large. They have stimulated a great deal of research activity and many of the results have helped growers and farmers in general reduce the amount of pesticides used. As I point out elsewhere, recently introduced materials are more pest-specific, they can be targeted and timed more precisely. Some can be used in conjunction with biological control [g], through what have become known as integrated pest-management programmes. Public concern has led to more and more stringent safety tests on the chemicals used, and the banning of the infamous broad-spectrum poisons so beloved of Victorian and Edwardian cultivators. Several of today's crop protection methods are deemed "acceptable" to organic growing, including the use of traps and attractants, while some materials that interrupt the life cycle or essential processes of pest species have proved to be at least partly effective in controlling their numbers. I doubt very much if wood-chip and bark mulches would have come to such successful prominence for weed control in amenity plantings without organic growers showing the way.

Studies in plant nutrition aimed at optimising the use of fertilisers from both the economic and ecological points of view have supported the now commonplace aim of optimising yield and profit rather than searching for even greater yields per unit area.

Nevertheless these trends do not of course satisfy the requirements of the organic-only movement. Organic growing in the form demanded by the Soil Association currently represents about 10 per cent of fresh produce production. This form of husbandry on commercial holdings and farms has reached a degree of sophistication and success far beyond that anticipated by many professional agronomists. In hindsight I think that this should not have come as a surprise, considering that "organic growing" was the only available option to supply the world with both staples and luxuries up until around 150 years ago. This having been said, the commercial success of today's organic production in this country must be judged within the economic framework of the developed world. Organic growing succeeds as a business based upon the enthusiasm of a sizeable body of customers. In order to discourage what they believe to be risky practices and avoid the resultant products they are prepared to pay a premium price for what is often lower-grade produce – lower-grade, that is, within the current quality parameters of the general marketplace. In many instances this so-called lower quality is of little import or hindrance to the consumer and, many would claim, is more than recompensed by their belief in an improved flavour. Other factors that exert a paramount influence on the flavour and texture of fresh produce are noted in Chapter 5.

Crop fertility in organic growing is based on manipulating the natural cycling of the elements of which all living things are composed, or at least those known as plant nutrients, in such a way that they are concentrated on the areas of land under crops. We have of course met precisely this approach before in the folding of sheep on medieval farms, and where else but the compost or manure heap did the old cottage gardener plant his marrows? Today's organic growers do not have to depend only on dressings of bulky materials such as farmyard manure. They have a range of carefully analysed and blended bag fertilisers to use alongside the traditional ones such as bone meal and dried blood. In a world where large quantities of organic matter are regarded as waste, gathering it onto cropland should be applauded regardless of any strict adherence to the "rules" laid down by the Soil Association, the authoritative voice of the organic movement in Britain.

These rules, if obeyed, provide the consumer with certain guarantees and as such lay down a useful benchmark for those that require them. But, and it is a very big but, I cannot take their transgression seriously. The kindest way I can describe these rules is to equate them with those that govern a sport. With them everyone knows where they stand – but don't search for a deeper meaning. Naturally enough, growers who wish to receive the Soil Association's accreditation must follow them to the letter.

Clearly it is incorrect to group together the "ban [almost] all chemicals" brigade with those that have taken advantage of the developments mentioned above to practice the minimum use of selected materials. Sadly there is at present no label for what many would describe as "best mainstream practice". It is equally wrong to confuse those outside the organic movement who avoid the use of crop protection materials with those inside it who additionally prohibit the use of inorganic fertilisers.

While many in the organic movement no doubt support the concept of sustainability, they do not claim that their methods provide it at any scale, from field to flowerpot.

CLEAR-FELL FORESTRY

The idea of any form of forestry as a cultivation system may seem strange to some people, but it would not be right to leave out such a huge part of man's endeavours to grow plants as a crop. Forestry has had its fair share of critics, both from the environmental lobby and, from those keen to preserve the – to them – traditional appearance of the British landscape. The planting of large blocks of a single species, particularly if it happens to be an exotic conifer, engenders the greatest displeasure. Such plantings were typical of the early days of the British Forestry Commission from the 1920s to the 1960s, although that work was only part of a much greater, virtually world-wide activity. Timber plantations leading to a final clear fell present a clear sequence of husbandry activities that show very clearly how the cultivation of timber trees has many of the same features that we are familiar with in agriculture and horticulture. The harvests are slower in coming, that's all. This kind of forestry involves raising plants from seed or cuttings, all the associated nursery work, transplanting, spacing and thinning, weed and pest control and pruning, even the use of exotic species that grow wild far away on other continents. Maybe it is the protracted time-scale that makes forestry seem so different. Historically there seems little love lost between woodsmen and agriculturists, a state of affairs not much helped by the obvious point that over large areas of Europe farming expanded at the expense of woodland. Things are a good deal easier if you mix foresters with horticulturists. In their different ways they do similar things to their plants and above all they both have an interest in individual specimens. Put the two disciplines together in an arboretum and it is not always easy to tell who is who.

For thousands of years timber was extracted from existing woodland; any planting that took place was primarily for other purposes such as game cover, shelter or scenic effects. Tree planting on farmland, heaths and moors or replanting old woodland after felling only became commonplace during the nineteenth century, first in those countries that became aware of the smallness of their timber reserves and hence their dependence on foreign imports, and later as the best investment for certain agriculturally poor areas. Today millions of trees are planted each year in some of the world's most forested lands such as Canada and Scandinavia.

Timber trees get a mention in the sections dealing with the various husbandry operations that go to make up cultivation, but a brief look at the production system as a whole reveals some basic bits of the cultivator's craft.

To me forestry is the art of taking the concept of "critical minimum inputs" to its extreme. This is the policy of doing only that which really matters; no frills, but do the vital bits on time and well. This approach is particularly suited to forestry, which is even then an economist's worst nightmare, high costs at the outset, profits, if any, anything up to a century later. The ultimate futures market. Such a business plan, if such a phrase is permissible over such a long time-span, understandably makes foresters reluctant to spend more on each operation than is absolutely necessary. Interestingly, this parsimonious approach has taught us all a lot about just what is important when dealing with young trees, and that however rough and ready we are we must respect their biology if we are to get the desired results. It has also shown up the unnecessary frills added by generations of gardeners, professional and amateur, who had the time and money to fuss over their decorative tree transplants.

Land preparation often combines drainage and seedbed or transplant tilth production. The final result is in stark contrast to anything a keen allotment-holder would aspire to. It reminds me more of a military tank-testing ground, yet this rugged terrain has, hidden within it, the key characteristic for establishing transplants: root-penetrable soil, which can be brought into close, firm contact with the roots. The transplants may seem to be treated roughly but they are never allowed to dry out.

At this point we come to some of the most interesting aspects of cultivating young trees. If we assume that the roots have re-established contact with the soil and have some new growth then we can turn our attention to the above-ground parts. Most but not all timber trees are woodland species adapted to growing in competition with their neighbours. Foresters have long held the view that some form of communal living was of benefit to young trees and advocated either the retention of tall weeds or else close planting with the crop species interspersed with a fast-growing "nurse" species. Both these ideas go completely against our understanding of good husbandry practice. They create the debilitating effects of high population densities. So who is right, the foresters or the rest of the cultivation fraternity? Well there is something to be said for both approaches. Competition undoubtedly does reduce the growth of the affected individuals, but so do other forms of environmental stress. One such stress is a shortage of water within the leaves, causing the stomata [g] to close. This stops the movement of gases between the inside of the plant and the outside world: no oxygen out, no carbon dioxide in; result: no growth. Young trees have evolved to develop below the woodland canopy where the air tends to be humid and their leaves are easily desiccated if exposed to dry, windy conditions. Weeds and nurse trees may help to slow down the wind and allow the air to become more humid, but it is a fine-run thing between this possible benefit and detrimental competition. It may well be that the most beneficial function of nurse trees in timber plantations comes a few years later as the canopies start to close. At this stage lateral buds and young side branches of the desired but slower-growing species are suppressed, ensuring that they produce singe, straight trunks.

A much safer way of keeping those leaves turgid and their pores open is to use tree shelters. Tree shelters are those ridged plastic tubes that appear in the countryside following civil engineering works and small-woodland grants. Inside each one should be a small tree transplant, but not for long as if all goes well, they should grow out of the top in one or at most two years. Invented by Dr Tuley of the Forestry Commission in the mid 1970s, they are truly an invention of their time, arriving on the scene at just the right moment to support the tree-planting efforts that have become perhaps the best as well as the most obvious manifestation of our concern for nature and the landscape. At first it was not clear why they increased transplant growth so much. Closer study showed that it has a lot to do with trapping moist air and keeping the leaf pores open, each little tree in its own woodland microclimate. And while it is true that in addition to this they also protect against rabbits, herbicides and strimmers, they were never claimed to provide more than part of a transplant's needs; site conditions, planting method, weed control and water can all make the difference between life and death, yet all too often tree shelters are the first and only form of husbandry on many sites.

One practice frequently neglected is pruning. Timber-tree

pruning differs from fruit-tree pruning both in the type of material being cut off and in the reason for doing so. The first consideration is a straight, single trunk for the distance you aim to crop as a bulk of timber, usually in Europe around 3–5m. To some people that may seem surprisingly little compared with either the length of the giant trunks taken out of tropical forests or the actual height of our home-grown trees at maturity. Of course the upper part of the tree, whose photosynthesis was vital to the trunk's development, has other uses, so it is not all waste. Achieving the right density in the early years goes a long way towards insuring that straight trunk, but it needs a regular check and the pruning out of one of any "double leaders" when a tree forgets what apical dominance is all about.

Once the single-trunk issue is settled, attention turns to the removal of the lower side branches, or "brushing up" as it is called. These initial side branches are doomed anyway; if the tree is growing under woodland conditions, they will be shaded out by those above and to the sides. In some species they soon slough off close to the trunk but in others, particularly conifers, their dead remains become knots in the timber if they are not cut off; as the tree increases in girth it grows round these horizontal dead stems, entombing them but not truly fusing with them. Years later when the trunk is sawn into planks they reappear, to downgrade the timber to knotty pine.

In recent years there has been an increased interest in managing productive woodland by selective felling and coppicing the understorey [g], whilst leaving many of the trees that form the main canopy standing. This is of course the traditional way of doing things. Some 150 years ago there were 40,000 hectares of such woodland in England and Wales, employing 20,000 workers from foresters to charcoal burners. Brought up to date to produce the range of products now in demand and making use of appropriate contemporary equipment, it is known as "continuous-cover forestry". As the name implies, the aim is to maintain the woodland ecosystem even to the extent of encouraging the natural regeneration of trees from both coppiced stools and seed.

Surface drainage by furrow and ditch preceded underground systems by many centuries. This medieval ditch-digger with his curious winged spade is taken from an illustration in Walter Blith's The English Improver Improved.

8 DRAINAGE

SOIL WATER AND ROOTS

Water and air are interchangeable. Under what circumstances can that possibly be true? It is not the circumstances but the location that is of vital importance to this story. The place is the space between the soil's mineral particles or their aggregated crumbs that form tilth. Water clings to the surface of the surrounding solids, producing the dark, moist soil we are familiar with in Britain for most of the year if we dig just a few centimetres below the surface. When a soil is dry these spaces are filled with air, when the soil is waterlogged the spaces or "pores" as they are termed are filled with water, and when things are as a root would wish to experience them there is some of each, air and water. It is not really a case of "wish", because apart from the obvious point about plants not wishing, it is a requirement. Roots need water to stay alive, let alone fulfil their function of water-gathering for the rest of the plant. Roots need air because they respire. As dynamic, actively growing organs roots have a high demand for oxygen which they get from the soil air. In this respect they are no different from a host of other life-forms in the soil. However, people get confused between this need and a plant's green leaves requiring carbon dioxide but giving off oxygen during photosynthesis.

Compared with leaves and stems, roots are particularly sensitive to water shortage for the obvious reason that a water-gathering organ can't be waterproof. In a drought plants are at risk from their roots losing water; in fact to prevent this the greater part of the root system of many semi-desert species dies off during the dry period of the year.

Soil scientists have identified the salient points in a soil's water-holding capacity. "Waterlogged" heads the list and describes the condition in which all the spaces between the soil particles are flooded. Next comes "field capacity" [g], the point where a soil with free drainage is holding the maximum amount it can against the force of gravity. As more and more water is lost, creating an ever greater soil moisture deficit, things become more and more serious for plants until they can no longer obtain moisture from the soil, although more than ten per cent of its volume may still be water. This is known as "permanent wilting point" and marks the end of the road as far as a plant is concerned. Finally, as far as conditions in the field go, we come to the soil in as dry a state as it is possible to be; it is "air dry".

Typically, land gets its water from one form of precipitation or another. In our climate most is as rain, with snow coming a long way behind. In a few exotic locations other forms of water are vitally important; fog supports the coastal redwoods of California and dew does the same for the vegetation on the borders of the North African deserts.

It is only in close proximity to springs and running water, and in places where the water table is so high that swamps, bogs or marshes are formed, that groundwater plays a significant part in the year-round supply to plant roots. This in spite of there being saturated rock below the water table, often only a metre or so beneath the surface. Unfortunately this subterranean reservoir is of little use because water rises from it only very slowly and to a limited height depending on the nature of the soil. Strangely, and against all the evidence, the belief in this upward migration of useful amounts of water remains strong in the folklore of gardening.

When water arrives at the soil surface it has to obey the laws of physics in its downward movement through the soil profile. In dry or slightly moist soil the pull of gravity is offset by the surface attraction of the soil crumbs and sand grains. Saturation describes the point at which there is so much water around these particles that gravity wins and water passes down the profile. Down, but only to the next crumb or grain where the whole sequence is re-enacted. As E. J. Winter puts it in *Water,*

Soil and the Plant, "Sadly neither a light shower nor a quick sprinkle from the hosepipe can dampen the whole depth of the root zone. It can only wet the surface layer." As the old-timers used to say of a summer shower, "It's not gone in far enough to do any good," or in Winter's words:

> Water arriving on the soil surface brings each successive layer to saturation before appreciable further downward movement takes place. In irrigation practice this means that it is not possible to raise the water content of a soil to any value except saturation. Any attempt to wet the soil only partially, by reducing the quantity of water applied, merely reduces the depth of soil which is brought to field capacity.

LAND DRAINS

We all know that at times the land is inundated with water, floods drown the landscape and dramatic pictures are shown on the television news. The impression we get is that the water starts in the river and then the river bursts its banks. That is clearly so, but it must have come from somewhere else earlier in the story. In Britain and over a lot of Northern Europe many rivers collect most of their water from the rain that falls on farmland, so how does that water get from the land into the river? Some will run off the soil surface, particularly if the soil is waterlogged, some will drain through the topsoil and, in nature, appear lower down the valleys as springs. But over millions of hectares of cultivated land its downward migration through the soil profile will be intercepted by field drains to emerge from outfalls into open ditches and so to streams and rivers.

I don't suppose many people outside the farming community ever give land drainage a thought, although it has had a massive impact on our ability to bring land into arable cropping. In my experience those that do ask about it find it all a great mystery, because it is so different from "the drains" at home. To start with, the pipes have open joints to let the water in; but won't that let it out? Then perversely most of the water enters from below. Finally they learn that, unlike the drains on the side of the road, it is only occasionally, and then not efficiently, that land drains remove standing water.

For practical purposes land drainage can be divided into two very different operations. There are the grand schemes such as the draining of the East Anglian Fens and the Somerset Levels, and the field-by-field soil drainage designed to prevent waterlogging. The great drainage works typically remove and control surface flooding. They cost huge sums and involve whole tracts of land, typically under many owners, and leave behind vast civil engineering works. Field drainage lowers the water table beneath farmland, it can be very localised, its installation is all over in a few weeks and it leaves hardly a trace on the landscape.

The main purpose is to set a limit to the water table, defined in the textbooks as the level in the soil profile below which the land is saturated. Land drains create a cut-off point above which the soil will not remain waterlogged. Over millions of acres of our most fertile farmland the natural water table in winter can be less than half a metre down. Without additional drainage, root growth and cultivation would be impossible.

A land drain is nothing more than a gently sloping porous tunnel set at an appropriate depth below the surface of a field. For hundreds of years this tunnel has been constructed by digging a narrow trench and then inserting something to hold up the soil before covering or backfilling up to the surface. That "something" has ranged from brushwood to arched tiles, ceramic pipes and plastic pipes. In the case of mole drains the trench is reduced to a slot cut through the topsoil and the tunnel walls are formed of nothing more than the compressed subsoil. Regardless of their construction all these porous subterranean channels or tubes collect and conduct water only when the surrounding soil is saturated, so there is no possibility of water leaking out of them, except of course at the outfall. Field drains cannot suck water from the soil. All they can do is to draw off water from the saturated strata above them. This has the effect of ensuring that the uppermost layers of soil are no longer waterlogged. Put another way, the drains lower the water table and by getting rid of that water provide crop roots with a deeper, oxygenated soil profile.

At first thought, drainage may seem to be very much a two-edged weapon, beneficial in wet weather but a real disadvantage in dry periods because lowering the water table inevitably lowers the "capillary plume", that trick of physics known in old houses as "rising damp" that keeps soil moist for several centimetres above the saturated zone. This is true, but in practice, on most arable land, the water table in the growing season very quickly drops below the level of the drains, so they hardly exacerbate the shortage of water in the root zone should there be a drought.

After all that cost and hard work, what is the practical value of land drains? They do two jobs; as we have seen, if the field has a standing crop the removal of water allows air into the soil which prevents roots from drowning. But drainage is just as valuable in the fallow time between crops for two reasons, temperature and workability.

Excessively wet land remains cold in spring. Water requires a lot of energy to heat it, so a wet field at several degrees below its dryer neighbours is a late field. A low soil temperature can be a real problem, but it is often not this direct effect on plant growth that's the biggest headache. That comes from the damage that results from trying to cultivate waterlogged soil or, if you are prudent and wait for the land to dry out, the loss of part of the growing season.

The damage is loss of soil structure through the destruction of the soil crumbs; these masses of fine particles are held together by organic glues but people, domestic animals and farm and construction machinery can break down sodden crumbs into a mire impenetrable to air and water, that can turn a fertile field into mud from which it can take years to recover.

All this may seem melodramatic, but if you doubt it reread the history of life on the battlefields of the Western Front in the First World War. That horrendous mud came by the denaturing of the once fertile clay soils of the floodplain of the Somme. Later the poppies grew on its surface, but recovery took years before it regained its natural tilth and drainage fissures. If such images seem remote and dependent on extreme acts of folly then there are two opportunities to study denatured soil much nearer home: look at the landscape of a green-field construction site when heavy plant has driven over it for a few wet weeks, or talk to anyone who keeps horses on heavy land in winter and find out what conditions are like round the gateways.

EARLY ATTEMPTS AT DRAINAGE

Cultivators have struggled for hundreds of years to get rid of surplus water. The Romans dug ditches and linked these back into the cultivated fields by constructing tile drains. These are formed from either flat or curved ceramic tiles; flat ones are placed together to form ducts of either square or triangular cross-section while curved tiles placed end to end have the appearance of miniature railway tunnels. Following the departure of the Romans, sub-surface drainage fell out of use and was not revived until the start of the eighteenth century. Throughout this long interregnum draining fields depended on ploughing in narrow "butts" or "braids" to produce the ridge-and-furrow formations discussed in Chapter 1. Although they must have helped medieval and later farmers remove surface water from part of their land, few were connected to ditches and, as one critic has put it, "Usually all that happened was that rain washed the best soil off the ridges into the hollows where it grew coarse grass and sedges while on the ridges the crops starved." J. R. Bond, writing in 1923, seems to take a less critical view and indicates that in his time they were still valued for drainage. Not only does he describe how to create ridge and furrow, but tells us that:

> On some soils it is considered necessary to preserve the ancient round backed form of the lands, the feerings [g] being set on the crowns of the lands for winter corn and the furrows for spring corn.

This may need a word or two of translation! Lands (or ploughlands) are the divisions of the field set out by the ploughman, and feerings are the first marker furrows. To overwinter successfully, autumn-sown "winter" corn needs well-drained dry conditions; "spring" corn benefits from the moisture retained in the furrow bottoms.

Following a wet spell it is still possible under permanent pasture for us to see, and sheep to exploit, the pattern of wet and dry strips. For hundreds of years ridging helped drain both pasture and arable fields and to both drain and irrigate water-meadows. Drainage ridging spanning many centuries can be found in fields scattered across the whole country, so we should be careful not to see it as proof positive of the site of a medieval common field. Indeed Walter Blith, no lover of such places, devotes most of one page out of the four carrying illustrations to hand tools designed to dig drainage furrows or ditches. And we know from written records that some ridges dating from the eighteenth century were made with the aid of specially designed draining ploughs. One such early model used on pastureland cut a trench a foot deep by over a foot wide, and capable of "casting the turf a great way off"; no wonder it

194

needed twenty horses to pull it.

The late eighteenth century was the time when huge areas of farmland were drained in what many claim to be the single most significant activity of the so-called agricultural revolution. This was however some 120 years after England's most dramatic venture into land drainage, an enterprise that ultimately gave us our largest single area of grade-one arable land, the East Anglian fens. The Dutch engineer Vermuyden was not the first since the Romans to tackle the challenge, an honour that goes to the thirteen "co-adventurers" in 1631, but his approach was by far the most flamboyant, a quality still rare in those parts. He was not the sort of chap to mess about with some pipes below a field; he went for the grand design. He schemes were based upon increasing the flow of water out of the whole area by digging new rivers and connecting them to the future farmland by drainage channels known locally as "lodes". The plan worked, but in its success were the seeds of its long-term failure. When the peat dried out it shrank to such an extent that the rivers were soon standing several metres above the surrounding land. The only solution was to "defy gravity and make the water drain uphill". The Dutchman had the answer: windmills, or in this case wind-powered pumps, some based on Archimedes' two-thousand-year-old design. It was quite literally an uphill task that became ever more challenging, and in 1820 the first steam-powered pumps were installed, to be followed some hundred years later by diesel engines.

If you want to see the impact of this scale of land drainage take a trip north from Cambridge. Start in the nature reserve of Wicken Fen, which is maintained in its pre-drained state of bog-land then go east to the New Bedford River. Follow the road that runs halfway up its bank; the land below you is the result of Vermuyden's work. In a matter of half an hour you will have been confronted by two of our countryside's most precious yet contradictory features – Wicken's wild habitat and our best farmland.

From the time of the Stuarts some turned, or perhaps we should say returned, to subterranean drains. They made them by burying faggots of blackthorn, gorse or heather, a technique that worked well enough for it to be still being advocated well into the nineteenth century. These brushwood drains were of almost exactly the same construction from Roman times to the

1920s. Even in a subject notorious for plagiarism that's some crib, but you could argue that if the Romans got it right there was not much new to say. The method suggested by one writer surely illustrates just how seriously drainage was regarded. Rather than dig and backfill a trench, he tunnelled beneath his fields. Man-sized pits were sunk every 16 feet (5m) in lines across the field and some unfortunate chap climbed in and half tunnelled, half poked a long pole to link up the holes. After that it was relatively easy to push the brushwood into place and backfill the pits.

As Tom Lehrer might say, such were the quaint and curious customs of the pioneers of land drainage, yet their methods not withstanding, their objective was absolutely correct. Drainage was the essential prerequisite to bringing millions of acres of unproductive land into cultivation. The question that bugged landowners at the start of the nineteenth century was how best to achieve it. What kind of drains, how deep, how far apart and even whether they should run down the slope of a field or along the contours. In hindsight, it is obvious that they understood little of the movement of water within the soil. Two pioneers stand out from the hundreds of enthusiastic trench-diggers, or should that be enthusiastic employers of trench-diggers? One was a Scot, James Smith, whose success was based on a well-thought-out drainage system with stone-filled trenches 30in (75cm) deep, every 5 to 7 yards (4.6 to 6.4m) apart across his fields. These he had linked at the lowest side of the field by even deeper main drains. His masterstroke was his recognition that no matter how good his drainage layout was it could do little good if water could not pass through his essentially impervious subsoil to reach it. To solve that he invented a subsoil plough, weighing three times as much as a normal plough but going three times as deep, though in places it took eight horses to pull it!

Smith's system was so successful that he became a celebrity and was invited to join government deliberations on the future of agriculture, but as we now know, no one system of drainage works best on all soils. Disappointed followers turned to his rival Josiah Parkes, whose system, devised for and excellent on peaty soils, used even deeper drains and, after 1843, ceramic pipes. Next it was Parkes's turn to fall from grace with some of his followers, as the one-inch (2.5cm) diameter of his pipes proved to be of far too small a bore, and his idea that such a narrow pipe would be self-flushing and so not silt up proved erroneous. Pipe drains fell from favour, replaced by ceramic (clay) arched "horseshoe" tiles resting on flat "sole" plates, an idea used by the Romans eighteen hundred years before.

As ever, we can turn to Arthur Young for an on-the-spot picture of things as he found them when compiling his report to the Board of Agriculture in 1813. In Oxfordshire he notes plenty of "under-draining" being carried out by the best farmers but writes not one word about tiles or pipes. Some are backfilling trenches with furze, blackthorn or "the green spray of elm which is best of all"; these were "in all cases covered with wheat straw" before replacing the topsoil. He regrets that stone backfill, although superior, is too expensive, but then finds Mr Bignal, "one of the best cultivators in the county", to be "hollow draining". Before backfilling he had the narrow base of the trenches capped with flat stones "so as to afford a free open channel for the water". Not quite tile draining, but near to it. By Young's time, brush drains may have been giving way to ceramics, but they hung on for a long while. In the 1920s the Ministry of Agriculture still recommended them, although it was recognised that they rarely had a life of twenty years; and it is on record that a few farmers were putting them as late as 1950.

Nevertheless in spite of a tileless and pipeless Oxfordshire, in 1839 the *Farmer's Magazine* reported "intense interest" in the Marquis of Tweeddale's "novel and ingenious apparatus" for drain tile mass-production which he set up "at Yester, the residence of the noble inventor". The tiles left his apparatus as flat "plates" but could be bent into an arch before being fired. Such tiles finally fell out of use when pipes 3 and 4 inches (7.5 and 10cm) in diameter were introduced, encouraged no doubt in 1843 when the Royal Agricultural Society offered a silver medal for the best design. Only two years later Thomas Scragg mass-produced drainage pipes by extrusion, a huge cost saving on the earlier method of wrapping soft clay round a mandrel.

By 1880 this period of massive investment in land drainage had resulted in some three million acres having been either brought into arable cropping for the first time or at the very least made far more productive. Many agricultural historians see these outcomes as providing the essential basis for the great developments which have taken place in farming since that date.

The second great flurry of drainage activity on British farms was triggered by a desperate need to increase production at the start of the Second World War when in its isolation Britain depended on the home-grown food. This time the work was in the hands of the all-powerful "War Ags", the Ministry of Agriculture's county-based War Agricultural Committees.   It embraced both improving the drainage of arable land and the reclamation of fields abandoned during the agricultural depression of the inter war years. As with so many aspects of crop husbandry, the demand for the maximum possible production provided the stimulus for mechanisation with equipment such as the Priestman Cub ditch-digger and prototype ceramic pipe-layers replacing handwork. According to farmer–author Duncan McGuffie, they speeded up these backbreaking jobs at least tenfold.

DRAINAGE TODAY

Every year miles of perforated plastic pipes are threaded into our lowland fields and the narrow trenches above them partly filled with graded aggregate. Once the field has been surveyed to establish the best pattern of pipe runs, highly specialised operators driving huge trenching machines put the drains in place. They carve their way across the land working to very close tolerances, with laser-determined gradients of as little as one in four hundred for the main drains. Often these subterranean arteries are fed by a network of tiny tunnels produced by a "mole". Mole drainage in a primitive form was invented in the late eighteenth century by Adam Scott, an Essex farmer. Even today the solid steel, torpedo-like "plug" has not changed much, although the power to pull it through the soil passed from human muscle to horse power to capstans anchored on the headland and then to steam power. Late nineteenth- and early twentieth-century mole drainage suited steam power; it used massive, cumbersome ploughs designed to be pulled slowly through the subsoil. They worked well either linked by cable to a winding drum on the engine or towed behind slightly lighter machines built to traverse the fields.

Today moles are pulled behind a subsoil plough linked to a powerful tractor. On heavy land, where they are most needed, the culverts they produce keep open for many years.

Whatever the details of the system, its aim is always the same: to open up an underground channel through which the water can drain away. Whatever the form of drainage below the field surface, it can only do its job if the water leaves the arable area. It must be taken away to some pond or stream. Historically it has been the job of ditches to collect drainage water along field margins and link with larger bodies of water.

The humble ditch, dug and kept open by up to fifty generations of farm workers, has probably had as large an impact on food production over the last thousand years as any other single operation in the farming calendar. Moreover, the lowly ditch-digger has helped fix the very pattern of our lowland landscape. The phrase "hard graft" comes from the work of these chaps, graft being an old word for digging. Today things are different, with large machines replacing man and spade. Indeed it seems ditch-making can now be fun; Dermot Bowler gives full instructions for blasting drainage ditches using lines of gelignite sticks fired in rapid sequence. But before risking the attention of both police and army please note he is writing for a readership living in the wide-open spaces of New Zealand, not overcrowded Britain where the ditches and the hedges that often followed them across the countryside create one of the most important of the man-made agricultural wildlife habitats.

Ditches take up a lot of land, however: 300 square metres for every 100-metre run. So it is not surprising that, over the last half century on the best arable land, miles of them have been piped in, many becoming incorporated into extended drainage systems when fields are amalgamated. Nevertheless, the Countryside Commission estimates that there still well over 100,000 kilometres of them, distributed surprisingly evenly across England and and Wales considering our diverse soils, geology and rainfall.

Superimposed on an idealised soil profile with topsoil, subsoil and parent material horizons, the familiar soil texture triangle shows clay at the top, sand lower left and silt lower right. Loam, that excellent blend of the three, is shown to have equal amounts of sand and silt but less of the potentially dominating clay.

9 THE SOIL

It seems logical to try and understand the role of the soil in the life of plants before weighing up the value of man's attempts to influence its composition and condition. Is all this hard work necessary? After all, who digs or ploughs the millions of square miles of the wilderness that are covered with vegetation?

Soil science, and that's a world-wide discipline in its own right, is concerned with all the chemical, physical and mechanical aspects of soil. The standard short description of the soil's roles in plant growth lists anchorage and support, retention and provision of a water supply, and a source of nutrients. This list may seem daunting enough, but it hides a deeper truth that none of these roles function unless the soil's physical condition is satisfactory. To understand that depends on studying both its mineral and its organic make-up, known technically as "texture", and the way those constituents are combined to produce what is known as "structure". Even then, soils cannot be fully understood without some engagement with the huge and challenging study of the soil's living organisms. Professionally, this has become a specialist branch of microbiology.

In the early years of the twentieth century, two men set out to explain this vast subject to "students of agriculture and horticulture, botanists and the general reader", as a writer in *Science Progress* put it. Both were in their turn directors of the famous research station at Rothamsted and both produced masterpieces. First to the press in 1903 was Sir A. Daniel Hall with *The Soil*. This was followed only nine years later by Sir John

Russell's *Soil Conditions and Plant Growth*. Both books became standard texts and ran to many editions, each reporting the worldwide progress in the applied and theoretical studies that established the basis of today's scientific cropping. Keeping Sir John's book up to date became a family business when, on his retirement from the directorship of Rothamsted Experimental Station in 1943, he handed over the revision of future editions to his son.

There is a strange paradox in that the natural world of the soil is in many ways far more complex and innately more diverse from place to place than the alternative root substrates used in some of the most advanced systems of crop production. So it is time I stopped referring to "the soil" as if it were a uniform material, evenly covering the surface of the world's land-masses. As every gardener knows, this is certainly not the case; in fact "good soil" is an elusive material that seems far more likely to be found in someone else's garden than just outside your own backdoor. Fertile soils are made up of a mineral component, organic matter, air and water.

The mineral skeleton of the soil is formed from rock fragments, ranging from the finest clays through silts to the sands and beyond to gravels and sizeable chunks of rock. Soil scientists regard these larger items as being outside the make-up of soil, as they can play no part in their interests. Agronomists may include them, if for no other reason than that they can appear in depressingly large amounts just where you hoped to find a rich loam. The proportion of each particle size affects the soil texture, which in turn hugely influences a number of related properties, including a soil's water-holding capacity, land drainage and the vital matter of air content.

Most people are familiar with the way these grades of mineral matter form the overall nature of a soil and give it its name: clay soil, sandy soil etc. Soils with a fortunate blend of sands, silt and clay that is generally good for crop production are known as loams, the ideal mix being around 20 per cent clay, 40 per cent silt and 40 per cent sand. Not surprisingly those with a bias towards one fraction or another are described as "clay loams", "silty loams" or "sandy loams". Loams make up the highest grade of agricultural land and command the highest price.

The physical nature of soil has more to it than just the particle size of its minerals. The mix of particles determines the soil's texture, but that is often not as important as its structure. These two terms, texture and structure, cause the novice no end of confusion, so perhaps an analogy would be helpful. Imagine a pile of concrete blocks. The basic materials are the cement, sand and gravel that formed the blocks; they are equivalent to the clay, silt and sand of the soil texture. Those ingredients have been formed into the blocks. Such blocks in the soil are known as peds [g] and crumbs, whose shape, size and bonding create the soil structure. It is that soil structure that influences all kinds of factors from drainage to aeration and bulk density [g], all properties that can have a huge impact on crop growth.

With skilled management quite a wide range of particle size mixes can become highly productive. One of the most important husbandry skills developed over the millennia by farmers and growers around the world has been the ability to know how to handle their local soils: when to cultivate them, what tool to use and how deep to set it. It is no exaggeration to say that this knowledge can make the difference between a successful harvest and crop failure, and most certainly between a miserable income and a large profit margin.

Soil cultivation should improve land drainage and increase the amount of air in the root zone. To do this it must produce tilth; it must prise apart the soil peds but not destroy the much smaller soil crumbs. Working the land under the wrong conditions smashes through peds and crumbs and reduces it to a homogeneous mass akin to either dust or mud. Soil cultivation may at specific times in the annual cycle be aimed at weed control or the incorporation of materials such as bulky organic matter, but these should never be achieved at the expense of the physical condition of the soil. Heavy clay soils have to be worked when they have just the right amount of water; too wet and they turn to something a potter would be pleased to use, too dry and the clods will have set as hard as concrete. In my youth we employed a horseman who if he had to harrow a field down to a seedbed would go out first thing in the morning and kick the soil, then decide if it would be "just right to work" straight away or best left until afternoon. No one challenged his decision; he was the first true "man of the soil" to influence me.

The fertility of a soil is a combination of its physical properties and its chemical content. Defining a fertile soil is either very easy ("a soil that grows good crops") or very difficult indeed if one tries to embrace all the factors that contribute to its success. The most important are as follows.

The soil must:

Be able to hold moisture yet be sufficiently free-draining to prevent waterlogging and ensure the presence of air within its pores.

Have a density such that roots can easily penetrate.

Be able to hold but slowly release the full range of plant nutrient minerals.

Have fine mineral particles, particularly the clays, combining to form soil crumbs.

Contain compounds that can release soluble forms of the mineral elements required for normal plant growth.

Have a pH within the range 5.5 to 7.5, ideally around 6.5.

Contain organic matter and the organisms that break it down to release nutrients.

This surface layer, the "topsoil" referred to in every book on cultivation from the most elementary to the most technical, is as one of my lecturers put it, "man's greatest possession". Tillage is all about how we handle and care for it.

SOIL FERTILITY

First Theophrastus then almost all the Roman writers on agronomy discussed soils and their suitability for various crops. A thousand years later al-Awam followed in their footsteps but went one step further by recommending testing soil fertility by taste and smell. He tells us to take the sample from the bottom of a pit "two elbows deep", put it into a glass container of clean water and let it settle. After this, "If the taste and smell of the water is good then the soil will be also [good]. If salty [or] of foul smell the soil will be putrid." Salinity and anaerobic conditions are still disastrous but today's students should be glad of the less direct techniques of detection available in a modern soil lab.

Unlike children, artisans and craftsmen seldom ask why. Why cultivators do what they do was precisely the question that early in the nineteenth century the first simple agronomy research labs such as Mockern in Germany and Rothamsted in Britain set out to answer. Not only did they ask the question, but also they added the codicils "Need we?" and "Is there a better way?" Credit for this understanding must go first to the botanists and chemists who started the transition from alchemy to chemistry in the seventeenth century. This heralded the time when analysts across Europe were enthusiastically investigating the composition of the world around them. Among their subjects were air, water, soil and plants. John Evelyn is rightly famous as the author of *Sylva* published in 1664, but his much longer-titled *A Philosophical Discourse of Earth Relating to the Culture and Improvement of It for Vegetation*, first published in 1676, gets my vote as his most interesting and, I think, valuable book. That having been said, it is easy for us to ignore the bits such as those dealing with transmutation, celestial influences and his claim that soil grows, to focus on his sound advice on tillage and the use of fertilisers, including the gruesome comment that an animal's flesh and blood are far more powerful fertilisers than its dung. Sir E. John Russell describes the book as giving the best available summary of soil science as it was understood in the seventeenth century. Miller's *The Gardeners Dictionary* of 1732 has much to say on soil fertility, and again the answers he came up with, however imperfect, helped provide the basis for others to try to show how and upon what plants "fed".

It was obvious that growing plants had to get their increase in bulk from somewhere, and the only things they were in contact with were air, water and soil. The question boiled down to determining the way in which these three were involved and how their substances entered a plant. It would be another hundred years before people investigated how, once inside, these inorganic substances combined to produce living tissues. These questions are still being answered at ever more fundamental levels. Over the last century the answers have revolutionised plant cultivation, particularly when our fundamental understanding gets translated and presented as practical advice to growers, farmers and foresters.

To follow this trail of discovery we had best start with the search for the make-up of a plant.

If we overlook the Greek philosophers whose astute musings recognised sap, soft tissue and fibre, but focused on the organs of a plant's anatomy, we may start the story with Jean-Baptiste van Helmont, who in the early years of the seventeenth century put all growth down to water. This deduction was based on a well-thought-out experiment in which he grew a young willow tree in a pot and recorded that in spite of it increasing in weight from 5lb (2.27kg) to 169lb 3oz (76.9kg), the soil only lost 2oz (57g). As far as he could see, the only thing added had been water, so QED. This is not the only erroneous conclusion for which van Helmont is remembered; the other concerns the spontaneous generation of mice!

> Press a dirty shirt into the orifice of a vessel containing a little corn, after about twenty-one days the ferment proceeding from the dirty shirt, modified by the odour of the corn, effects a transmutation of the wheat into mice.

He claimed to have seen this happen and that the mice were born full-grown.

Half a century later Sir Kenelm Digby, in a lecture to the Society for Promoting Philosophic Knowledge by Experiments, attributed plant growth to "a balsam in the air", stating that "there is in the air a hidden food of life". How right he was, but it would be for others much later to unravel the role of carbon dioxide as that balsam. This was not the only occasion when he was ahead of his time in this lecture. He seems to have recognised the role of compounds dissolved in the soil water acting as fertilisers:

> The mere water which is common to them all, cannot be it; there must be something else enclosed within it, to which the water serves but for a vehicle. Examine it by spagyric [alchemical] art, and you will find that it is nothing else than a nitrous salt, which is diluted in the water.

It seems he had experimented with potassium nitrate, or, as he and most people then and since have known it, saltpetre. Clearly he got tantalisingly near to recognising the role of fertilisers in solution and had by luck or good judgement chosen a compound that supplied two of the three most important soil-based plant nutrients.

Meanwhile the Reverend Stephen Hales was delving deep into the physiological processes that take place within plant tissues, and publishing his results in *Vegetable Staticks, or, An Account of Some Statical Experiments on the Sap in Vegetables.*

Jethro Tull, famed for the seed-drill and the horse-hoe, was convinced that the answer lay in the soil. As Crichton Porteous says, he "was a man of very strong opinions who believed that others should follow his lead". He seems the sort of chap that would have made General Montgomery look a timorous wimp. He believed the only way to make plant nutrients available was to break down the soil into ever finer particles, by, you will have guessed, the use of his beloved horse-hoe. He spoiled an argument that contains a germ of logic by claiming that fields so treated would henceforward need no manure.

Charles Bonnet, a Swiss naturalist, started a chain of thought that eventually solved one part of the mystery, the origin of the carbon found in such abundance in plant remains. During these investigations he observed that leaves give off bubbles of gas. Appropriately it was Joseph Priestley, the discoverer of oxygen, who determined that such bubbles were execrations of his gas, as he put it. But it was left to John Ingenhousz writing in 1779 to establish that this was only so in sunlight. Curiously, the story ends where it started, in Switzerland, through the work of Jean Senebier, who showed that the absorbed gas was carbon dioxide, which the plant "decomposed", releasing the oxygen and assimilating the carbon.

Today most people probably link carbohydrates, oils and proteins with information on foodstuffs. They are of course the main components of plants after water, which is often by far the largest component of fresh produce. We need to go a bit deeper and look at the elements that form these complex compounds, the chemical building-blocks a plant assembles from its surroundings.

As cosmologists never tire of telling us, our planet is made from the debris of long-dead stars. So as part of that chemistry, and as Joni Mitchell's song *Woodstock* reminds us, "we are star dust", and so are plants!

Of the seventeen elements of star dust that come together to make plants, oxygen, hydrogen and carbon come from the atmosphere and water, and the rest are gathered in solution from the soil. For the record, those known as the major elements (macronutrients) are nitrogen, potassium and phosphorus, followed by calcium, magnesium and sulphur, while at the other end of the scale are the micronutrients or trace elements – iron, zinc, sodium, chlorine, boron, molybdenum, copper, manganese and cobalt.

How they get into the soil water is not straightforward. Some are derived from the weathering of rock fragments, most of which will have been reformed several times over geological time. But in rare instances a plant will absorb what we might think of as fresh material only recently weathered from igneous rocks, themselves derived from magma below the earth's crust.

So most rock minerals are on a slow, endless cycle. Sometimes they are chemically bound fast within a sedimentary rock, sometimes they are released into the soil water, often from their entrapment on the surface of clays. When that happens a plant can dip into the soup and borrow them for the few years it is alive. After it dies it may succumb to fire, when its ashes rejoin the cycle, or its organic remains will decay to contribute to the merry-go-round, first as partly decomposed "organic matter" and then as its derivative, "humus", those two much-loved icons of the organic gardener's world.

Those who like to muse on these things estimate that apart from the elements weathered from igneous rocks, all the molecules will have been in and out of living things from people to pineapples many times in the last million years. Regardless of whether they currently accrue as mineral deposits or derive from the compost heap, they will have passed through countless specimens of single-celled organisms over the 3.5 billion years of life on Earth. This is a thought that might give both the organic and non-organic camps cause to ponder.

The study of the soil's micro-inhabitants is beyond the scope of this book, but recognising their importance is certainly not. Topsoil is home to a large number of unrelated groups including the protozoa, nematodes, algae, fungi, actinomycetes and bacteria. Each of these vast assemblages contains a huge number of species with comparably diverse life styles. To stand in a field and comprehend that such a large number of different life forms are living literally beneath your feet is hard enough. To appreciate the many studies that have shown that the lump of soil stuck to the toecap of your shoe can be home to one thousand million individual organisms defies the imagination.

Some of this multitude cause plant diseases but can live in the soil apart from their hosts for long periods; and some rob the soil of valuable nitrogenous compounds by converting them into nitrogen gas. But the vast majority are the saprophytes that run the second half of that great cycle of which all living things are part and upon which all more complex life forms depend.

Farmers and gardeners both benefit from and influence this microscopic world. By living off plant and animal remains and the debris left by larger creatures these micro-organisms complete the decomposition process. Each of the various groups plays its part in breaking down these remains. And in their turn the bodily remains of each of the group's members join the cycle that finally releases plant nutrients in the form of compounds that can be taken up by roots.

The cultivator's influence starts with the choice of crops as the roots of different plants stimulate different micro-organisms, but the basic acts of cultivation, including tillage, drainage, irrigation, and the use of fertilisers and crop protection chemicals all exert an influence. Remarkably, in spite of such intrusions into their terraneous world, there are few examples of man having rendered once fertile soils lifeless.

Important and beneficial as the soil micro-organisms are, growers have developed cultivation systems that turn their back on them. They are typically but not exclusively intensive glasshouse systems and include the partial sterilisation of soils, hydroponics and, most aseptic of all, in-vitro micropropagation.

Of the mineral nutrients available to plants, the amount of each present in a soil at any one time is dependent on its rate of release from its insoluble state, balanced against its rate loss by being leached from the soil in drainage water. The amount taken up by plants, although vital to them, is not a very large proportion of the total in solution at any one time.

Keen gardeners will know that they buy fertilisers for the nitrogen, phosphorus or potassium they contain, and that adding extra amounts of one or more of these elements can have a big effect on the growth of their plants. That does not alter the fact that most plants are around 90 per cent water, and of the remaining 10 per cent dry matter less than a tenth comes from the three main elements listed on the fertiliser bag. The interwoven cycles by which elements pass into and out of living things can seem confusing, so let's start with the simplest, hydrogen.

The hydrogen within a plant's make-up comes from water, obtained when H_2O is split during photosynthesis. It goes into the living chemistry of the plant via the large sugar molecules produced in that process. It is that splitting of water that results in the net surplus of oxygen upon which we and all air-breathing animals depend.

In spite of producing a net surplus of oxygen, plants use it in their respiration much as animals do; it comes from two sources, directly during the splitting of water or from that previously released into the air, where it makes up twenty per cent of our atmosphere.

The oxygen the roots need to breathe defuses from the atmosphere above ground, if there are open cracks and spaces for it to pass down. A soil can become anaerobic when it is so compacted that there are no such spaces. This rarely happens in well-tended gardens and on arable farms, but it frequently causes plant losses following the passage of heavy machinery during construction and civil engineering works.

Carbon is confusing, as we think of it as a black powder (unless you have diamonds in mind), but the plant gets all its carbon from the invisible gas carbon dioxide, which it "fixes" during photosynthesis. That's a simple sentence but it happens to be the key to life on Earth. Earthly life is based on carbon chemistry, which incidentally is why the latter is also known as organic chemistry. Once the plants have done their job those carbon-based compounds get passed along the food chain until decay finally returns the element to the air, ready for the next round. It is this carbon cycle that more than anything illustrates the saying, "All life is grass," or, as the cannibal higher up the food chain would have it, "We live from hand to mouth."

Finally we come to nitrogen. It also has its cycle from inanimate compounds incorporated into living tissues and later released back into the inanimate world. This is a complex web of processes, succinctly summarised by Professors Fox and Bandel as mineralisation, immobilisation, nitrification, denitrification, leaching, volatilisation and erosion. Mercifully we need not go into great detail.

In a way this story is the mirror-image of carbon. Most people think of nitrogen as the gas that represents four fifths of the air we breathe. Unfortunately, plants can't use that source any more than we can; they need to take in nitrogen from compounds dissolved in the soil water.

In nature nitrogen gets from being a gas in the atmosphere to being in solution by two routes, the fast and noisy or the silent and slow. The dramatic way is when the process is started by lightning during electric storms, when the massive energy discharges fuse nitrogen with oxygen. The gentle way depends on the activity of micro-organisms. Some bacteria and some algae can start the cycle afresh because they can do what the rest of us can't: take nitrogen from the air and incorporate it into their living matter. Some of these bacteria are free-living. Others exist within the roots of some plant species, including many members of the vast pea family. These lucky hosts can in turn obtain this fixed nitrogen. This symbiosis gives the legumes, as the members of that family are called, a huge advantage at sites deficient in nitrogen, a boost evident if you look at the growth of clover on some neglected lawns and gorse on many quarry faces.

So much for the capturing of nitrogen gas, but there is another bug-assisted part to this complex story. By now you will be familiar with the idea of these elements being passed from one living thing to another as the natural world eats its way up the food chain. Likewise, you will have guessed that nitrogen's return to the atmosphere is, like the carbon story, when decay after death is complete and the nitrogen is lost to the living world. The bugs that release the nitrogen, the nitrifying bacteria, are, as far as plants are concerned, nutrient-wasters.

However, there are other micro-organisms at work earlier on in the process of decay that do an extremely valuable job. They break down dead plant and animal remains and animal excreta and release soluble nitrogen compounds into the soil. These heroes are behind the story of organic fertilisers. As to the role of nitrogen, suffice to say that it is part of virtually every giant molecule in the chemistry of life. Whilst that cannot be said for the rest of the elements listed above it is true that each plays one or several vital roles in either the biochemical processes that form the basis of plant physiology or they are essential components of the plant's cellular and subcellular structure. Many amateur gardeners will be familiar with the somewhat over-simplified idea that some nutrients are especially required for some crops, for example potassium for tomatoes and phosphorus for root vegetables. A good idea of the importance of these nutrient elements and the role they play in complex metabolic processes can be gained from reading *Diagnosis of Mineral Disorders in Plants*, while its coloured plates show just how sick plants become in their absence. This publication was based on Professor T. Wallace's pioneering work during and shortly after the Second World War at Long Ashton Research Station.

THE SEARCH FOR INCREASED FERTILITY

These then are the substances a plant needs from its environment if it is to grow to maturity. Over most of Earth's land surfaces that are not too cold or dry they are present in sufficient quantity to support a successful flora. Why then has the "need" to augment them played such an important role in the story of cultivation?

The early cultivators of Asia, the Middle East and the Americas all discovered that their crops grew larger if they added materials to the soil. The most famous and first mineral top-dressing must surely be the silt from the annual Nile flood, although much of its fertility would have come from the decomposition of micro-organisms as it dried out. It was not only valued but also venerated as a gift from the gods. The Egyptians were not alone in using river silt to fertilise their fields. My ancestors in East Anglia did the same thing, although they called it "warping". Apparently warping "made a rich top-dressing for the land whose effect will be seen for from 15 to 20 years", as one farmer put it.

Perhaps early farmers found it strange that the most effective dressings they used on their arable land were either the dead remains of plants and animals or their waste or ashes, and that through the cycle of life and death their land became more fertile. It has been suggested that the increased growth of herbage stimulated by blood spilt at the site of a kill, be it for food or for sacrifice, might have been taken as an augury from the gods.

In addition to such grisly leftovers from the slaughterhouse, early farmers recognised the value of both animal manure and decomposed plant remains. Today most gardeners convert plant debris into compost by stacking it in either a heap or one of the multitude of plastic bins designed specifically for the job (the job, that is, of making the manufacturer a profit). The who, where and when of the first composters is not known, but it is well established that farmers at about 3000 BP ploughed in both purpose-sown crops and crop debris as green manure. It is the familiar story: such an understanding precedes any written record, so as soon as we get any reference to it, it is already standard practice with growers in Asia, North Africa, Persia and the Americas.

The cultivation of legumes to increase soil fertility is closely linked to green manuring, as several species such as lupins were grown at least in part for that purpose. Even when the haulm [g] was not ploughed in after harvest, the plants would have already improved fertility through their hosting nitrogen-fixing bacteria in nodules on their roots. The benefit to subsequent crops was fully recognised two thousand years ago by Roman writers, who give the impression that it was a long established practice. Cato notes that cereal fields are manured by lupins, beans and vetches, while Columella prefers medic clover to "dung the land". Sadly they have left us no clue as to how they imagined such increased fertility was achieved.

In pre-Columbian South America, seabird droppings – guano – were spread on the land; however, fertility from the ocean could be more direct. Some Inca farmers planted fish heads alongside their maize seeds, just as thousands of miles to the north, Chief Squanto taught the Pilgrims to do before sowing their first crop of maize. This must have been a success, as 150 years later East Coast market-gardeners were ploughing in 10,000 fish per acre (25,000 per hectare).

Marl-spreading is by far the most ancient form of mineral fertiliser used in Britain, and a technique we may have introduced to the Romans, indeed Pliny described it as an ancient British agricultural practice. Marl is a chalk–clay mix with useful traces of magnesium, phosphorus and potassium. In its various forms it is found as a rock deposit over considerable areas of the country. It was dug, carted and spread to great effect on acid sandy soils, where the chalk neutralised the acidity and the clay helped to hold and then release nutrients. The amounts used were huge; estimates vary greatly, but around 100 tonnes per hectare is a conservative figure, which must explain the frequent marking of "Marl Pits" on local maps.

Medieval texts bear witness to marl's continuing use. Later, according to Chambers and Mingay in *The Agricultural Revolution, 1750–1880*, an early sixteenth-century local historian in Pembrokeshire gives us a vivid description of the work, if a rather fanciful idea of the origin of the material:

> Claye marle is of nature fat, tough and clammy. The common people are of opinion that this marle is the fatnesse of the earth, gathered together at Noah's flood: which is verie like to be true ... It is digged or caste out of the pitte, carried to the lande, and there caste either upon the fallow or ley ground unplowed, and this in the summer tyme ... where it lyeth so on the lande all the somer and winter, the rain making it to melte and run like molten ledd all

over the face of the earthe.

Marling was a recognised occupation. Bands of men went from farm to farm finding, digging and spreading the marl. Like all clays, marl is gut-wrenching stuff to dig, so to give it less to stick to, the marler's fork had only three widely spaced tines. The leader of a typical gang of six or so was known as the "Lord of the Pit" or "Lord of the Soil"; he no doubt negotiated terms with the landowner before work started. Itinerant landworkers of all kinds and in every age live a tough, rough life. It is not hard to guess that it is the impact they made on a village community that is the main reason why their customs and exploits were so well recorded. Surely both their demanding of money from passers-by and their response, if successful, must have been well known. Apparently the Lord of the Pit shouted, "Oyez, Oyez, Oyez! This is to give notice that X has given us marlers part of £100 and to whom so-ever will do the same we will give thanks and shout." Then the gang joined hands in a circle danced and cried "Largesse, Largesse!" The "part of £100" was typically a few pence.

The marlers' weekends of singing and drinking in the local pub no doubt disturbed the rural idyll and offended some, but their work was seen as so significant to the future fertility and hence prosperity of a farm that its completion was marked with Finishing Day Celebrations. These were followed by a feast and inevitably more drinking and dancing, this time at the landowner's expense. Perhaps it was the marlers' departure that gave the locals most to celebrate.

Christina Hole in her book *British Folk Customs* describes an almost identical custom from the harvest field. This time the gangmaster is known as the Lord of the Harvest. Once again he solicits money from passers-by, and when he is successful, gratitude is shown by dancing and shouting "Largesse, Largesse!" And once again the accumulated money is spent on drink at the end of the task. At least our jolly marlers did not have to mix the lumps into the soil; once roughly spread on either a ley or a fallow they were allowed to weather until they could be harrowed down before being ploughed in. In the last quarter of the eighteenth century Thomas Coke, that irrepressible enthusiast, used the technique on the acid sands of his 43,000-acre (17,200ha) estate at Holkham. Its success and his promotion of it at his annual gathering, known to the agricultural world as the

"Holkham Shearings", contributed significantly to his fame as a pioneer of modern farming.

By this time the value of farmyard manure had been established for millennia; however, feeding livestock with nitrogen-rich "oil-cake" [g], as much to increase the quality of their manure as to nourish them, was new. Most purchased fertilisers came in the form of waste from the towns, with London supplying much of that used in the home counties. The most common materials include malt dust, rabbit dung, night-soil, soot, ashes and bones, burnt and boiled. Some such products came from much farther afield: poudrette (night-soil plus lime or gypsum) was imported from Paris, while taffo (night-soil plus clay) came all the way from China. This was no catchpenny trade; indeed by 1800 there were recognised application rates per acre for each of these materials for cereal and root crops on heavy and light soils.

Lime, marl and sea sand had been applied to crops for hundreds of years in the quest for better yields, but it was only after the nineteenth-century chemists had established what plants were made of that a wider range of simple compounds were used. These early scientists' ultimate contribution was to find new sources of these essential plant nutrient elements within what became known as "artificial manures", an inappropriate term from whose emotive ring we still suffer. As Crichton Porteous says:

> Whether these nutrients are given in the form of pig hair, sawdust, or horn shavings, or as sulphate of ammonia, superphosphate, muriate of potash, or whatever other modern fertilizer it may be, the principle remains; we are helping nature. To call modern fertilizers "artificials" is an error, for they are no more "artificial" than were pig hair and horn shavings. Fertilisers are produced from natural sources, as is everything.

Another scientist, Professor Robert Warington of Oxford University, deserves the final word on our search for fertility. It was he, in the closing years of the nineteenth century, that did so much to put the role of the agricultural chemists we meet next into context. He saw that a soil could be considered fertile only if it had the right physical and biological as well as chemical characteristics. He understood that soil structure, tilth, humus and drainage were all as important as ever, and must not be swept aside in the rush to apply fertilisers. His own work on the role of bacteria in the soil makes him a pioneer in agricultural microbiology, whereas von Liebig, who features so strongly in the story of agricultural chemistry discussed below, had called the idea that "corruption is the mother of vegetation" nonsense, Warington showed it to be true both in nature and to a great extent in arable fields. We still need his wisdom and balance in the current impasse between "the Greens" and science.

AGRICULTURAL CHEMISTRY

Agricultural chemistry, as opposed to the chemical make-up of plants outlined above, is generally considered to have started in 1795 when the Earl of Dundonald's *A Treatise, Showing the Intimate Connection That Subsists Between Agriculture and Chemistry* was published. His introduction leaves us in little doubt about his view. After such a confident start it is something of an anticlimax however to realise that the science had only reached a point at which he was able to declare that "plants consist of mucilaginous matter, resinous matter, matter analogous to that of animals, and some proportion of oil".

Things developed apace, though; by 1802 Sir Humphry Davy was telling us that:

> The surface of the earth, the atmosphere and the water deposited from it must either together or separately afford all the principles concerned in vegetation, and it is only by examining the chemical nature of these principles that we are capable of discovering what is the food of plants, and the manner in which this food is supplied and prepared for their nourishment.

A long sentence, but in language everyone could understand. This was his introduction to a series of lectures given to the Board of Agriculture. His focus is clearly on the link between the constituents of the living tissues of a plant and the chemicals that surround it. These are the substances that scientists now know as plant nutrients, cultivators call fertilisers, and most popular writings still refer to as plant foods.

In 1804 Théodore de Saussure's *Recherches chimique sur la végétation* recognised the ash residue from the burning of plants as material that had been essential within the living plant. Indeed, by combining the evidence of his own experiments with those of earlier workers he postulated that plants obtain their carbon from the carbonic acid gas in the air under the influence of sunlight. At last the pieces of the jigsaw were falling into place. There was however a vital one missing – the source of nitrogen. One might even say that they had the piece but could not decide which way up it went! Did the nitrogen found in all plants come from the air or the soil?

Around a quarter of a century later two minor aristocrats started to experiment on crop production on their estates. One was the Frenchman Jean-Baptiste Dieudonné Boussingault at Bechelbronn in Alsace, the other an Englishman, Sir John Bennet Lawes at Rothamsted in Hertfordshire. Boussingault was slightly ahead of his English colleague in developing the idea of combining science with practice through field-based experiments and by building a laboratory on a farm, the forerunner of the today's hundreds of agricultural, horticultural and forestry research stations.

If agricultural chemistry was said to have started in 1795, then 1840 was declared to be "an epoch in the history of the science", thanks to the publication of a report to the British Association that set out the bones of our understanding of plant nutrition. Its author was agricultural science's first academic giant, the German chemist Justus von Liebig.

A measure of Liebig's stature can be judged from his academic record. At 21 he became Professor Extraordinarius of Chemistry at the University of Giessen; at 23 Professor Ordinarius; at 42 he was created Baron, and at 49 appointed Professor at Munich University. Although the chair at Munich has no adjectival embellishments it was extremely influential and became the platform from which his international reputation spread.

Liebig's 1840 report did three things: it reviewed and integrated much that was worthwhile from previous workers; it introduced findings from his own laboratory; and above all it set out how in the future experimental science should work to improve crop production. In his own words,

> A rational system of agriculture cannot be formed without the application of scientific principles; for such a system must be based on an exact acquaintance with the means of nutrition of vegetables, and with the influence of soils and actions of manure upon them. This knowledge we must seek from chemistry, which teaches the mode of investigating the composition and of studying the characters of the different substances from which plants derive their nourishment.

There is no arguing with that, although there are still a few who would wish it otherwise.

At last we knew the major elements of which plants were made and that air, water and soil minerals all played their part in supplying the essential ingredients. Liebig argued that enriching the soil with the appropriate compounds could boost crop production. So far so good, but it is at this point that the great man is found wanting. It was known that the air was four-fifths nitrogen, that nitrogen was a vital component of plants and that they "breathed" through pores in their leaves. Many, including Liebig, drew the obvious conclusion: plants got their nitrogen from the air. They do not; it is taken in as compounds dissolved in the soil water, as are potassium and phosphorus etc.

Based on his belief that nitrogen was literally as abundant, available and free as air, the fertilisers Liebig recommended contained only phosphorus and potassium. So they were not, as claimed, "universal fertilisers", but nevertheless produced good results in soils containing sufficient nitrogen. They stimulated a huge amount of interest, that in turn led to the search for available sources of potassium and phosphorus in large enough quantities for farm use, materials that were to become known as "artificial manures". It was Liebig's faith in his misguided theory that a plant gained its nitrogen from the air that made him so critical of the work at Rothamsted, the institution that, as we shall see, ultimately proved him wrong.

The first large-scale source of phosphorus was bones. Jennifer Davies points out in *The Victorian Kitchen Garden* that bones were used as early as 1774. According to Liebig, Britain three quarters of a century later was not only importing animal bones from the slaughterhouses of Europe, but had "turned up the battlefields of Leipzig, of Waterloo, and of the Crimea; and already from the catacombs of Sicily had carried away the skeletons of many successive generations" – not the sort of thing that gives either the British or progress a good name!

To begin with, in what was essentially a pre-industrial economy, anyone wishing to use bones as a fertiliser had to crush them themselves, and specifically designed horse-powered bone-mills were sold to farmers and growers. Perhaps there could be a renewed demand from self-sufficiency organic producers. It was however the Baron himself that escalated the demand by discovering a way of making bones more useful by increasing the availability of the phosphorus in them by treating them with sulphuric acid.

Bones are of course "organic" but once treated they were

nevertheless classed as an "artificial" fertiliser. So was guano, which Professor A. P. Aitkin called "the first artificial manure to be used in large quantities", but to me there seems little artificial about seagull droppings, nor apparently to the Qurchua when they called it "*huano*", their word for dung which the Spanish changed to guano. However, long before the professor's time the manurial strength of bird droppings had been recognised. Thomas Hill in 1577 claimed that "doves dung is the best because the same possesseth a mighty hotnesse", and that knowing this the ancient Greeks "willed this dung to be strewed the thinner, and in a manner as seeds on the earth".

The story of guano's collection, importation and use almost rivals the bone saga. Most was quarried from ancient and massive deposits dropped on the islands and rocks along the extremely dry coast of Chile and Peru. Guano had long been used by the Incas before it was brought to Europe by the geographer and naturalist Humboldt – he of the current. It was however a member of the British military elite, General Beatson, that laid claim to being the first European to test its nutritional value. Manurial trials are not often in a senior army officer's line of duty, but the story takes an even stranger turn when we learn that he carried out the tests on potatoes on St Helena – perhaps hardly the place one might have expected to be at the cutting-edge of crop research, though probably safe from visitors trampling on the experimental plots.

Lord Derby introduced guano to British agriculture, and within a few years growers were reporting results "little short of miraculous", such that "This wonderful brown powder gave a most powerful impetus to intelligent farming." With that kind of promotion it is no wonder that demand took off, but bearing in mind its origin it still amazes me that the deposits were great enough for us to import five million tonnes in the first fifty years. That's an awful lot of bird droppings. The trade made fortunes for some of those involved, not least the Gibbs family, who bought the Tyntesfield estate and built the huge neo-Gothic pile of that name recently purchased by the National Trust. Add to their wealth the title of Lord Wraxall, and it becomes clear that the benefits of guano were not chicken-feed, even if its origins undoubtedly were. Pressure from farmers in the United States to have a secure supply of guano led to Congress passing a law empowering US citizens to take possession of any island with guano deposits not under the control of another government. As a result Midway Island flies the stars and stripes. Many writers warn of its not surprising variability, which no doubt is the reason why Newsham includes a number of tests for "high class guano". Along with colour ("coffee and milk"), smell ("strong"), consistency ("oily to the touch"), flame ("blazes up quickly"), comes taste ("strong, salt, piquant and caustic"). Now there's a challenge for both the health and safety officer and the organic grower.

Around the middle of the nineteenth century, following the lead set by Liebig's 1840 report, scientists started to apply their new-found knowledge to many aspects of crop production. Perhaps Henry Stephens had read the great man's report before writing in his *Book of the Farm* of 1851 that "no art bears so close a relation to so many branches of science as agriculture". These early researchers' ability to change the plant's circumstances revolutionised crop production. Man the cultivator was slowly becoming less dependent on conditions as he found them. There was nothing fundamentally new about his crops growing in a man-made environment – that had happened when the first field was established. What was novel was the use of manufactured products to bring about environmental changes, "artificial" fertilisers, pest-killers and disease controllers available from the newly established chemical industry.

Early British investigations into the science behind the craft of cultivation took place in several locations, each the home of an independent, dilettante experimenter. Two of the best-known and most productive centres for both field and laboratory investigations were the Woburn Experiment Station on the ninth Duke of Bedford's estate in Bedfordshire and Rothamsted Manor in Hertfordshire.

The record of the research carried out at Rothamsted reads like a history of the last 150 years of our developing understanding of crop husbandry. It is remarkable to realise that this world-famous research station was then the private estate of the Lawes family, and that John Bennet Lawes carried out some of the first crop analyses in his study in the manor-house. What would today's crop scientists give to be able to say to yet another review committee, "Welcome, coffee's on the side table, but please remember, it is my land, my room and I decide what I investigate"? The snag is you have to be able to add, "And it's my money."

The story starts with Lawes's investigations into plant nutrition and his recording of huge increases in yield when he applied phosphates; it goes on to his discovery of a method of achieving the first large-scale production of an artificial manure from bone debris: superphosphate of lime. His technique could also, and most significantly, be applied to mineral deposits of "rock phosphates". In 1842 he started large-scale production at his works in Deptford, and although the business was based on the phosphate story it was not long before his "Patent manure" contained ammonium phosphate and potassium silicate as well as "supers", as calcium phosphate became known. The use of various plant nutrients containing chemical compounds was under way.

Bennet was joined by his friend Dr Joseph Henry Gilbert and in 1843 they formed a partnership that lasted for sixty years; indeed they are still close together, both buried in Harpenden churchyard. Together they extended the field-scale experimentation on Lawes's estate. Incredibly, their most famous investigation is still ongoing 160 years later: the world-renowned Broadbalk Trials. Ostensibly these were to compare the effects of different fertilisers on the same cereal crop. It is said that it is thanks to Gilbert that the trials were not stopped when their planned end arrived. He could see that such work could go on yielding useful data; however not even the meticulous Gilbert could have known how right he would turn out to be. The sheer length of the trial with its continuous, uninterrupted monitoring has allowed many other issues to be studied such as the comparison of the development of soil structure with and without the use of farmyard manure. Laws and Gilbert worked tirelessly to resolve what became known as "the nitrogen controversy", and in so doing met the full force of Liebig's arrogance. One hopes that being proved correct was some compensation for receiving some very unfriendly comments from across the North Sea

Perhaps Rothamsted has never forgiven the Baron; as why else should Jean-Baptiste Dieudonné Boussingault's portrait, rather than his, form the frontispiece of Russell's *Soil Conditions and Plant Growth*, with the caption "The Founder of Modern Agricultural Chemistry"?

If agricultural chemistry was not to remain a solely academic study, news of its findings had to spread to the farming community. The two ways that this happened were through places of learning and learned societies. In 1881 John Pilley wrote a student text with the very modern-sounding title *The Elements of Scientific Agriculture*, in which what we now know as soil science took pride of place. To help his student readership he includes specimen exam questions such as "Explain the chemical changes taking place in the preparation of farmyard manure for the land," "What are the principal substances found in the soil and which of these do plants require?" and "What are reduced superphosphates and what is their action in the soil?" You may start writing now!

Dr Augustus Voelcker used both these channels to convey the results of both his and other people's research. During his distinguished career he held the posts of professor of chemistry at the Royal Agricultural College at Cirencester, consulting chemist to both the Bath and West of England Agricultural Society and the Royal Agricultural Society of England and Director of the Woburn Experiment Station. A German by birth, he worked tirelessly for the improvement of farming in his adopted country. Among many topics he investigated were the movement of chemicals within the soil and their loss in drainage water, information vital to the best use of fertilisers. Becoming a British patriot did not curtail his scientific curiosity across wider horizons. Indeed, he gave us the first answer to a question that cultivators had been asking for at least five thousand years. His analysis of the floodwaters of the Nile showed why the annual inundation brought such fertility to the floodplain of Lower Egypt.

The story goes that to improve his English Voelcker banned the speaking of German at home as "his accent and method of making sentences were interfering with his success as a lecturer". Knowing how little agricultural students relish chemistry classes and how they are prone to seize on a lecturer's eccentricities I am sure they were!

MINERALS AS FERTILISERS

In summary, by the mid nineteenth century science had established the basic composition of plants and soils and had shown that crops responded to additional applications of what had become recognised as the most important of these. As a consequence, scientists were asked why, if the soil contained these "plant foods", upon which wild vegetation seemed to thrive indefinitely, was it necessary to add more to cropland? They gave three basic reasons.

The first was that there might not be available at any one time as much as the plant can use. Cultivators have always wanted to get the most out of a given area of land, either because they have limited space, or because the basic tasks of growing a crop are the same per unit area, whether you get a high or a low yield. So increasing yield per unit area increases output for effort and profit margin. This basic plank of agricultural economics is however now under question, in some circumstances, with some crops; a low-input, low-output approach may be preferable both for the producer and for the environment, and much more is likely to be heard of this debate, as European farmers and growers search for a fresh approach to profitable crop production.

The second reason was that soils of some otherwise suitable locations might be deficient in one or more of the required elements.

Finally there was the possibility that plants vary greatly in their demand for nutrients and crop plants tend to be greedy; thus a piece of land that grows a fine stand of trees or a dense cover of heather may not produce even a light crop of potatoes or cabbage.

It matters not one jot to a plant if the chemical elements that it combines together in its growth processes are derived from an organic, a mineral or an industrial source. Any material that contains nutrients that can be released into the soil water can be used as a fertilizer unless it also has some other phytotoxic [g] constituent. As G. J. Leigh remarks in his book *The World's Greatest Fix*, "Once a fertiliser is applied to the soil, the plant absorbs nitrate (or whatever) and it has no mechanism for detecting its origin, whether industrial or 'organic'." (Incidentally, G. J. Leigh is Emeritus Professor of Environmental Science at the University of Sussex.) As we have seen, the partly decayed products of a once live organism, plant or animal, are classed as organic fertilisers. This includes composted plant remains, faeces and urine, parts of dead animals such as bones, blood, hooves, hair and, as in fishmeal, whole creatures.

Nutrients can also come from the air and the land; both are

natural sources that feed into the cycle of life and death. Such "Inorganic fertilisers" are either minerals mined from the earth or compounds produced in a chemical factory. Over time, depending on their solubility and the prevailing conditions, they dissolve in the soil water and the nutrient element becomes available just as it does from an organic source.

Discussion of organic growing appeared in Chapter 7. So suffice to say that neither the crop nor the chemist has yet been found that can tell the difference between a second-hand atom of potassium of organic origin and one straight out of the mine. It is the quantity and timing that influences yield and flavour.

As part of this cycle of the quick and the dead, organic fertilisers typically contain all the nutrients a plant derives from the soil. In contrast, we can buy inorganic fertilisers either as "straights" containing only one nutrient or as "compounds" containing several nutrients. If the compound fertilizer has been blended for a specific task, a particular crop at a particular time of year for example, then it is often called "balanced", in the same way as a human's diet might be so described. Within the EU the law requires every container of fertilizer sold to show the amount of each nutrient it contains. Of course, if you have the amounts you also have the ratio between them, which allows you to estimate both the size of the feed and its balance.

Of the seventeen elements found in most plants, the typical British agronomist buys less than a third. Fertilisers in the frenetic world of glasshouse and container growing will get special consideration in their own chapters. Nitrogen, potassium and phosphorus, the so-called macro elements, are far and away the most sought-after, followed by calcium and magnesium. These latter two are sold in the form of crushed limestone and have been much more often spread on the land to change the soil pH or to improve the structure of heavy clay soils than to counter a shortage of their metallic elements. In the story of the eighteenth-century agricultural improvements and long before the chemistry was worked out, farmers spread as much as 2000 bushels ($70m^3$) of lime per hectare.

Early in the century Daniel Defoe writes of Kentish chalk being exported by water for

> country farmers to lay upon their land, and that in prodigious quantities; and so valued by the farmers of those countries, that they give from two shillings and six pence, to four shillings a load

for it ... Thus the barren soil of Kent, for such the chalky grounds are esteemed, make the Essex lands rich and fruitful, and the mixture of earth forms a composition, which out of two barren extremes, make one prolifick medium; the strong clay of Essex and Suffolk is made fruitful by the soft meliorating melting chalk of Kent which fattens and enriches it.

A little further to the east in Hertfordshire, at the end of the eighteenth century, Arthur Young found farmers liming their land with the chalk that lay just a few metres beneath the surface. Specialist three-man gangs dug pits, one for every six acres (2.4ha), going down 20 or 30 feet (6 or 9m) before tunnelling sideways into the chalk. Hauled to the surface in wicker baskets, it was spread at the backbreaking rate of 1000 barrow-loads per acre (2500 per hectare). Young thoroughly approved the use of barrows, as he considered carting to be such hard work that it often injured horses!

Limestone deposits were often converted into "quick" or "burnt" lime before being spread. Whichever form the lime took, it was known to make clays less sticky, by the process we know as flocculation, while "sour", acid land was made "sweet", so bringing it into profitable production.

All the rest of the nutrient elements, although vital in very small amounts, are applied only under the unusual circumstances of a deficient soil and/or a very demanding crop.

The following is typical of the kind of statements we get from today's apologists for "agribusiness":

> It is no exaggeration to say that the introduction of the practice of artificial manuring has revolutionised modern husbandry. Indeed, without the aid of artificial manures, arable farming, as at present carried out, would be impossible. Fifty years ago the practice may be said to have been unknown; yet so widespread has it now become, that at the present time the capital invested in the manure trade in this country alone amounts to millions sterling.

Though the estimate of fifty years may seem a bit low, in 1894 it was not, and *that* was when C. M. Aikman wrote this in the introduction to *Manures and the Principles of Manuring*! He based much of the book on the researches of Britain's most famous pioneers in agricultural chemistry, the by then knighted Sir John Laws and Sir Joseph Henry Gilbert at Rothamsted.

This quote suggests to me that a significant amount of land and its produce was being "exposed" to these chemicals by 1880. Yet most people's idea of a golden age of organic produce seems to extend to the 1950s. It seems that they may have to revise this and go back to their great-great-grandmother's day to find out what, in their opinion, really safe, healthy, flavoursome food tasted like! The fact is that we, our crops and our soil have had the benefit of well over one hundred years' experience of these materials. It is not the source of these plant nutrients that matters but the amounts used. Groundwater is just as much at risk from cattle effluent as from nitram.

Attitudes change; in 1762 Jethro Tull in *Horse Hoeing Husbandry* made plain his dislike of manure, believing the soil contained everything that was needed if only one could pulverise it sufficiently to release the entrapped goodness, preferably by the use of his horse hoe. As the following quotation shows he seemed particularly revolted by the use of animal and human waste, seemingly finding it impossible to envisage it breaking down into anything less noxious.

> It is a wonder how delicate palates can dispense with eating their own and their beasts ordure, but a little more putrefied and evaporated; together with all sorts of filth and nastiness, a tincture of which those roots must unavoidably receive that grow amongst it.

Nearly one hundred and fifty years later Helen Nussey and Olive Cockerell faced the same attitude, as they explain in *A French Garden in England*. The couplet

> Nothing on earth is half so pure
> As vegetables grown withOUT manure.

seems to have been known to some of their potential customers who expressed doubts about the use of farmyard manure in intensive market-gardening.

> It was not surprising that several customers wrote asking us to explain our position. We however felt quite justified in what we were doing as when the facts are stated it will be seen that there can be no risk whatever from vegetables [so] grown.

Clearly the women took the queries in their stride and reason prevailed. I can picture the grandchildren of those concerned customers now writing to insist on organically grown produce!

SOURCES OF FERTILISERS

Of all the plant nutrients, the element nitrogen leads by far the most complicated life. Before it can be absorbed by plant roots, both the nitrogen from organic remains and the gaseous nitrogen that makes up four-fifths of the air has to be converted into a soluble state. In fact both sources produce the same chemicals.

Until the start of the twentieth century virtually all the nitrogen fertiliser used throughout most of the world came from the rather grisly list of organic remains we encountered in the nitrogen story. The exceptions were Europe and the USA, which had by then spent over fifty years spreading South American guano over fields and gardens. Over the same period farmers and gardeners had also used a fertilizer with a more straightforward chemical composition: potassium nitrate, known as nitre or saltpetre. As early as 1834 it was reported that a dressing of a hundredweight per acre (125kg/ha) was "productive of the most luxuriant effects". This must surely make it the first simple inorganic chemical compound to be so used, but there was nothing artificial about it. It was, and still is, a naturally occurring crystalline salt found and collected from extremely dry places. This brings the story back to South America, but now to the Andean deserts. Nitre was so valuable an export that control of the trade led to war between Chile and its neighbours Peru and Bolivia. The resolution of the conflict redrew the political map of that part of the continent. It seems that while the organic people are wrong to brand it "artificial" they are right to view having it around as a potential source of trouble!

Dependence on these naturally occurring sources of nitrogenous fertilizer all changed, thanks to the work of a German chemist, Fritz Haber. His discovery, still known as the Haber process, achieves the fusion of nitrogen gas from the air with hydrogen to produce ammonia. This is the vital start of a series of chemical reactions that can form other nitrogenous compounds. Across the world cultivators now use more than 100 million tonnes a year of fertilisers derived from the Haber process. It would be nice if Herr Haber had offered the world nothing but the blessing of more food from bigger harvests, but unfortunately there are other uses for the compounds of nitrogen: in explosives. So whilst German farmers were spreading the first factory-produced fertiliser the Kaiser's army were using the same chemistry to participate in the horrendous artillery duels of the Great War.

Haber's story has yet another twist; look again at his name. As a Jew, in 1933 he was forced from his homeland, to die a year later, in exile, at the age of 65, a one-man symbol of the extraordinary mix of the progress, benefits, war and hatred of his time.

In the strangeness that is world trade, most of the nitrogen used in British agriculture today undergoes that process in what was the Soviet Union. Our crops flourish on Russian air.

All seawater contains dissolved salts of potassium and phosphorus washed down from the surrounding land. The drying-out of ancient seas in past geological eras can leave these salts behind, rather like the common salt deposits deep under Cheshire. Much of the phosphate we use is imported from North-West African rock phosphate deposits. Potash is usually mined as sylvinite; unfortunately this mineral is a mixture of potassium chloride and common salt, so the latter has to be removed before it can be used as a fertilizer. Potassium sulphate, still known to gardeners by its nineteenth-century name "sulphate of potash", is preferred for many more-demanding glasshouse crops as it is free of chlorine; needless to say it is also more expensive.

The fertilizer industry could be thought of as playing a part in one of nature's never-ending cycles, engaged in the extraction, formulation and redistribution of deposits of these compounds. Nowadays there are a number of legitimate concerns as to how these resources are used. Should they be employed almost exclusively in the developed world because we can pay for them? Should their use on cropland be controlled to safeguard the local ecology and purity of the water supply? I understand these concerns, which are fairly presented and professionally evaluated by Professor Leigh, but not the concept of one source of a vital element being beneficial and another harmful. This is a discussion that would have been an intellectual embarrassment a century ago. Perhaps the problem is one of terminology. Does the phrase "artificial fertilizer" conjure up a dangerously unnatural image to those who have forgotten every word of their school science? The irony is that it was coined to describe the treatment of bones to speed up their release of phosphorus.

The boot on the spade became the icon of Britain's "Dig for Victory" campaign of the Second World War when those responsible recognised that digging symbolises tillage in the garden just as ploughing does on a field scale.

10 TILLAGE

Tilling the land has dominated man's efforts to grow crops, indeed many writers claim it to be the seminal act that marks the start of agriculture. The extent to which that meant clearing the whole "field" of the local vegetation and disturbing the whole surface, let alone penetrating deep into it, remains unknown, but I suspect it is likely to have been a rather local and superficial affair. Nevertheless even this must have been a huge amount of work whose benefits are still debated some eleven thousand years later, so we must take a hard look at what value all this use of energy to push, pull, stir, lift, and mix the soil really brings.

Of course the effort required to make a seedbed is a long way away from the subsoiling, deep ploughing and double-digging practised over the last two hundred years, but it is still pretty demanding if the only tool you have is a pointed stick. Unfortunately we don't have much evidence of the early style of tillage, or how things developed up till the time of the great civilisations of the Middle East four thousand years after the start of agriculture. These have left us paintings, tools and in some cases written descriptions, from which it is clear that by then the cropland was ploughed overall rather as it is today.

Over the last half-century, archaeologists in Britain have found many traces of cultivation, some as far back as the Neolithic, and they are impressive. As I mentioned in Chapter 3, the evidence comes from scratch marks in the subsoil considered to have been made by the tip of an ard. As is so often the case in archaeology, the discovery both informs and at the same time creates further questions. Assuming we are right in attributing these marks to "ploughing", it is our best insight into early tillage and shows that fields were cross-cultivated (at least once) to some 30cm below today's surface with furrows set about 30cm apart. That depth, spacing and cross-working is exactly what we would now recommend if a piece of land were to be thoroughly broken up using a chisel plough. The problem is to reconcile this with what we can regard as today's typical surface "seedbed scratchings" of an ox-drawn ard in the Third World. Archaeologists seem satisfied with the idea that these very deep ard marks were produced as part of a land "reclamation programme", to be followed henceforward by shallower between-crops tillage. Again that sequence is very good practice, and the depth could have been achieved by making several passes down the same furrow; but did our very early farmers really assart with such vigour and care?

In a modern textbook, tillage is credited with several attributes, including helping to control weeds, incorporating manure and, according to fairly recent research, releasing soluble nitrogen compounds by improving conditions for the oxygen-requiring microbes that produce them, but its prime function remains as it has always been, the making of a seedbed – a seedbed to provide the best possible conditions for the seed of annual crops to germinate and their seedlings to establish. This is the tillage that can make the difference between life and death: the life and death of the seed, and hence in some cases the life and death of the sower. Inevitably there is a down-side, with erosion heading the list, and not only in tropical countries. The 1998 *MAFF Soil Code* devotes a significant section to the problem. Foremost among the preventative techniques is good practice in both the timing and mode of tillage to minimise soil loss by wind and water.

Given its key role in the development of crop production, it is perhaps surprising to find that the need for tillage under some circumstances is still debated. Indeed there is a strong following for reducing the depth of soil disturbance. The American text *No-Tillage and Surface Tillage Agriculture* is sub-titled "The Tillage Revolution". This is a fair description for many British readers, but in fact there has been masses of research into soil conditions, fertility and yield following the application of reduced tillage in American prairie farming.

An ever decreasing depth of cultivation has gone from

mouldboard "plowing" to no-tillage sowing via the use of chisel ploughs, disc harrows, V-sweep ploughs, tandem disc harrows, seedbed conditioners, roller harrows and combination tillage-seeders. Today a significant acreage of cereals around the world is sown following minimum tillage on land still carrying the remains of the previous crop. Some is even "direct-drilled" into undisturbed stubble; isn't this where we came in eleven thousand years ago? Textbooks tell you the reasons for tillage are to make a seedbed, allow water to penetrate, aid root penetration and kill weeds. All are valid, but it is wise to add the rider "to more or less a degree dependent on local circumstances". The American authors end their book by saying that "The no-tillage revolution is well under way, but still has a long way to go," which seems a fair summary of the preceding 450 pages. In Britain the then Ministry of Agriculture, Fisheries and Food commissioned a ten-year study that produced very interesting results which were both crop- and soil-type-dependent. On heavy soils direct drilling rather than ploughing gave heavier yields of winter wheat, but winter barley and spring-sown cereals were slightly better after ploughing, particularly on light soils. To those of us brought up to think of ploughing as *the* essential activity the most impressive finding must surely be that regardless of soil or crop type the depth of cultivation never affected yields by more than 5 per cent.

Minimum tillage in horticulture usually takes us into the realms of protected cropping, where the soil is not so much subjected to limited disturbance as replaced altogether by some other kind of substrate. However, there have been horticultural systems that very closely parallel the farmer's surface tillage approach. One used to produce salad crops on a large market-garden was expounded by Rosa Dalziel O'Brien in 1956 in *Intensive Gardening*. She describes the production of traditional vegetable crops such as lettuce, cauliflower, carrots and tomatoes, but there is nothing in the slightest traditional about her soil management. Out go the plough, rotavator, spade and fork, all to be replaced by what she calls a "scrapper"– an appellation derived from the Dutch "*skraaper*" meaning "scraper" – and I would say was an onion hoe: a diminutive swan-necked draw-hoe some 17 inches (43cm) long with a blade 6 inches (15cm) wide which should not "penetrate the soil more than 3.5 to 4 inches [8 to 10cm] for any purpose". The hoe is drawn through the soil towards the user but as the instructions for its use occupy some four pages we must leave the user "kneeling or squatting on the path", where "apart from involuntary muscle reaction in the legs there should be no movement of them" as "the body movements are from the waist".

It is easy to regard such an approach to soil tillage as yet another way-out theory but the photographs of Mrs O'Brien's crops tell a different story, as do so many of her comments on soil management. She continued to expound the advantages of the system until her death in 1977. Do growers know of the O'Brien method when they complain that it's hard to scrape a living from the soil?

PROVIDING TILLAGE POWER

For millennia, tillage power came from human muscles, expended as they wielded digging hoes across the clearings around their villages. In the backwaters of the Third World it still does. Animal traction was the breakthrough that made it possible to cultivate sufficient land to grow enough staples to reduce gathering to a sideshow; there have been, and still are, a lot of different species used: ass, horse, ox, water buffalo, camel and even elephant. Early animal-assisted tillage amounted to some domesticated beast dragging some form of chisel-ended spike through the soil. Once men had achieved the no small matter of taming and training the animal they could turn their attention to converting horse power to horsepower.

Landwork is massively energy-demanding and, as those that do it will tell you, energy-sapping. The two most significant changes to have occurred in the story of tillage must surely be the harnessing of draught animals and the coming of the tractor.

Draught animals: the ox and the horse

The animal that powered agriculture, or more accurately land tillage, for over four thousand years was the ox. These wonderful, hardworking and docile beasts tilled the early fields of the Middle East, plodded their way across the farmland of Greece and Rome and followed agriculture into Europe.

No one knows exactly how much arable land, cropped and fallow, there was in medieval England but it is possible to make some estimates based on a number of separate strands of evidence. It has been reckoned that farmers kept one ox for approximately every 14 acres (5.7ha) of ploughland. In reality they worked in teams of up to eight beasts, hence in a year a full team was reckoned to be able to plough eight bovates, known as a carucate. That most meticulous of researchers Oliver Rackham considers that there were 648,000 draught oxen in the country when the Domesday census was taken in 1086. Excluding calves and heavily pregnant and suckling cows, that bovine population should have been able to plough between 9 and 10 million acres (3.6 and 4 million hectares). Another way of approaching the question is to base it on the seasonal output of a plough team. I estimate that the 81,000 ploughs recorded by the king's men would have been able to till between 8 and 9 million acres (3.2 and 3.6 million hectares). Other ways of arriving at a figure are based on the area of arable land in the common fields around villages. Of course, village landholdings varied in size, and there can be only a vague estimate of how many of the 13,400 place-names (mainly manors) occurring in Domesday qualify as villages, yet again the guestimate gives just over 8 million acres (3.2 million hectares).

All these calculations quite correctly include both productive and fallow land, as both were part of the arable area and both were ploughed. By far the lowest figure comes from calculations based on Lord Ernle's estimate that a person consumed around 7 bushels (approximately 200kg) of grain per year. The following fully deserves the contemporary designation "guestimate", but serves to remind us of several factors that must be taken into account before embarking on the maths. We must remember three things: first, between a half and a third of arable land would have been fallow; second, that some arable land was used for non-grain crops; and third that whereas gross yield may have been as much as 1.5 tonnes per hectare, demands for re-seeding, stock feed, brewing and storage losses might have reduced that to 0.4 tonne for human consumption. Using this figure, the estimated population of around 2 million would require the grain harvest from only about 1 million hectares, which with the addition of the fallow and land used for other crops makes a total arable area of at most 2.5 million hectares, roughly the equivalent of 6 million acres.

Rothamsted's Broadbalk no-fertilizer plots yield a lower average than I have used, but the same study found that yield could almost double the year following fallow, which would of course be very significant in a two-field rotation. The briefest comment comes from Richard Muir, in *Portraits of the Past*, where he comments that "a little over a third of England was devoted to ploughland"; Oliver Rackham gives the same estimate, which I make 10.6 million acres (4.3 million hectares). A table in R. J. P. Kain and H. C. Prince's book *Tithe Surveys for Historians*, based on original records, estimates the arable land at the start of the nineteenth century to be around 11 million acres (4.5 million hectares). Today, two hundred years later, DEFRA's officials give almost the same figure. The recurrence of this estimate seems to suggest that Britain's farmers and growers reckon that between 4 and 5 million hectares of land are generally suitable for arable crops. But, while I do not think it simply a coincidence that this figure keeps turning up across the centuries, we should remember that it is not always the same land that is cropped, as the histories of Salisbury Plain and the East Anglian Fens show us.

It was not until well into the nineteenth century that the horse replaced the ox on many European farms, and then still only to plough and prepare the seedbed while sowing, weeding and harvesting remained handwork. In Britain the horse's reign lasted less than two hundred years. Around 1810 Arthur Young, one of the most respected voices in British agriculture and the first Secretary to the Board of Agriculture, argued strongly for the ox, while his colleague Thomas Davis regretted their impending demise, claiming that farmers are "too fond of their stout fine horses and their men too proud of showing them, to give them up for oxen". More impartial observers credit the ox with being cheaper to keep, and that it pulled more steadily and was less liable to disease. Not only that, but when slaughtered its hide and flesh were more valuable. The horse had only one card but it was the ace of trumps: speed of working. And it won the day – eventually; so much so that today horses alone have become the symbol of animal power on the land.

Records from one mixed farm in southern Britain show them keeping 16 "plough horses" to cultivate some 300 acres (120ha), that's just under 19 acres (7.7ha) per horse, about typical for heavy land. Indeed the farming statistics for 1900 show arable land to be some 7 million acres (2.8 million hectares) and a farm horse population of 1 million. Its not surprising that, as one authority puts it, "The impact of these beasts of burden was not limited to their work in arable fields; horse maintenance required a quarter of our arable farm acreage." Add to this the working horse's need for around a further 2ha for grazing, and winter hay and no wonder that the disappearance of the two or even four hungry mouths at the front of those ploughs had a significant impact on the appearance of the countryside. Horsepower was not just a quaint expression for measuring work-rate; in its literal sense it was the energy source for carting, tillage and harvest. Barrie Trinder and Jeff Cox's analysis of the probate inventories of over 200 Shropshire farmers living between 1660 and 1750 gives us another angle on just how important the horse was even at that time. Time and again horses and their tack were the most valuable possession on the arable side of the farm, typically worth several times the total value of all the very basic cultivation equipment they pulled.

Steam power

Our first attempts to mechanise land work were truly awesome. Steam power in the second half of the nineteen century came in large containers. After several somewhat unrealistic patents had failed, "traction engines", weighing in at some 15 to 20 tonnes, reached the headlands of the largest fields of a handful of the most progressive farmers. The first successful design was patented in 1836 by the Devonian John Heathcote, a man of many and varied parts being also a lace manufacturer and MP. From then on, burning a tonne of coal a day and using 200 gallons of water per acre (2160 litres per hectare), via pulleys, drums and very long lengths of steel hawser, these anchored leviathans pulled ploughs back and forth across the fields. The early enthusiasts had designed tillage equipment to be towed across the land behind these monsters whose successors, pulling ten-furrow ploughs, played a significant role in opening up the prairies to arable farming. But on British farms their weight was against them; even if they avoided bogging down they damaged soil structure and destroyed land drains. By the 1860s John Fowler, perhaps the greatest name in traction engines, had developed a method that used only one engine that pulled a cable to which the plough was attached. The cable stretched back and forth across the field turned on the headland opposite the engine with the aid of a large pulley wheel mounted on a "cable anchor cart". Confined to the headlands, their power ensured that plough depth was no problem to them, but it could be to the farmer months later when the exposed subsoil would not break down to a seedbed. Soon routine ploughing on most soils returned to more or less its old depth. Steam cultivation was at its peak around the turn of the century, with many hundreds of these engines at work in Britain tilling more than 1 million acres (400,000ha) of land.

As in the factories and on the roads, the early years of the twentieth century saw the internal-combustion engine oust steam on the land; steam's last toehold in agriculture came from specifically designed thrashing engines that saw service well into the Second World War.

The tractor
This book never set out to be the story of the development of the tractor, and if it had it should have found itself another author, but you can't explore the story of cultivation without reference to its single most influential invention. The first tractor was made in the USA in 1889; by 1900 they were using 10,000 and we had 50! Britain continued to lag behind; by 1920 the score stood at around 20,000, yet in 1923 Bond was still able to write in his scholarly book *Farm Implements and Machinery* that "the horse is the motor or prime mover in most farm operations". However in the next decade the number of working horses on British farms fell by 100,000. By 1939 there were 50,000 tractors, but three years later under the impetus of war it had shot up to 120,000; what was even more of a shock to the old school was that most were driven by land-girls!

Unlike the steam engines, these early designs pulled or carried tillage tools onto the field and the idea of a prime-mover with attached but changeable kit was born, or with due respect to generations of draught animals, reborn. The appearance of the tractor changed neither the tasks nor for a long time the tools that did them; what changed was the amount of power available. Of course, the early models make our generation wet themselves – young farmers through laughter, health and safety officers through sheer terror.

One measure of the tractor's significance must surely be the number of histories of its introduction and development that have been written in virtually every language used in the developed world. The derivation of the word "tractor", first used in 1856 to describe a steam-driven traction engine, reminds us that the first requirement of any land-working machine was, and still is, its ability to pull. To do that it must grip the land but not sink under its own weight.

The early machines simply pulled trailed equipment, much of it originally designed to go behind horses. Joining tractor and tool by more sophisticated and direct means had to wait nearly forty years for the development of tractor-mounted hydraulics and the three-point linkage, which was devised and developed by Harry Ferguson in the 1930s but did not become commonplace until after the Second World War. The adoption of hydraulics made tractor and tool act as one, and allowed the operator to lift the tool clear of the land when turning, or travelling on the road. Anyone wishing to be convinced that the mechanisation of cultivation has become a science should read Professor Brian Witney's book *Choosing and Using Farm Machines*; behind that innocent title hide some formidable equations and a remarkable insight into our scientific understanding of the relationship between the machines and tools of cultivation and a plant's environment. It is a relationship that ranges from the difference in a wheel's traction on heavy and light land to the effect of speed when ploughing on soil structure or the link between spray droplet size and leaf coverage.

As the twentieth century progressed the engineering got cleverer, the power greater, the control more fingertip, and the doable tasks more numerous. I suppose the moment the plough-boy could sit down his life got easier, but anyone who has spent a day winter ploughing on a pre-1950 tractor is very unlikely to describe it as a luxury cruise. We should remember that the professional tractor-driver (and the Second World War land-girl) was doing that for months at a time. Hard work or not, the impact on farming and the very pattern of the landscape was dramatic.

The power of the modern tractor, all 160hp (120kW) of it, allows more to be pulled. The combination of broader seed-drills, wider spray-booms, more furrows on the plough and faster speed across the field has resulted in a huge increase in output per unit time. This has allowed folk, for the first time in the history of cultivation in the temperate parts of the world, to seize the moment and do the job both when the calendar or the crop tells them it is time and when soil and weather conditions are reasonable. Agricultural scientists have worked out an optimum "establishment date" for most of the important crops and calculated the yield loss if a grower is either early or late. For example, a fortnight's delay in planting maincrop potatoes can reduce the harvest by around a tonne per hectare. The turn-round from harvest to autumn seedbed can be as little as a few days, with one tractor ploughing as much in a day as ten teams of horses.

In 1930 there were still over a million workhorses on British farms, but virtually all would go over the following thirty years. Horses may have been the farm animal whose numbers have been most affected by all this mechanisation, but they are not the only one. Landworkers, once almost synonymous with countryfolk, are now almost an endangered species. In round figures the number of people engaged full-time in agriculture and commercial horticulture has gone from 1,000,000 to 250,000 in my lifetime, with a reduction of similar proportions in part-time workers. Just as significant has been the escalation and change of skills required following mechanisation. Photographs are a powerful way of bringing such statistics to life and I have found none more so than those used to illustrate the "state of the art" in the 1946 third, revised edition of Dr H. I. Moore's textbook *Crops and Cropping*. There are the horses pulling a wooden-framed plough. And there are the workers in their droves like people from another age: there are 7 in one field hand-pulling flax; in other pictures the same number are similarly engaged in harvesting overwintered carrots into wicker baskets and there are 36 pea-pickers in one field. In other photographs solitary labourers are spreading farmyard manure, lime and fertilisers by hand, while 2 are pulling a bag soaked in paraffin across a huge field to control flea-beetle. Perhaps most amazing of all to today's young farmers is the picture of 7 chaps *on their knees* crawling across the East Anglican flatlands singling beet.

When I started work the chances were that if a landworker had soiled clothes at the end of a working day it was due to just that: soil. Now the "s" has gone! The skilled landworker's dungarees are indistinguishable from the garage mechanic's.

In recent years a whole bunch of refinements have taken place on the tractor and its equipment, that together might be described as providing control and accuracy. There are some wonderful bits of kit, most of which are computer-based; they allow a driver to set output rates and monitor the function of such devices as sprayers, fertilizer distributors and seed-drills. Today's tractors monitor and inform their drivers to a level not far short of that found in racing cars. The cabbage you brought today was probably planted by a computer-controlled hydraulic marvel and your sprouts harvested by something the length of a London bus.

The working life of a horse and a tractor is not very different, but the difference in capital investment is huge, with tractors costing between £50,000 and £100,000 and the precision equipment they use ranging from £5000 to £20,000 an item. That's the cost to a grower, but should the land have to pay a price as well? There are some that would give an emphatic NO. There are real concerns about damage to the physical nature of the soil. It is those peds and crumbs and bulk density again. Soil, as no doubt you are beginning to appreciate, is fragile stuff. The tractor's weight of some 8 tonnes and the vibration from all its moving parts combines to damage soil structure and cause compaction. As we know, that is very bad news for both drainage and roots. Soil scientists are concerned. The matter is being looked into, as they say.

The latest tractor designs now supersede their predecessors at ever increasing rates. Today's models provide the driver with a stereo sound system, heating and a degree of soundproofing. On the technical side they have 16 forward gears and several for reverse, with an ability to pick up equipment without leaving the cab. Having a way of relating forward speed to tool speed ensures that the quality of the work is not jeopardised by having to drive at a constant speed regardless of local conditions.

The horticultural tractor or rather its equipment has had as much impact on field-scale horticulture as larger tractors have had on agriculture. Today's horticultural tractor is simply a smaller addition of its big brother out on the cereal farmer's broad acres. Fifty years ago things were very different; horticulture was deemed to need only two wheels, not four. To say that you walked behind these machines would be a gross simplification, From start to finish you wrestled with them in near-mortal combat for the supremacy of man over machine. As ever in such conflicts, collateral damage claimed its victims in the form of crop plants mangled beneath wheel, tool or foot as the wretched machine took off across the field. Some horticultural holdings such as those along the Tamar Valley were, and still are, too steep for tractors to work. Local growers came up with an ingenious do-it-yourself solution whose design owed much to the days of steam power. The description in the book *Sovereigns, Madams and Double Whites* says it all:

> An old car was stripped down and a wooden axle attached to the drive from the engine. A wire rope was connected to the axle going down to the bottom of the plot where a plough or earth scoop was attached to it. The wife usually drove the engine while the husband ploughed up-hill. Earth was brought back up to the top again in the scoop.

Today the basic tillage tasks facing the horticulturist remain the same, but there is a range of specialist kit mounted on four dependable wheels. Most of it has two characteristics in common: precision, and high cost!

There are drills that space the seed at the required distance apart in the rows. There are transplanters that position seedlings at the required spacing; in one operation they make the hole, backfill, and firm the soil around the roots. As the crops grow, yet more precision equipment is employed to weed and spray. Finally the largest and often most expensive machine appears at the field gate, the specialist harvester. Come to think of it, the field gate has long since disappeared on most of these holdings simply to make room for just this kind of kit. Of course all this equipment needs understanding, calibrating, driving and servicing; it can still go wrong and it does.

Forestry, as I have said before, is a world of critical minimum inputs. Foresters have recently developed some amazing harvesting equipment, but their in-crop cultivation consists mainly of cutting and spraying. This is a world of knapsack sprayers, slashers and chainsaws. It is a form of applied Darwinism, with the forester playing the part of nature in the phrase "natural selection".

Forestry tillage is rather akin to land reclamation, but in the case of established forestry it comes into play between crops following clear felling, rather than when land is being brought into production. Throughout the world trees get the short straw when it comes to TLC. To start with, as a crop they have been driven into the toughest sites and the worst topsoils, if any!

Pre-planting tillage usually focuses on the big "critical" issues, the life-and-death problems of waterlogging and compaction. Machines get involved to smash up woody weeds and the debris of the previous vegetation, subsoil, and throw up ridges so that new transplants have better soil and drainage. Typically, huge crawler-tractors pull toolbars armed with wing-tined rippers capable of penetrating to around a metre. These machines are not for the fainthearted or the orchid collector. The fact that the site still looks like a First World War battle field when the job's done may dismay that glasshouse grower with his digging machine, but it gladdens the heart of a forester and it seems to equally please oak and sitka spruce – everyone to their own.

Reclamation has produced some strange episodes and some equally remarkable machines. The Second World War provided the setting for both, but back in 1932 our old friends John Fowler & Co. (Leeds) Ltd produced one of the stars, the Gyrotiller. Never ones for miniaturisation, they mounted their massive tillage machine on its own half-track prime-mover; the business end consisted of two horizontal rotating discs, each fitted with four massive tines. As the machine moved forward it literally stirred the top half metre of the field into huge clods. It came into its own spearheading the wartime drive to bring more land into food production, a story told so well by Alan Bloom – including the episode when a huge area of Fen reeds was set on fire. Some in Cambridge with vivid imaginations but a limited grasp of geography thought the smoke came from the Battle of Dunkerque.

The next generation of tractors, already under development, will use ground positioning satellite (GPS) monitoring to "know" exactly where they are in the field. Following a crop inspection that provides appropriate coordinates, they will use this knowledge to alter their workrate. Nutrient-deficient patches of "hungry" land will get extra fertiliser and only weedy or diseased areas will be sprayed. Even driverless ploughing based on stored electronic memory of how best to set out the field is said to be on the cards.

THE TOOLS OF TILLAGE
The early hand-tools
Viewed from an airliner, agriculture is seen to be truly a matter of scratching a living. What scratches those faint marks on the surface of the earth are the tillage tools designed to disturb the soil, to loosen it up, to lift and invert it. The equipment to do this job, first by human muscles then animal power and finally by

machines, ultimately evolved into today's ploughs, harrows, rotavators, spades and forks.

The interesting question is: What was the seminal tool? Many writers opt for the digging stick. This ancient implement, excellent for excavating postholes, almost certainly started its "agricultural" life not in tillage but in gathering. It was a digging-up stick used for harvesting wild roots long before we started to grow crops. If the evidence from the recent past by anthropologists is to be believed, those used for excavating soil from a planting pit or for breaking new ground were pointed poles, probably the height of a man and made of a heavy dense wood, whereas smaller, lighter designs were used to weed or maintain a tilth on arable land. Some archaeologists consider that the digging stick was the only tillage tool for several millennia before it evolved into either the spade or the digging hoe. If that was the case, I suspect that it applies only in those cultures that domesticated tuber and root crops. At its most basic their tillage amounted to little more than harvesting the perennating [g] organs and putting a few back before filling in the hole. In contrast to this very casual approach, some cultures such as the Melanesian people of the Trobriand Islands situated to the east of New Guinea still used only digging sticks to cultivate their yam and taro gardens, albeit that they had many highly developed horticultural skills such as crop spacing, weeding, staking and training. Bronislaw Malinowski points out that the sticks were so basic that they were not saved from day to day, but that a fresh one was gathered and sharpened each time a villager went to work. Other anthropologists have observed the use of digging sticks with somewhat flattened ends, giving them something of the form and function of a spade, perhaps somewhere such a development was indeed its origin.

Although in living memory "digging" sticks have been used as dibbers for sowing seed, I find it an unlikely tool with which to till well over a hectare, the area of land necessary to support a family, even when it received its "updates" in the form of a bone or stone tip and a weight part way up the haft, made from a stone with a hole in it. As I have suggested earlier, after a lifetime of working the land I find it easier to imagine the start of crop production without tillage. It is when cultivation spreads both beyond the area of summer drought and onto heavier soils that pre-sowing tillage becomes a necessity. On these sites the cleared harvest would reveal a rather compact, moist soil supporting a strong weed growth probably dominated by native grasses. Sowing the next crop onto such a field would be disastrous; by some means the soil surface has to be loosened to form a tilth and the majority of the weeds removed. A tillage tool capable of doing this over a sufficient area of land to make cereal growing worthwhile became essential to the spread of a grain-based agriculture. Archaeologists consider that tool was the digging hoe. It most certainly has been, and continues to be, used for just such work when fitted with an iron blade. What little we know of such tools in their wooden or bone form before the use of iron suggests that the energy and time required would hardly accelerate the adoption of this revolutionary form of self-sufficiency. There are however output figures for people using iron-bladed digging hoes in very traditional forms of arable cultivation. Although it would be foolish to extrapolate too closely from twentieth-century Tanzania to the spread of agriculture in the Middle East, it has been observed that it takes some 400 hours of hoe "digging" to cultivate a hectare of land. In this study each worker managed to cover about 0.7ha in a tillage season of some ten weeks. If the development of such tools took place early in the story of arable farming then we had better greatly reduce the "Iron Age" yields reported from the Butser Ancient Farm experiment; nevertheless, seven tenths of a hectare might well have produced enough grain to feed three people the year round.

Dr A. Steensberg of the University of Copenhagen writes of flattened wooden implements he terms "paddle spades" found associated with regionally early cultivation sites. These look to me like really serviceable tools that could act as primitive spades. He goes on to describe what could be a development from such a tool, a wooden shovel with an "ace of spades"-like design not unlike today's Cornish shovel. Some of these have been found with two holes through the upper part of the blade. It is believed that this served to attach the spade to a pulling rope, creating what he describes as a "rope traction ard": now we are getting somewhere! Nevertheless, it is important to point out that this tantalising sequence of tools has not been found in any one area, let alone a single site.

Peter Reynolds, of Butser Ancient Farm fame, had a most attractive alternative or perhaps addition to this evolutionary sequence. He used, to very good effect, what he called a "sowing stick". When drawn through previously tilled soil this single-pronged "hoe", formed from the natural shape of a pole with a side branch, both loosens tilth and makes a seed-drill. Could it be that row cultivation preceded the broadcasting of seed? I doubt it, although I think the "sowing stick" could well have found a really valuable use in European Iron Age crop husbandry. Of one thing we can be certain: advances in the design of the tools in day-to-day use did not take place simultaneously across the farming world. Even today we can find virtually every form of tool still in use, from those crudely fashioned from a log, a faggot or an appropriately shaped local tree through those forged by the village blacksmith to factory products of extreme sophistication and complexity.

Returning to the very beginning, Marek Zvelebil puts forward an alternative to the digging stick which to me offers a more plausible approach for seed raised crops. He writes that "In the archaeological record of hunter-gatherer Europe, we can find tools which have clearly been used for digging the soil. These include wooden hoes and mattocks." He then goes on to suggest that many of the more common antler implements may well have had the same use. Such finds from the pre-agrarian Mesolithic Age remind us that people dug before they grew crops. If we follow that line to its logical conclusion, soil tillage can be thought of as a technology transfer that required neither the invention of new tools nor the advent of metalworking. There is however a snag – it depends on what you mean by "digging". These tools were far better for excavating than for cultivating large areas of surface soil.

The division between spade and digging hoe is so clear that archaeologists speak of there being two cultures. We could think of them as the prodders and the swingers. The former uses muscles in both arms and legs, and can call upon the principle of the lever. The latter swing the tool down from arms extended above their heads using the kinetic energy of the mass of the implement to penetrate the soil with a pickaxe-like action. Both are hard work! The hoe is particularly so if you set out to dig a spit deep; however, cereals are now being successfully sown after breaking up a few centimetres of soil. Maybe we are returning to the form of tillage that saw us through the first millennia of our farming history. Perhaps it is because the British long ago ceased to use such tools to till the land that we call them "hoes", a term that is bound to confuse digging and weeding. The Romans gave the various designs separate names: "*dolabra*", "*marra*", "*ligo*", "*ascia-rastrum*" with blade and prongs, and the "*bidens*" with just the two prongs.

Some designs such as the bidens seem most likely to have been used to break down clods to produce a tilth. Another group are virtually identical to a still popular digging implement with an extremely long lineage, known in parts of West Africa as a "*daba*". In its many forms it remained the basic tillage tool until well into the twentieth century, when for larger scale cultivation, the ubiquitous spread of western technology replaced it with the modern plough. We should not however belittle either the spade or the digging hoe. Together they have, for thousands of years, sustained millions of people spread round the world in various cultures, and they still do.

The ard and the plough
Jacob Bronowski called the plough "the most powerful invention in all agriculture"; indeed it is, yet as we have seen there is still debate as to its value. One thing is however very clear, neither the prodders or the swingers won control of the broad acres; that went to the draggers, who invented the ard that evolved into the plough. One way to begin to appreciate the significance of this tool is by the number of words it has generated. Within the United Kingdom there are not far short of one hundred describing just the plough and ploughing. There are nouns that put a name to every object no matter how small, verbs that describe each and every action and, most revealing of all, the adjectives and adverbs that allow the speaker to describe and criticise the nature and quality of the finished task, maybe when looking over the neighbour's hedge!

Here are seven:

Bulk – an unploughed strip of land or ridge left to mark the boundary between fields.

Beam – the main body of a plough to which all other parts are attached.

Stilts – the handles of a horse-drawn plough.

Mouldboard – the curved metal plate fixed behind the plough shear which turns over the slice of soil cut from the furrow.

Headland – the strip bordering a field where the plough is

turned between runs; also known as a "hedrig" or "forracre"!

Gathering – a method of setting out a field so that already ploughed land is circled in a clockwise direction.

Casting – the mirror image of gathering, in which the ploughed land is circled in an anti-clockwise direction.

It seems we know little of the early origin of the ard, the precursor of the plough, but if, as is commonly stated in the archaeological literature, the digging hoe provided the wherewithal for the idea of "dragging" then "the big moment" came when a cultivator pointed it the other way!

You stand on your finished work when you swing a digging hoe. Having swung it you then pull it towards you to break off a bit more of the face of the uncultivated land. In even the earliest illustrations I have seen, that action was helped by the blade being angled towards the user.

Now for the about-turn. Imagine starting a fresh patch of land; go through the same swinging action but, with the hoe blade embedded in the soil, pull the tool towards you across the undisturbed area. If you were strong enough, and if the hoe blade was not too broad and the soil not too hard, you would draw the start of a furrow. Of course, pulling or pushing something through the surface layer of soil is not easy – go into the garden and try! It is however a lot less exhausting to undermine a weed cover than to have to chop through it with every stroke of a hoe. It is also much less work the next time around; then it is like using a Dutch hoe in a well-managed vegetable garden. If the "draggers" drew the first furrows by their own muscle power then I believe that we have yet another reason for looking for the birthplace of tillage somewhere where there is a very light sandy soil and a distinct dry season to burn off the vegetation.

The most primitive ploughs we have any detailed knowledge of were in use thousands of years after the origin of cultivation but before farming reached most of Europe. "Ards" are first glimpsed in prehistoric cave paintings; then they appear as both graphic representations and as funerary offerings revealed by archaeological digs in the Middle East. They are made of wood, some, based on nothing more than a carefully selected tree branch configuration, being no more difficult to fashion than a digging hoe. Others were of a more demanding construction requiring several pieces of wood to be joined. Regardless of design they were no longer powered by human muscle but by draught animals, whose domestication surely ranks alongside cultivation as the second great achievement of early agriculture. We do not know for certain that these tools travelled across Europe at the same rate as the crop seeds that introduced agriculture, and it is very probable that some communities tilled by the hoe while others used a form of ard. We do know however that ards were in use across Northern Europe and in Britain some 3000 years ago and the remains of stone shares found on Orkney and Shetland suggest they were in use on those northern islands throughout the first millennium BC. It seems that field-scale cultivation might well have arrived in Britain already equipped with what we may call its essential tillage tool.

Though perhaps first dragged or pushed by humans, the ard comes first to our knowledge when pulled by domesticated animals, when even in its primitive form it has been estimated to have speeded up seedbed preparation tillage tenfold compared with the digging hoe. The development of the ard required the invention of both the tool itself and a harness to join the animal to it. If you try using an animal-powered digging hoe it soon becomes apparent that to get it to travel through the soil at a constant depth whilst being pulled along, handle and blade must be at the correct angle. Too shallow and it rises to the surface, too steep and it digs down like an anchor.

It is clear that the digging hoe needed to develop a fair bit before it could be usefully harnessed to any animal. That development produced the ard; at first still made totally of wood, it was nevertheless well along the road to becoming a plough. Its beam formed the body of the tool and carried attachments for pulling; to the rear the stilt formed the handles by which it could be controlled and the sole [g] made a primitive share whose stone tips have survived. In time, beam, stilt and sole became the three essential parts of the plough: the beam, shafts and share. But it is not only as the plough's precursor that this primitive-looking tool deserves its place in the story of cultivation. It was the tool by which the Old World civilisations fed themselves for thousands of years. Recent reconstructions demonstrate that even in its early form it could very effectively disturb the soil quite deeply enough to produce a seedbed, particularly if the field is cross-cultivated. Criss-cross ard scratch marks in subsoil layers exposed during archaeological digs have been dated to around 3000 BC.

Engineers can now write you an equation for the calculation of the optimum angles between those three major parts of the plough and the forces involved. Although the first written attempt to do this seems to have been by James Black in 1779, the relationship between them must first have been worked out by trial and error while hanging onto one or other of those none-too-cooperative four-legged power sources.

The ard evolved into the plough within the civilisations of the Middle East and the Mediterranean basin. It is generally accepted that the Romans developed the sole into the two soil-cutting tools that above all others define the plough: the coulter [g] that slices vertically through the soil, followed by the chisel-like share whose wearing parts were protected by metal cladding. The mouldboard in its earliest form was a simple plate angled behind the share, its job being to create an open furrow by deflecting to one side most of the soil loosened by the shear. The Romans took ploughing very seriously. It is virtually the first operation Columella deals with in his major work, *On Agriculture*. He starts with the qualities to look for when hiring staff, or in his case buying a slave:

> In the case of the ploughman, intelligence, though necessary, is still not sufficient unless bigness of voice and in bearing makes him formidable to the cattle. Yet he should temper his strength with gentleness ... so that the oxen may obey his commands.

Columella goes on to say that strength and height are of the greatest importance

> both for the reason I have just given and because in the work of the farm there is no task less tiring to a tall man; for in ploughing he stands almost erect and rests his weight on the plough-handle.

Exactly with whom and when early mouldboard ploughs reached Britain is unclear. Historians seem as interested in tracing the appearance of the wheeled plough, the Gauls' *"caruca"* (a name with clear links to the ploughland measure a carucate). Its impact on cultivation is often attributed to the depth of tillage it could achieve but, although important, is not I think, so significant as its mouldboard. To start with, the mouldboard was no more than a flat plank of wood that did no more than shove soil to one side, produce a distinct furrow and cover over some of the superficial weed growth. Most archaeological opinion seems divided as to whether the honour of introducing the mouldboard should go to the Celts or to the Belgae. Its arrival before the Romans was just as well, as their *aratrum* plough was designed for the light land they favoured for cropping at home while our most fertile soils tend to be heavy with a high clay content, added to which, to produce a good seedbed, they have to be cultivated in the autumn and winter when they are wet and even more intractable.

Christopher Taylor in his book *Fields in the English Landscape* seems to champion a minority view that the mouldboard plough might have been a Roman introduction from their conquests in mainland Europe. Whoever deserves the credit, they seem to have become the victim of some early brand piracy, as nowadays it is usually referred to as the Saxon heavy plough, and indeed it was in general use in Saxon times, well before the Norman Conquest. Not only is its arrival in Britain hard to date, but its evolution over some six hundred years before, during and after Roman times, is extremely sketchy. As Taylor points out, "No ploughs of definite Saxon date are known from the UK."

Most writers tell us that Romano-British farmers used the "simple" mouldboard plough such as I mentioned above, but G. E. Fussell describes early medieval ploughs as still being "a simple wedge hauled by means of a beam or pole fastened to its heel". Simple they may have been, but he goes on to claim that this basic design survived alongside later improvements and "was still in use a thousand years later". It would seem that the mouldboard let alone its development we will met later was very slow to reach every British farmyard. Had Fussell looked a little further afield he would have found his "simple wedge plough" still unchanged and in everyday use well into the middle years of the twentieth century. My hero, the Russian agricultural scientist Nicolay Vavilov, photographed three, one each from Iran, Crete and Sicily, that would grace any museum of medieval if not late Iron Age life.

But the ard's lineage does not end there; the Channel 4 television evening news for 8 March 2006 showed villagers in Iran making an all-wood "simple wedge plough" of precisely the same design. Bizarrely, their main concessions to modernity seemed to be the use of an electric drill and a coat of varnish!

In the Middle Ages ploughs were typically pulled by anything between 4 and 12 oxen. From the noses of the first beasts to the feet of the ploughman that could be as much as some twenty metres. We are told that ploughmen curved the ends of their furlongs to help in turning round on the headland. Unfortunately our mentors don't explain how to overcome the disadvantage of the furrow now veering the "wrong" way on your return. Large ox teams were guided by a boy who controlled them, not by the crack of a whip but, as many contemporary illustrations show, by a dig in the ribs from a wand 5.5 yards (5m) long – the rod, pole or perch of land measurement. Later, mixed teams of horse and ox reduced the number of animals but maintained productivity, with 4 oxen and 2 horses ploughing an acre (0.4ha) a day.

John Fitzherbert of Norbury is often credited with writing the first farming manual in English dated 1523. *The Boke of Husbandry* puts ploughing at the top of his list of required skills for any farmer and the plough as the farm's "moste necessaryest instrumente". The key to a good seedbed and effective "wede" control was, he claimed, to "plowe a brode forowe and a deep so that he turne it cleane and lay it flat". He kept "sturrynge" his fallow by ploughing in spring, midsummer and again in August, this time leaving ridges ready for the autumn sowing of wheat. No wonder he rated the ploughman's craft so highly.

Notwithstanding the survival of its basic shape, the heavy plough evolved into many local variants, often named after their place of origin. Regional patriotism supported the Hertfordshire, Norfolk, Suffolk and Kentish designs. Over the course of the eighteenth and nineteenth centuries these more sophisticated tools emerged. They had a wheel, and the all-important mouldboard now took on the form of a helix. The twist on its face turns the lifted sod and inverts it enough to bury surface weeds and trash. This capability of partly inverting the undercut slice of soil as it falls into the previously formed furrow reveals a part of the soil profile with a good crumb structure, capable of very quickly weathering down to a fine tilth suitable for next season's seedbed. The awards given to designers and manufactures by the Society of Arts and various agricultural societies no doubt encouraged the later stages of these improvements.

The story of the eighteenth-century rush of new shapes of plough has within it an all too familiar cameo of British social history. Our hero is one James Small; as G. E. Fussell says, he was "the first ploughwright who tried to lay down the principles of plough design in as scientific a manner as the mechanical knowledge of his day allowed". His approach to the optimum shape of the mouldboard embraced mathematical theory and practical experimentation, resulting in both a *Treatise of Ploughs and Wheel Carriages* and the manufacture of the real thing. Then the attacks from the establishment came, deriding poor Small's efforts because as a humble wheelwright he lacked a formal education. Happily it is self-taught Small and not his detractors that are remembered in the history of British farming.

Ploughing is so dominant a part of cultivation that it is not surprising that the development of the plough is so well recorded. But among all the contributors one memorable name stands out, and then more for his patrons than his engineering. In an age of innovation few inventors could have had the privilege of showing off their brainchild at a private audience with Queen Victoria and Prince Albert, but it happened to Theophilus Smith and his plough. Back home in Norfolk among his God-fearing fellow-Baptists, he told how he had "testified before his sovereign" that its design came to him as a result of prayer. Apparently the Dissenter and the Defender of the Faith hit it off, and her Consort, with his usual enthusiasm for progress, lent his name to the "Patent Albert" plough.

At the start of the twentieth century a new name comes to the fore and one whose company was long to remain pre-eminent in the manufacture of farm equipment; in 1903 Robert Ransome patented the cast-iron self-sharpening ploughshare.

The mouldboard plough so dominates the field in Britain that other designs hardly get a look-in. Starting with the most complex, one might say improbable, there is the digging machine. The idea can be traced back to the days of steam power, but the first designs in the form we know today date from the 1960s. This is a piece of equipment that pushes a series of spade blades into the soil one at a time, then lifts and turns each sod in a very similar action to that of a person with a spade. It is mostly used in horticulture, including glasshouses. According to its devotees, although slow it does a better job than a mouldboard plough and is kinder to the soil structure. Not only that, but the finished job looks like hand-digging. Could it be that some growers still hanker after the old skills?

In contrast there is the disc plough, a go-anywhere design whose business end is a large, dished, circular steel plate that cuts and turns the land. Part of its go-anywhere quality comes from its ability to ride over buried obstacles like rocks or large roots, whereas the mouldboard ploughshare gets stuck. The Third World and forestry tend to favour disc ploughs – not, I hasten to add to my sylvicultural friends, that I would ever confuse the two.

As someone who has had rather a lot to do with development sites, my favourite piece of kit for busting up compacted land is the chisel plough. It consists of between three and five very robust tines mounted on a frame; given a powerful enough tractor, these can shatter soil along its naturally occurring fracture lines to a depth of over 60cm and dependent on their design produce varying degrees of surface disturbance.

Ploughing became the quintessential husbandry activity of an importance far beyond all other forms of tillage, and the ploughman emerged as a named and respected craftsman within the farming fraternity. His skills not only produced the basis of soil conditions for the following crop, but gave us one of the most enduring features in the countryside, the 10-metre- (11-yard-) wide ridge-and-furrow undulations mentioned in Chapter 1. There is clearly a difference of opinion as to how the ploughman produced these. We know they used single-furrow mouldboard ploughs that therefore always cast the soil in the same direction – ridge to the right, furrow to the left. With this design of plough they could have done it by ploughing up and down the field in a series of 5-metre-wide, back-to-back strips. Over time, and the practice continued for more than three hundred years, it would produce the 10m-wide and up to 1m-deep corrugations we can still find today. The problem with that approach is that at the end of the furrow they would have had to turn their 16m-long span of eight oxen plus plough back on itself. We know that to prevent such gymnastics ploughman have for centuries "set out" the field into a series of blocks known as "lands" before starting to plough. I suspect that their medieval forebears might well have done the same.

Freed from the strange conventions of medieval land tenure, we no longer have to operate within the stricture of the strip. But at least up to the use of the modern tractor, a ploughman often set out a field into a number of lands by ploughing a series of marker furrows known as "ridges" or "rigs". The dimensions he worked to remained based on those medieval measurements the rod and the chain. A land was 11m wide, or one rod (5m) to each side of the rig; they were ploughed in sequence to reduce the time lost turning on the headlands.

Before we leave the facts, figures and dimensions of ploughing with animal power, armchair yearners after yesteryear's countryside please note that the acre (0.4ha) a day mentioned earlier required steering plough and team (both with minds of their own!) while walking along some twelve miles of open furrow. As for the animals, they had to lift some 800 tonnes of soil and invert it; today a tractor pulling a four-furrow plough does the same area in just over half an hour.

Although autumn ploughing comes at the end of the farming year, it is really the first act of the new season. As the stubble fields of set-aside now remind us, you certainly don't do it unless you intend to grow a crop the following year.

Now we come to yet another ploughing mystery. The importance of the task is evident by the church celebrating Plough Sunday, blessing the plough and offering "the work of the countryside to the service of God". My difficulty is that this takes place on the first Sunday after Epiphany, that is at the end of the twelve days of the Christmas festival at a time when the soil might well be frozen solid. Some books tell us that this was a blessing at the start of the ploughing season, yet there are lots of references to autumn ploughing when weather and soil were at their most favourable and the following frosts could produce tilth. Michael Wood, quoting from a contemporary text on Saxon labour services to the lord of the manor, gives the example of a villein who "from the time when they first plough until Martinmas" (11 November) must plough one acre (0.4ha) of his lord's land each week. Clearly this lord knew about the advantages of autumn cultivation. We know they ploughed a second and even a third time just before the spring sowing of barley between Hoketide and Pentecost, but that's weeks later, well into the spring. One reliable source, among others, speaks of "resuming ploughing to finish any outstanding work, albeit that the ideal was to finish ploughing before the end of the year".

There is another reason for delaying at least some cultivation, and that is to do with the role of post-harvest fallow in feeding stock. In a three-field rotation, fallow started at the harvest of the second crop, and we can be confident that by autumn the stubble would have had a fair covering of "weeds" and, no doubt, seedlings from seed of the previous crop lost at harvest. That mixed vegetation supplied some sorely needed end-of-season grazing, and it had a name: "Michaelmas shack". In their study of the open-field system at Laxton in Northamptonshire, the Orwins provide the data that allows me to produce the following summary of the management of a three-field system:

Year one: Wheat – Harvested in late summer; then the stubble "shack" grazed until mid October.

Year two: Spring corn – Autumn: ploughing following "shack"; seedbed prepared and sown with spring corn. Late summer: harvest; then the "shack" grazed until late November.

Year three: Ploughed fallow – First ploughed soon after stock removed, further tillage to control weeds. Early autumn: seedbed prepared and wheat sown.

We know that fallow was tilled throughout the growing season, presumably to try to clean the land of weeds, but as the Orwins have shown, the first ploughing was delayed until the stock had taken advantage of this free grazing, and the land of their manure.

It is clear however that none of this insight into the medieval farming year helps to explain the turn-of-the-year date for Plough Sunday, but that is when the Church gave its blessing to the task (and one hopes the men and animals who did it). A more secular activity followed the next day, Plough Monday no less, when gangs of farm workers, variously known as "plough bullocks", "jacks" or "stots", decorated with horse ribbons, rosettes and brasses, pulled ploughs round villages. Accompanied by Morris Men, "the fool" and cross-dressing "Bessy", they called for alms and threatened to plough up the dirt road in front of any defaulter's house. An early form of rural trick or treat, but before the Reformation at least some of the money went towards the maintenance of the continuously burning Plough Light placed before the Ploughman's Guild altar in the parish church.

Another ploughman's escape from the solitude of the furrow, and one still with us, is the ploughing match. Introduced in the middle years of the nineteenth century, it could, according to one writer, "do more towards correcting the [then current] imperfect and expensive system of ploughing than all the advice that could be given" – and to a lot of people, if the Liverpool Agricultural Society's 1839 attendance figure of 3000 was anywhere near typical. Ploughing matches succeeded in improving standards of work; but I think Allen Ransome went a bit too far in claiming that a match "extends a beneficial influence to each class of the community, and leads to that unity of feeling in a common cause, which is one of the best securities for the common good order of a neighbourhood, and the happiness of a country." Can they be the Holy Grail of social cohesion that today's politicians seek? To describe a ploughing match as an outdoor winter sport does little to convey the full experience of standing as a spectator for two or three hours in the middle of a vast, open stubble field. The classes are each based on strict rules, among which are the following:

Three setting sticks are allowed.

Competitors to strike from same end of plot. Each competitor to plough three rounds at his ridge before starting to cast towards the next competitor.

All ground to be cut and judged before ploughing continues.

All competitors to finish their furrows towards own ridge with a grate furrow.

Plough bodies must not be removed or raised out of position at any time.

So that's all clear to everyone! But not in Ransomes' home county of Suffolk, where ploughing competitions were often "furrow-drawing matches". The contestants ploughed only one furrow, the winner being the one with the straightest furrow as judged by the "stickers". These searched for the "worst place"; once this was found and marked, "the deviation" was measured. Winners rarely wandered off the true line by more than 2 or 3 inches (5 to 7.5cm) across the whole length of the field.

The mysticism apart, the craftsmanship is superb, but it is the application of the hip flask that gets most contestants and spectators through to the traditional post-match supper.

So for one reason or another, or most likely several, man cultivated the land between crops. Before the advent of the tractor this rarely went below 12cm, and even today routine field cultivations disturb only around some 15cm of earth. Only drainage works and subsoiling go deeper.

Traditionally, things were very different in the intensive world of the garden, where the rule was "one spit deep" and two in the case of double-digging. A spit, the measure of a spade's depth, has truly ancient roots. It derives directly from the Old English "spittan", to dig, and has absolutely no connections with any nasty habits. Just how far back that rule can be traced I don't know, but medieval illustrations are full of chaps digging exactly as we do today, indeed the design of spades has changed little in two thousand years except for one rather curious detail: many late medieval illustrations show spades with the blade on only one side of the shaft. I cannot but think that they would have been extremely unwieldy to dig with, with a tendency to twist under the weight of the soil. Indeed I was half inclined to dismiss such a strange image as an artistic distortion, but there can be no doubt about it: one-sided spades were commonplace, even appearing on seventeenth-century tombstones. Apart from adding the other side to the blade, the biggest change started to appear towards the end of the medieval period; before that, spades had wooden blades with only the cutting edge and sides clad in iron, then, as iron became more commonplace, the whole blade was forged.

The contrast in depth of tillage between agriculture and horticulture is indicative of what amounts to a fundamental difference in attitude towards working the soil. It marks a basic difference between intensive production and extensive field cropping. Unlike arable farmers, horticulturists have worked to ameliorate, extend and even change the soil within the whole root zone of their plants. The impact all this huge amount of manual labour has had on crop production is hard to quantify. Perhaps the most positive point, and the kindest thought to the memory of all those aching backs, is that up until a few decades ago gardens typically out-yielded fields by severalfold.

When we look at today's field-grown vegetables it is hard to claim that the gardener achieves much improvement in the quality of individual specimens. And incidentally, that's not just a matter of rigorous grading: many vegetable growers are achieving around ninety per cent of their crop at the standard we see in the supermarkets. Farmers and growers working on a field scale have always regarded the gardener's approach to tillage as over the top and in some cases downright unnecessary. As I have mentioned, subsoiling takes field tillage to greater depths, at times as much as 60cm deep. This is by no means an annual task; indeed in some situations it is a once-in-a-lifetime event. However there are circumstances in which the very machines that make contemporary agriculture so productive consolidate the land some distance below the surface to such an extent that it needs to be "busted up" every few years. By choosing conditions when the soil moisture is midway between wet and dry, the single tine of the subsoil "plough", like the larger and more energy-demanding chisel plough, causes a shattering action, loosening the land well into the subsoil and opening up the naturally occurring cracks between the soil peds without bringing the subsoil to the surface. This improves drainage and breaks up any over-consolidated soil horizons, often referred to as "iron pans" or "plough pans".

So, to summarise, land tillage is about making a seedbed, allowing water to percolate, aiding root penetration and killing weeds. There is however one further rather complex function; tillage can "make" topsoil and increase the volume of soil available for roots to explore.

Topsoil can be produced by bringing subsoil to the surface, exposing it to air and increasing its organic matter and humus content, but only by a few inches each year – weathering subsoil takes time! Increasing the depth of topsoil was one of the ideas behind "bastard trenching" that inverted the first and second spits. More generally gardeners practised "double digging" that kept the soil horizons in their original sequence. Whichever the approach, years of hard work paid off and many old walled gardens still have 50cm of man-made topsoil while in the field just the other side of the wall there may be as little as 20cm.

It is a fair approximation to say that the vast majority of a plant's roots stay in the topsoil. Deepening the topsoil by deep cultivation does not encourage more roots, but does provide a bigger root territory. The greater the soil volume explored, the greater reservoir in times of drought and the larger the potential catchment of nutriments.

The next set of tools found in almost every agrarian culture are the seedbed preparers. But before looking at the tilth-makers we must briefly consider one of the most miserable of tasks but one that often fitted into the sequence at about this point: stone-picking. Root crops, especially potatoes, are easiest grown and harvested on stone-free land. Today otherwise suitable land is stone-picked mechanically, rocks over around 2 inches (5cm) in diameter being lifted and carted off the field or at the very least cleared from the planting beds. Stone-picking has been a precursor to field cultivation for millennia and by tradition was one of the winter jobs reserved for children and women. No doubt the removal of the rocks made cultivation with primitive equipment easier, and their use in both building field boundary walls and roads added some extra value to the drudgery. An example of just how far landowners would take this work is well illustrated by the Lancashire farmer who removed just short of a thousand cartloads from one field; the size of the field is not recorded, but I think the story makes its point regardless.

The effectiveness of tilth-makers depends partly on soil moisture, partly on the length of time since the basic cultivation and partly on the weather during that time. Freezing and thawing and wetting and drying all help to crumble the clods. The tools should not probe deep into the land but leave unweathered soil well below the surface. Their job is to work with the material that has been weathered after being exposed by ploughing. If that's happened over the winter you should have a useful depth of tilth or "frost mould" to work with, so with land that is in good heart this is not an exercise in brute force. After a little weathering, and with the right moisture content, all that is required is a nudge and the lumps fall apart.

The traditional gardener used his boots to crush the clods, in the time-honoured act of treading or "heeling" the seedbed. The hand-tool that followed the footwork was the rake, a tool that requires more skill than almost any other to produce its desired result, an even depth of tilth and a level surface.

To a modern farmer the most primitive field-scale tilth-maker must surely be the "clodding mell". It was nothing more than an over-large wooden mallet used to bash clods of earth. In our labour-saving world it is staggering to realise that it was used on a field scale! The horse-drawn wooden scrubber provided an up-market solution to the same problem. Superficially this looks like a sledge, but instead of runners fixed from front to back for ease of movement, the scrubber has the opposite: angled slats running across the frame. An even more basic tool performed the final act in tilth production, a "harrow" made from brushwood faggots dragged behind an animal, the same device being used to cover broadcast seed.

Throughout the nineteenth century and well into the twentieth, farmers used often locally made stone or wooden animal-drawn rollers to produce the desired result by crushing the clods, but it is risky unless the ground is on the dry side; too wet and you are making a road rather than a seedbed. The story of implement development coincides with the start of the slow replacement of the ox by the horse. In the nineteenth century things looked up in the world of roller technology with the appearance of a prototype of today's "rib", "ring" or, to many, "Cambridge" roller. It was made from a series of alternating wood and iron wheels brought together on an axle. Having done their job they give the resultant tilth some lateral space to move into rather than simply squashing it down into a continuous smooth finish. By now readers must be getting used to things being named after their place of origin, but in this case it is not the famous city but the roller's less well-known inventor Mr W. C. Cambridge who gave it its name.

Around the same time, the "spiky" roller made its debut, thanks to the inventive mind of Mr Clarke, Mr Ellis or Mr Randall, each of whom claimed the glory. The idea was to concentrate all the weight of the roller through a line of spikes onto the clods, thereby shattering them. You can see the same idea today in the design of lawn aerators and the massive sheepsfoot rollers used in road construction.

The alternative to clod-crushing is clod-knocking-sideways, and to do that you need a series of iron spikes dragged through the surface layer of the soil. The heavyweight forms are known as cultivators, the lightweight as harrows. Harrows were and still are little more than a set of spikes fixed to a stout frame. The trick is to so arrange both the spikes on their frame and several frames in a pattern behind whatever is pulling them so as to push the soil about, smash clods and make the maximum amount of tilth. Harrows tend to collect dead weeds and trash from the previous crop and although this was seen as a valuable part of their function, clearing them was a slow and awkward job, hence the value of "Finlayson's Self-Cleaning" harrow. This clever design went a long way to making the job easier, and gives me an excellent excuse to emphasise how much of the early development of tillage equipment took place in Scotland. On the other side of the Atlantic the harrow had evolved into several forms of horse-drawn, surface-soil-shattering spikes, prongs or blades. An American catalogue of 1895 offers "Hinge", "Reversible", "Smoothing", "Common

Square", "Pulverizing", "Butterfly", "Spring", "Flexible Disc", "Revolving", "Spading", "Spring Tooth", "Float" and "Gardeners" harrows as variants on the theme. All are designed to do the same thing: loosen up the surface soil and produce tilth by smashing the clods into their constituent crumbs. Taken together they represent a valuable legacy left to twentieth-century farmers by European and American agricultural engineers. This is not the place to explore each type's finer details, but just in case you find an old set rusting away in a hedge bottom and think its skew-whiff rhomboid shape comes from it having being knocked out of square, it is not. From early in the nineteenth century harrows were made that way to prevent the tines lining up one behind the other.

Around the middle of the eighteenth century, an extra implement was added to the traditional list of plough, harrow and roller. It was the cultivator, "to perform functions intermediate between those of the plough and the harrow" – needed, it was said, to help keep the land clean of weeds when fallowing went out of practice and to aid in the preparation of spring seedbeds for the newly introduced root crops. Early cultivator designs were generally known as scarifiers but even this fearsome title was outdone by Robert Fuller who maybe had to search his thesaurus before coming up with "Fullers Extirpator". Unlike a correctly set plough, the tines of early cultivators tended to dig ever deeper into the soil, the huge effort required to pull them earning them the gruesome nickname of "horse-killers". Rival implement manufacturers offered many and varied designs of early cultivator including those with spring tines and others with duck feet but if I were to pick out one make it must surely be "The Tormentor", not just for its splendid name but because it is clear that it could do the job, was built to last and set the style for the next 150 years.

All these tools had to be somehow hitched to either one or several animals, and in Britain by the middle of the nineteenth century that meant horses. The design and arrangement of the harness had to maximise the pulling power of the animal while at the same time ensuring that it did not cause either immediate discomfort or long-term harm. The farm tack room was even richer in leather, rope, chain and wood and brass artefacts than today's counterpart in a riding stable. The biggest difference was in the size and weight of the harness and such extra items as the collar by which the horse pulls and the pad that takes the weight of shafts or pole. The actual attachments between bridle, collar or pad have the inevitable "specific terms" associated with any long-standing craft. "Traces" from the bridle allow the horseman to control his charge, while the wooden "whipple-tree" between horse and tool sets the traces wide enough to prevent them rubbing the horse's flanks.

Using the huge power of the modern tractor, tilth-making today can even be combined with ploughing, but is more often done by the first part of a compilation of machines that end with a seed-drill. A recently developed technique is known as minimal tillage. The idea is to produce a seedbed tilth without disturbing more than around 7cm of soil; typically it is done on the stubble from a recently cleared cereal crop. The technique needs one of today's massively powerful tractors to which is hitched two sets of disc harrows, a spiked and a ribbed roller. The result of this concert of tillage devices is a 3m-wide strip of tilth ready for drilling with the next crop.

As an example of just how far mechanisation has progressed to serve every type of arable crop, let's have a look at potato production on the deep soils of East Anglia. Growing potatoes on a field scale has always meant shifting large volumes of soil; they are not a crop for the minimal-tillage enthusiast. For some 200 years after potatoes were first grown on any scale the land was ploughed, then, using a double-mouldboard plough, "stitched" into ridges. At that point the work switched from the horseman to the general field workers, often women, who spent days on end in gangs of two or three bent double either carrying planting baskets or dragging chitting trays along the ridge tops and dropping the potato tubers one at a time about 25cm apart in the furrows. Then the horses returned to "split" the ridges and bury the tubers with the same double-mouldboard plough.

Today, thanks to the massive power of today's 160hp tractors and specialist equipment manufacturers such as Richard Pearson Ltd, it is somewhat different procedure. Start, often some months before planting, with putting on the fertilisers: farmyard slurry and bag fertilisers, each distributed by the appropriate kind of spreader. Then plough to around 35cm.

Wait for the right soil conditions at planting time and bring on the specialist kit. First the Jumbo bedformer followed by the Rotoforma then the Megastar declodder and destoner and, at last, the Starfeed planter. From start to finish that's between £100,000 and £150,000's worth of equipment, so what does it all do? Well, the muck and fertiliser spreaders' jobs are straightforward: even distribution at the required rate. The plough is nothing untoward except for its draught; 35cm is three times the depth our horse managed. Now for the specialist equipment. The Jumbo bedformer's adjustable, deep ridging bodies form a two-ridge bed within the wheelspan of the tractor, whilst its subsoiler tines ensure that the earth below the furrows is loosened. The Rotaforma's rotors break up clods and produce a deep, even tilth, then its ridging bodies reform the furrows. When conditions require its services the Megastar Actiflow grades the soil, removes stones and any remaining clods and drops them along the wheel tracks on the edge of the bed. The planter does a number of tasks in rapid sequence. It can place fertiliser alongside the furrow bottom before dropping the potato sets at a predetermined distance apart, then, with its closer-discs, cover and protect them before the main ridging bodies split the ridges to bury them. Each piece of specialist equipment forms a part of one complete set; under good conditions that set of equipment can start with ploughed land and finish the day with some eight acres (3.2ha) planted; and in spite of the complexity it is worth it.

So far I have found this chapter fairly easy to write, as it can follow a straightforward progress from ploughing to drilling, but I have a nagging problem; where do I fit in the rotary cultivator?

The precursors of rotavators, a proprietary name now often used generically for rotary cultivators, were powered by steam engines. Several enthusiasts are involved in their invention around the middle of the nineteenth century. However, little came of their ideas until some seventy-five years later. The machine's business end consists of a rotating horizontal shaft mounted with blades that cut into the soil, shatter it, then, beneath a cover, throw it into the air from which it falls as a loose mass. You may have noticed that I did not describe the product as tilth or soil crumbs, for the good reason that it is neither. On appropriate soils with the appropriate moisture content these tools, in their various sizes, do a good job. They have been successfully used to replace ploughing or digging and achieve seedbed preparation. The problem comes when they are misused, when not all the "appropriates" are in place; then they destroy tilth that can take years to reform.

This illustration, adapted from an original, shows a medieval forester planting giant hardwood cuttings. Both willow and poplar will propagate successfully from such "wands".

11 THE RAISING OF NEW STOCK

It must be evident to everyone that the perpetuation and increase of crop plants lies at the heart of man's success as a cultivator. I have an English language glossary of plant propagation that defines some five hundred "technical terms". Surely the extraordinary length and etymological precision of such lists reflect the attention paid to each detail of the work. For centuries every act and every result deserved a name but, as so often in the past with craft words, many varied from region to region.

Here are seven for you to try and decipher: chit, crab-stock, double-worked, whip-and-tongue, bottom heat, steckling, watershoot.

And the answers are:

Chit: the first growth from a seed or tuber.

Crab-stock: an apple rootstock used for grafting, raised from the seed of a wild crab-apple.

Double-worked: a grafted tree formed of three parts: the rootstock, an intermediate scion and the desired variety.

Whip-and-tongue: a commonly used form of joinery used in grafting young trees and shrubs.

Bottom heat: the application of warmth beneath a propagation bench designed to raise the temperature of the cutting compost.

Steckling: small, overwintered root vegetable transplant selected to produce a seed crop.

Watershoot: a vigorous, soft, juvenile shoot produced from a dormant bud on the trunk or old branches of a tree.

SEEDS

Seeds are nature's most common way of producing new individuals of most species of flowering plants. As the result of sexual reproduction they represent the beginnings of a new generation. Seeds are therefore the way a species perpetuates itself. Yet because they are produced as a result of genetic recombination, they are also the way a species changes. To growers, seeds have always presented this two-edged ambiguity. Uniformity meant a dependable harvest; diversity offered the chance of improving future crops.

"Fixed" cultivars breed true from seed. To achieve this genetic uniformity can take plant-breeders a lot of time and effort, but once it has been achieved it means that a grower buying from a reputable company can expect to get a crop of similar individuals that are also the same as their parent's picture on the seed packet. Gardeners know they can depend on this being the case for vegetables, but not with many perennial flowers and fruits because once "a winner" has been produced there is no attempt to fix it; it is propagated vegetatively as a clone.

There is another form of seed that produces a crop of identical plants: the F1 or first-generation hybrids. These are the offspring from two true-breeding but genetically different parents. Based on the laws of inheritance, all the seedlings are identical, with characteristics from both parents. Their offspring will however be made up of a range of genetically different individuals known as the F2 generation. Such a mixture gives a diverse and unpredictable crop, so growers cannot use such seed. Each season they must start again by sowing F1 hybrid seed.

As agriculture and horticulture in different parts of the world have slowly become businesses, so specialist seed-producers have taken on the task of offering dependable seeds of all kinds of annual crop plants, even when it means growing promiscuous kinds in isolation to prevent cross-pollination between cultivars. Of course, however important this is it is only one part of the seed merchant's task. Customers not only expect seed to be true to the name on the packet; it must also be viable. Seed quality depends on a series of operations spanning the whole period from the cultivation and harvest of the parent plants to cleaning, grading and storing the seeds. The seed industry is now an international trade, with production taking place where the climate can be trusted to provide good growing and harvest conditions. In practice this means that little seed is grown in Britain, although it may be processed, stored and packed here.

There are several husbandry tasks that the seed-producer tackles in a specific way. Sowing dates, irrigation and fertiliser programmes may well be different for a seed crop compared with the same plant grown for its usual harvest. Biennials such as beetroot, parsnips, carrots and sugarbeet have to be carried over for a second year, when the overwintered roots sprout and run up to seed. Plant spacing can have a significant effect on seed quality, since many plants produce flowers in a sequence, starting with the central spike and progressing through a series of lateral and sublateral branches until either the plant runs out of steam or the growing season comes to an end. This sequential flowering and seeding presents the grower with a dilemma. Harvest the first heads, which are often the best, immediately they are ripe and you are in danger of gathering up a lot of poor, underdeveloped seed from the later flower-heads. Delay long enough for them to mature and the first seeds will have fallen. If however you plant closely the shady conditions around the flower stems suppress side-shoot production and each plant produces just the one primary shoot (see Chapter 15). The close planting ensures that the yield per area remains the same, but this time it is all top-quality seed. It is routine to rogue the crop at the critical stage, when "off types" can be detected and got rid of before they have had a chance to pollinate the rest.

Early cultivators could be excused for feeling cheated by the gods if seeds failed to grow. After all, the local flora in its various natural habitats seemed to manage very well, not to mention those species that had taken advantage of man's efforts and become weeds among the crops. What was going on, and why should crop seeds not germinate? Well there are a lot of answers to that question, including some that have taken us the best part of ten thousand years to discover. Let's begin with the parent crop. Some plants produce a mixture of fertile and infertile seed, in which case you are not going to get the number of plants you thought you were from any given sowing rate. The seeds of many plants have an inbuilt dormancy that prevents them from germinating until either a period of time has elapsed or certain environmental conditions have been met. For example, the germination of holly seeds benefits from the chemical treatment they get during their passage through the gut of a bird. As an alternative to this somewhat difficult-to-manage treatment, Sir Isaac Newton suggested storing them in wet bran; not perhaps one of his best-known contributions to science, but for many easier to follow than the *Principia Mathematica*.

Another cause of failure occurs when the seed is gathered too soon; most have to develop fully on their parent plant, as immature seeds won't grow. All these hidden snags add up to you not necessarily sowing the number of get-up-and-grow seeds you thought you had.

The very early cultivators may have depended on seeds falling at harvest time to resow their fields or plots, but for thousands of years their successors have set aside a percentage of their harvest for sowing the following crop, indeed eating the seed-corn remains the surest indication of a famine. Supposing you had succeeded in gathering good seed; you could be excused for not worrying too much about how or where to store it. After all, nature seems to manage without any special provisions. In fact in the wild there are huge differences in longevity between species; it ranges from a few days in the case of rubber (*Hevea brasiliensis*) and willows to over fifty years for many members of the pea family. Over and above the natural lifespan, we now recognise how significant storage conditions are in maintaining and extending seed viability in many species, but not all. Indeed the challenge of keeping seeds viable in the tropics concerned the White Raj over a hundred years ago, at a time when seed storage and testing in Europe was beginning to improve your chances of getting seedlings when you sowed a packet of seeds. Dr van Hall recommended sending the usually very short-lived cocoa seeds in their pods on the six-week voyage from Dutch Guinea to Java.

> The pods were first thoroughly washed with a tooth-brush and soapy water, then placed in 70 per cent alcohol for a minute, and afterwards in a 5 per cent solution of corrosive sublimate for a few minutes, so as to kill the germs on the surface. A piece of string being then attached to the stalk end of the pod, the latter was dipped in the molten paraffin wax; it was taken out immediately and hung carefully by the string, so as not to break the thin coating of the wax adhering to it. When cold, each pod was again dipped in the paraffin, thus making the coating more complete. The pods were then packed in dry sawdust and despatched by post.

I am glad to report the seed germinated.

In the past, warm-and-dry were an inseparable couple, so as gardeners came to recognise the value of keeping their seeds dry as well as out of reach of vermin they hung the storage bags from the rafters above the heater in the potting shed or garden office – as we now know, a far from ideal place. In some establishments melon seed was made an exception; that the head gardener carried with him in his waistcoat pocket, convinced that the resultant seedlings would be stronger and more fruitful. It was not only humble gardeners that had this strange belief; Gilbert White in his diary entry for 15 March 1755 records that before sowing he "Carry'd Mr. Garnier's Cantaleupe seed in my Breeches-pocket 6 or 8 weeks."

The honour of establishing the earliest seed-testing stations is shared between Germany in 1869 and Denmark in 1871. They were sorely needed: in Copenhagen they still have museum specimens of the dyed sand used to adulterate seed lots. Nowadays seed management is so well developed that the husbandry of a new crop effectively starts with the harvest of its parent's seed. Temperature, oxygen and above all the moisture content of the seed influence its lifespan. The long-term stores usually referred to as seed banks run at –20°C and the seeds have been dried down to a fraction of their natural moisture content. These conditions so increase the life of seeds that the scientists in charge are predicting that many samples that under natural conditions might have lived for around five years will remain viable for over a hundred. By the same token, seeds for both crop-producers and amateur gardeners are dried and sealed in moisture-proof packets to ensure the customer gets live seed. Don't open until you want to sow!

There is one more very long-standing worry that is no longer a problem in most parts of the world; it was not about seed viability but, put simply, could you believe the name on the packet? Sadly you could not, until trueness to name became part of the seed inspection story.

Sowing the seed

The cycle of sowing, growing and harvest is ingrained in the calendars of every civilisation. Implicit in this annual cycle is the need for the wherewithal and skill required to raise the following crop regardless of whether the plants are propagated by sowing directly into the field or by being raised in a nursery.

The first cultivators sowed seed and moved transplants in order to bring a crop from some place out in the wilds to a spot that they had chosen. Presumably a site selected for a combination of security, good growing conditions and their own convenience. For thousands of years the sowing of seed has been seen as a symbolic act signifying the start of every cropping cycle, but it is more than that. It is perhaps the most audacious of all the husbandry activities. Whilst all the rest assist plants to grow and have their parallels in nature, seed-sowing reorders the natural distribution of species.

Seed testing tells us the percentage of viable seed in the sample we sow, but there are many reasons why some of the live seeds fail to produce seedlings. In addition to the wrong sowing depth and badly incorporated fertiliser, Professor Peter Salter and Professor John Bleasdale, two outstanding horticultural scientists working at the then National Vegetable Research Station at Wellesbourne, Warwickshire, list soil moisture, tilth, capping, compaction and temperature. They go on to give the example of lettuce seed, where these "field factors" can account for the failure of some 50 per cent of the live seed sown. Most of these causes remained a mystery up until the mid nineteenth century, so it is not surprising that people all round the world called upon supernatural assistance. Christian Britain chose the extra sanctity of St Valentine's and St Mathew's days to sow their crops while the less devout used natural indicators of the progress of the season in their district. One was "when the elm leaf is as big as a mouse's ear". Another, traditional in East Anglia, took a very direct assessment of that most important environmental factor is of course the state of the soil, its moisture and warmth: to test this, the farmer dropped his trousers and sat on the bare earth.

Goodness knows what the local Baptist tabernacle had to say about that and all the undertones it carried from a pre-Christian era! Day-to-day conditions right for landwork depend on the weather, so it is not surprising that our folklore is so rich in ways of predicting snow, rain, sun and wind. It must have been comforting to believe that: "If Candlemas Day be clouds and rain, winter be gone and won't come again." On the other hand, "Saturday moon and Sunday full" would surely make you abandon plans for Monday's seed-sowing because, as the saying continues, it "allus brings rain and allus 'ull." Now all this may seem to be no more than a few old wives' tales, but the farmers of medieval England ran their cropping programmes by the church calendar. Seed-sowing was no exception; the sowing of wheat and rye could not take place before Lammas Day and must be completed by Hallowmas (21 July and 21 October in the old calendar). Today, to get the maximum yield, we are far more precise (see page 24) – indeed thirteen weeks seems a large work window – but we should remember that with undrained land and the slow pace of ox teams to produce a seedbed there must have been many occasions when Lammas seemed to come round all too soon.

Metaphorically speaking, the sowing of seed is generally associated with male sexual activity, but the farming world placed the fate of the real thing in the hands of female icons; this may reflect the recognition of maternal tender loving care or perhaps the ancient role of women in the raising of crops. If you have a knowledge of classical mythology you will recall that Ceres carried seed in a shallow basket held on one arm while scattering it by a sweep of the other. Britannia, our British female icon, looks like a frigid debutante at a fancy-dress party, but across the Channel the French take their inspiration from not one but two more comely creatures, the confident Marianne and her rural sister La Semeuse. Anyone who remembers French stamps back in the 1950s will recall that not even French culture is so sophisticated as to loose sight of the symbolic role of the seed-sower in the prosperity of the state. I am delighted to see that she is still with us, having even survived the disappearance of the franc to reappear on the euro. From her basket she sows the next crop by broadcasting seed onto a prepared seedbed just as it was done throughout the Roman empire and then across Europe for more than another thousand years before the adoption of the seed-drill. Her skill ensured the even distribution of the seed at the right density to produce the desired harvest. Two-handed sowers scattered seed to right and left as they coordinated strides with arm movements. According to Ian Niall, a skilled nineteenth-century worker covered a total width of 5.5 yards (5.04m) at each pass across a field. Surely it can be no coincidence that this is one pole, rod or perch, a very old unit of land measurement, exactly the width we found between the ridge and furrow in medieval ploughlands. If this is so then the ridge and furrow, first found in the open fields and later the product of ploughing in lands, acted as a perfect guide to the sower and prevented both overlaps and missed areas. Perhaps the skill that ensured that you covered all your own land and none of your neighbour's persisted for several hundred years after the disappearance of the common fields. Being able to broadcast seed or granular fertiliser evenly over the ground while walking along is a simple but satisfying skill, and one that gives me a lot of pleasure and an almost tangible link with the hundreds of generations of cultivators who have played out this annual ritual.

Seed-sowing is such a seminal act (no pun intended!) that it has been the subject of hundreds of paintings stretching back over two thousand years. Almost all show the same swinging arm action, but in some the seed is carried in a basket, known in the nineteenth century as a "seedlip" or "seedcote", while in others the sowers wear a "sowing sheet", attached at the shoulder and one forearm to form a cradle, from which seed is drawn and scattered with the free hand. It is rather reminiscent of the kind of carrier my grandmother would make from her apron to collect hen's eggs if she unexpectedly discovered a nest in a hay barn.

With practice the seed could be spread evenly and at the required density, but it was still on the surface and there much of it remained. No wonder the old rhyme tells of one for the master but one each for both the pigeon and the crow. It fails to mention that in addition to this risk of avian predation there is the difficulty of meeting all the necessary conditions for germination from such an exposed resting-place. The broadcasting of seed was mechanised by the invention of the seed barrow and the seed fiddle. The barrow consisted of a wheelbarrow-like structure across which balanced a long wooden trough holding a rotating spindle. Its circular brushes swept seed out of a line of small holes. The fiddle used a rotating disc beneath a seedlip to fling seed over the seedbed. The disc's centrifugal force was powered by the reciprocal action of the fiddle bow as the operator pulled it back and forth, walking across the land. Both these mechanical principles are still used, the rotating spindle in simple seed drills and the spinning disk in fertiliser distributors and crop protection sprayers.

We don't know if any sown seed was raked in, however there are numerous medieval illustrations of various devices, from the "harrows" we saw used earlier in tilth production, made from faggots of brushwood or gorse, to flat rafts of planks and even old squares of stack cloth being dragged over seedbeds to brush seed into the crevices between the clods. The large-seeded field beans became a popular stock feed before many farmers had seed-drills. Some had the seed sown in the furrows as ploughing proceeded while others recommended driving cattle over the land after broadcasting the crop to trample in the seed.

Nowadays, using today's machinery the major events of the farming year are over in a few days. Historically they took weeks of arduous work. Not without reason, they often ended with a celebration. A rest for the men, more work for the women! This poem dates from Tudor times:

> Wife, sometime this week, if the weather hold clear,
>> An end of wheat-sowing we make for the year.
> Remember you, therefore, though I do it not,
>> The seedcake, the pasties and frumentie [g] pot.

It was not until the invention of the seed-drill that, on a field scale, seed could be placed below ground. As usual, gardeners took more care and greater precision when sowing their crops. Even on broadcast beds they raked the seed in or sprinkled a layer of soil over it.

The sower of seed and the inventor of the seed-drill face four challenges in common: density, distribution, insertion and contact. As ever, these one-word summaries have more to them than meets the eye, so let's unpick this list and see what really has to happen.

Density and distribution

As we will see in Chapter 13, plant density can have a huge effect on the growth of the individuals concerned, so it is no surprise to learn that both gardeners and farmers have long seen the even distribution of the right amount of seed as the cornerstone of a good harvest. The putting of plants into rows meant traditionally that they were crowded in one direction (along the row) and spaced out in the other (between rows). Modern precision seed-drills are designed to reduce this rectangularity, but a crop of sugarbeet plants will still have roughly twice as much space between rows as within them, i.e. a rectangularity ratio of two to one. Some crops of root vegetables do even better and are grown almost "on the square" – that is, with equal space between the

273

plants in the row as between rows.

Now what does "at the right density" mean? Well, as we saw in Chapter 5, it is not what is best for the plant as a prize specimen but for the harvest as desired by the grower or customer. In other words, the spacing varies not only between crops but also between batches of the same crop plant when grown for various uses.

Insertion

Seeds are rather fussy about how deep they are in the ground; too deep and most types won't germinate, too shallow and they are vulnerable to rapid and lethal fluctuations in moisture. To some extent the optimum depth can be linked to soil structure and to the natural form of the seedling and its germination strategy. The Romans understood this, as Columella makes clear, but their way of achieving the right depth I find surprising, and a long way from what Salter and Bleasdale would recommend. He writes of broadcasting the seed of field crops before cultivating the land. This could take the form of harrowing but in some cases he recommends ploughing the seed in. I guess we should remember that the Roman plough did not go very deep and they tended to select light soils for arable cropping. Today research has produced an optimum for farmers to aim at for most important crops, for example wheat 2.5cm, peas 4.5cm and sugarbeet 2cm. Now 2cm is very near to the depth below which many seeds remain dormant in a typical undisturbed soil profile, which clearly indicates how much all that effort to produce a seedbed changes conditions, particularly by allowing light and fresh air to penetrate the soil surface between the crumbs.

The old gardening books used to give a rule of thumb, recommending a covering "equal to twice the size of the seed", which I take to mean that if you were sowing a seed 0.2cm in diameter you would take out a drill 0.6cm deep. Few would argue against that advice under the ideal conditions you might find in a greenhouse, but it would be risky in the garden or field. Today's agricultural and horticultural seed-drills are designed to follow research findings and sow at least twice that depth, in part to help prevent the seed drying out during its vulnerable germination phase. In contrast, some mass-production glasshouse units producing half-hardy bedding plants do not cover the seed at all, but use blacked-out temperature- and humidity-controlled germination rooms. Writing this has prompted me to look up some rather strange sowing recommendations from the seventeenth century. The author insists on sowing depths of several inches for virtually all garden vegetables. He claims to have experimented to find the best depths, but time and again experiments and observations from those times defy repetition in these more sceptical days. I can't help feeling he must have had some very disappointed readers.

Foresters tend to raise seedling trees by broadcasting seed over carefully prepared beds. Then comes the unusual bit: they bury the seed by covering it with a layer of grit, or as some people would describe it a very coarse sand. Once again we are back to achieving a good balance around the seed between moisture and air. The extra benefits of easy seedling emergence and a weed-free start to the first year are important bonuses. For a truly inspirational account of raising forest transplants from seed under tropical conditions read *How to Plant a Forest*. It is far and away the best cultivation-for-conservation manual I have seen, sound in its science and with very practical instructions ranging from how to make your own seed composts to the advantages, as well as the disadvantages, of having wild elephants on site!

Contact

This refers to the physical contact the seed has with the solid components of the soil. In a seedbed with a fine tilth it is the soil crumbs that touch the seed, but contact can also involve fragments of organic matter and even the sides of clods of soil. This contact allows a continuous film of water to develop between soil particle and seed, providing the sustained supply of moisture, which is of course vital throughout the process of germination. Seedbed rolling and the old gardening ruse of tamping down seed-drills with the back of a rake are both aimed at producing sufficient compaction to keep both surface tilth and seeds moist. But always check on soil conditions before performing this trick, as there is a fine balance between encouraging capillarity and reducing the amount of air that reaches the seed.

Seed-drills

Furrow opened, seed in, seed covered – all in one pass across the field. The crop sown at the right depth and density in lines so you could hoe out the weeds and eliminate much of the backbreaking task of hand-pulling. No wonder the quest for a functioning seed-drill plays such an important part in the story of agricultural progress.

My understanding of the story of the seed-drill, like so much in this book, comes from other people's hard work. Source material such as that used by G. E. Fussell throughout *The Farmer's Tools* has proved invaluable when trying to link the mechanical "how" to the biological "why" of cultivation. Fussell makes it clear that cultivators have long known what was required of a seed-drill, and there is plenty of evidence from the literature that long ago seed-sowing equipment was constructed that came near to doing the right things to the right degree and in the correct sequence. Evidence for very early seed-drills in the Middle East comes from Sumeria in the form of a toy-sized model and from a Babylonian illustration. In the model the seeding density was controlled by a person dropping the seed into its hopper, but it looks as if the rest of the operation follows very much as today. However, according to the US Department of Agriculture, early as these examples are they are not the first; that comes from China around 4800 years ago. None of these early technological breakthroughs seem to have reached Europe.

The first alternative to broadcasting we hear anything about is what we would now call sowing in stations, that is making a series of holes and putting one or more seeds into each. I know that sounds like a back-garden kind of approach, but in fact it was done on a field scale, and the title page of Edward Maxey's *A New Instruction of Ploughing and Setting*, published in 1601, carries an illustration of two chaps using a pair of wooden planks with lines of holes in them. Armed with these "setting boards", they followed across a field behind a plough team. It appears that they are benefiting from earlier trials. In the first, according to a contemporary, Sir Hugh Plat, the sower made the holes with his finger but found the work "to be very long and tedious" – and, I would guess, hard on the finger! The next step was to make the holes with a multi-dibber on a pole. That in its turn was discarded in favour of the setting board for "not making sufficient riddance of the ground". The first attempts at space sowing were abandoned; all had proved too slow even for those unhurried times.

If the setting board was scrapped the dibbling iron was not, so I cannot see how Norfolk folk can claim the method was invented by a tenant farmer on the Hethel Hall estate years later. Promoted it certainly was, and became so commonplace that dibbling or setting irons are still to be found in some collections, including that at the Museum of Agriculture and Rural Life at Lackham College in Wiltshire, where they have both a short- and a long-handled model. They are heavy forged iron rods with a pointed knob on the bottom that opens up a hole to receive the seed. To my surprise I found the most graphic details of this quintessentially handwork in D. J. Smith's book entitled *Discovering Horse-Drawn Farm Machinery*; here is his description of the task:

> The dibblers walked backwards in a crouching position making dibble holes both to right and left with both hands clutching dibble sticks. Each dibbler was followed by a dropper, often a woman, who put two or more seeds in each hole.

Dibblers and droppers were followed by horse-drawn rollers or harrows. A single dibbler could normally cover half an acre (0.2ha) a day in good weather. I make that to be around 35,000 holes, so that's a million dibbles for every 14 acres (5.7ha) of cereals. This form of seed-sowing is such an extreme example of cultivation drudgery on a huge scale that I cannot resist quoting Mary Russell Mitford writing on sowing beans in the early years of the nineteenth century. She describes "troops of stooping bean-setters, women and children in all varieties of costume and colour", slowly plodding "through the main business of this busy season". Usually one to see poverty and drudgery as God-ordered features of the rural idyll, even the leisured Miss Mitford is compassionate enough to declare:

> What work bean setting is! What a reverse of the position assigned to man to distinguish him from the beasts of the field, only think of stooping for six, eight, ten hours a day drilling holes in the earth with a stick and then dropping in the beans one by one.

We can only hope that such thoughts did not spoil her afternoon ride as she set out to pick wild violets.

The first European seed-drill for which we have a good

description dates from 1602. It was the brainchild of Tadeo Cavalini from Bologna. We do not know if it was ever manufactured, but as Fussell says it is clear from the surviving description that it had all the necessary bits and pieces:

> A coulter shaped like the bow of a ship to open up a shallow, even sided furrow; a hopper to hold the seed, a mechanism to control seed flow and deliver it to the furrow and a simple trailing iron bar to drag some tilth back to cover the seed.

Indeed, that's an exact description of my father's 1930 model.

The challenge has always been to control the seed's flow rate. The answer appeared to be to make the hole from the hopper just large enough to allow one seed at a time to escape. Unfortunately, the seed of crop plants varies from giant broad bean to tiny turnip, so you have to be able to adjust the size of the hole. Sadly, that sophistication does not prevent jamming, even with round seed like peas and kale, and such drills are even more unreliable with less regular shapes such as the all-important cereals. The solution came much later; it required the introduction of moving parts.

The British did not come on the scene until a few years after Cavalini, but once started there was no stopping them: Alexander Hamilton 1623, Daniel Ramset 1634, Gabriel Plattes 1639, J. Sha 1646, John Worlidge 1716. Sadly it would seem all these gentlemen suffered from one or more of the following problems: their machines could not be built, were never built or did not work when built.

Enter Jethro Tull; it appears he produced and used a series of drills from the end of the seventeenth century, but they received little or no publicity until his *Horse Hoeing Husbandry* was published in 1733. Historians are loath to give him all the credit he may deserve for producing the first practical seed-drill because success seems to have gone to his head; he appears to have wanted all the glory, making the very unlikely claim to have read nothing of any other's efforts before starting work on his prototype. Once Tull showed that the idea could be made to work, others followed: Ellis 1750, Sharp 1772, Winter 1787, and on into the next century with designs by Cook, Morton and Garrett. You might think that the entry of such machines marked the end of the superstitions that characterised earlier farming, but not a bit of it: it added more. Well into the nineteenth century a blank row across a field, usually caused by nothing more supernatural than a blocked drill or poor alignment between "bouts" [g], was taken as a dreadful omen, as a missing row supposedly meant losing one of the family.

Until around 1740, seed-sowing on a field scale meant producing cereals of one kind or another; no other annual crop occupied a fraction of their acreage. But the development of the seed-drill promoted the cultivation of another field crop, turnips. This story starts with Charles I's ambassador in Holland, Sir Richard Weston. People had eaten turnips in Britain since before the Conquest but it is Sir Richard that deserves the credit for introducing us to the turnip as winter stock feed, but all good ideas need both a publicist and a means of delivery. Turnip promotion was the forte of Lord Charles Townshend of Rainham, indeed so much so that he became known in the farming fraternity as "Turnip Townshend". By 1721 he was a Secretary of State, but nine years later out of politics after a row with Walpole, he turned his attention to his lands in Norfolk. His "handsome, burly, brusque manner and hot temper" were just what the turnip needed if it was to make an impact on British agriculture. Nevertheless turnip technology, and with it field production, had to wait until Jethro Tull introduced his seed-drill. "Turnipamania" took off, but there was more to come, appropriately enough from Scotland, the country already leading the way in the cultivation of *Brassica rapa*, or, as they are still known north of the border, "neeps".

In 1777 Mr Airth sent his father a bag of "turnip" seed to try on his farm in Forfarshire; they were an outstanding success. There was nothing very unusual about such a filial gift except that Airth Junior lived in Gothenburg, and his turnips were, strictly speaking, not turnips at all. They were derived from a different but related ancient bloodline originating with *Brassica napus*. Inevitably this new root crop became known as swedes. For an assessment of their importance I turn to a somewhat taxonomically confused Sir Robert Wright in the 1908 *Standard Cyclopedia of Modern Agriculture and Rural Economy*:

> From this parcel of seed has been derived all the numerous varieties of swedes which now cover by far the greater part of the turnip area. Prior to this date only white and yellow turnips had been grown and the introduction of varieties of superior, hardiness, nutritive value and keeping powers extended the

utility of the crop in a very high degree. That this remarkable advance was due to the almost accidental transmission of a small parcel of seed from Sweden has perhaps hardly been fully appreciated. From that date onwards the turnip has occupied a leading position among British crops.

And so it did; at the beginning of the twentieth century, some 150 years after the start of this story, around one and a half million acres (600,000ha) of Britain were "down to turnips", three times the area of potatoes. Just in case you are wondering who ate them, winter feed for sheep and cows accounted for the vast majority, but they feature strongly in old farmhouse recipe books everywhere, from the West Country's love of "Devon" swedes and Cornish pasties to Scotland's mashed neeps.

Lord Charles Townshend was not the only one promoting the turnip. Arthur Young never tired of encouraging farmers to grow them. Young was one of the great figures in early nineteenth-century British agriculture. Technically, as secretary of the Board of Agriculture, he was a civil servant, but with indefatigable energy he acted more as a messianic journalist in his promotion of agricultural improvements. So effective were his writings and lectures that one historian has given him most of the credit for Britain, over that period, increasing its arable land by ten thousand square miles and doubling production per acre. Had that been only half-true, it would still have been no wonder that King George III told him: "Mr Young I am more obliged to you than to any man on my Dominions." No doubt Swift would have approved the complement!

Today the acreage under swedes has shrunk to far less than one per cent of our ploughland. This relic is now linked to stock-rearing in the North and West of Britain, with hardly a trace in the Norfolk of "Turnip Townshend".

Today's drills still have to meet the same criteria that confronted the Babylonian designers, and they still have to perform the same procedures to satisfy them: open a shallow furrow of the required depth, drop a controlled amount of seed per unit length of furrow, cover the seed. Seed-drills continue to evolve, but all the progress has come at a price. Around 1750, Ellis's drill cost four guineas (very roughly equivalent to £4000 today); now the largest and most sophisticated models cost around £25,000.

Controlling seed number and dropping at exactly the required frequency has made the greatest progress. Many drills use rotating circular brushes to sweep seeds into the outlet while at the same time preventing an avalanche. This design works, but cannot give the accuracy of seed placement that some of today's crops and high seed costs require. Precision drills are the answer, but they need very compliant seeds. Rubbing off the spikes, hooks and hairs helps, but pelleting the seed in a clay jacket, plus seed dressing and fertilizer if appropriate, turns even the most asymmetric types into perfect spheres. Within the drill the pellets are collected one per hole along a perforated belt, rather like the little ball-bearings in those infuriating puzzles. Having collected them the belt turns to drop them out, one at a time, at the required distance apart, into the furrow.

As usual, once people start to address a problem several solutions appear. One successful idea that deserves a mention as an example of lateral thinking is fluid drilling. Mix the seed in a viscous paste and squirt this into the furrow. If you have the right ratio of seed to paste, the seed density will be even and as required. Following this invention came the really clever bit: chitted seed. Why not partly germinate the seed before sowing? The gel protects it and it gets off to a flying start.

The contribution precision drilling makes to cultivation stretches far beyond giving the seed a good start, to providing the optimum plant population at the optimum spacing. We shall meet these benefits again in that most primitive of fights for survival, the story of competition.

VEGETATIVE PROPAGATION
The immortal clone

It may come as a surprise to some people, but many plants have the key to immortality. It is called vegetative propagation – the ability of bits to develop into complete individuals so that in a very real sense the old individual is kept going in perpetuity, its genes intact and unaltered. If several bits of the same plant perform this trick, the result is a clone, that biological conundrum beloved of science fiction, an entity that is at one and the same time both a single item and a group of separate individuals.

Those more at home with how things are done in the animal kingdom will know that virgin births tend to make the headlines, be they in Bethlehem or, in the case of Dolly the Sheep, a research station in Scotland. In contrast, many species of plant seem to have a lower sex-drive and exploit their ability to multiply by the separation of parts that can develop into complete fully functioning individuals. The part in question is usual a stem of some modified form such as a tuber, corm or rhizome, but there are examples of leaves, roots and even fruits being involved. As a method of spread, vegetative propagation is fairly slow unless an outside agent can be utilised – for example water in the case of floating pondweeds and fly-tipping human beings with Japanese knotweed.

Gardeners plagued by couch-grass may well regard vegetative propagation as all *too* successful, but biologists argue strongly that sex adds a vital something to the process that cannot be lightly dismissed. To a geneticist, all the offspring form a genetically identical clone and are therefore best regarded as a single individual. This causes a great deal of confusion and not a little argument among conservationists when a single specimen of a species on the brink of extinction is found. If we cultivators manage to propagate a hundred from it by vegetative means, how many have we now: 101 or still only 1? This dilemma reaches its most extreme condition if the species is dioecious [g], because the individual in question will then only produce offspring of its own sex and is doomed to depend on human help for evermore. The most famous example of a plant without a mate has sat alone in the Palm House at the Royal Botanic Gardens Kew for more than a hundred years; it is a cycad named *Encephalartos woodii*. No female has ever been found, so it is doomed to be the last of its line. Suppose in the future a way of vegetatively propagating it is discovered; to many conservationists that would be a pointless operation: after all you could hardly return it to the wild. Yes but – and now comes the point of telling this story – it is the same for most of those cultivars in the herbaceous border and shrubbery. They will not breed true from seed, indeed many are sterile. Their perpetuation depends on the propagator, but we don't dismiss them because of this. The garden centre certainly regards each member of the clone as an individual when we buy them, and so do we when working out how many to plant. Finally, I wouldn't mind betting that should that cycad at Kew ever be cloned, botanic gardens round the world will be clamouring for a specimen; after all, it's only natural, isn't it?

Vegetative propagation is both a way of reproducing a crop year after year and also the way of perpetuating and multiplying plants that carry precisely the same genetic material. Establishing a crop that is made up of one genetically identical specimen (or a handful of them) can be a huge advantage to the grower when predictability is an advantage, as it typically is in the First World. Those working in less-developed areas point out that a more heterogeneous population can however have its benefits. It is a matter of not having all your eggs in one basket.

Vegetative propagation has another very strong justification for its own place in this book. The delicate, intricate and precise techniques used today require skills and attention to detail that single out contemporary nurseries as pinnacles of the application of the theory and craft of cultivation. They are a unique fusion of the husbandry tradition of tender loving care, applied science and almost industrial mass-production.

We don't know the details of the early cultivators' first use of vegetative propagation, but it is possible to piece together some general clues that suggest how it may have begun. We know that as far as the origins of agriculture in the Middle East are concerned, all eight foundation crops are annuals, raised from seed each year. It is much the same story in North America, with the focus there on corn, sunflower and squashes.

There are however specific areas of the world where the oldest cultivated staples are perennial plants started each season from the vegetative propagules that nature has equipped them with. Typically, these are the very same perennating organs that make up the edible harvest. Among the better known are the yams of West Africa, taro from South-East Asia, sweet potato from tropical America and, most familiar to us, the potato from South America. These specialised bits of stem or root are a natural method of survival and spread. They now have distinct names such as tubers, rhizomes and offsets, but they all do much the same thing: store reserves to carry the plant over from one growing season to the next. To plant a field of potato tubers is a lot easier and faster and demands much less skill than it does to raise plants from seed.

The introduction of vegetative propagation techniques such as grafting and the taking of cuttings is lost in the mists of time, some stretching back before recorded history. In Europe, at least as far back as Tudor times, much of the work was done out of doors, using division, layering and hardwood cuttings. But in spite of the painstaking work of John Harvey giving us an excellent account of the pioneers of the British nursery trade and of the plants they offered for sale, his writings throw very little light on the dates and names of any of the nurserymen who introduced significant improvements. Dr Rune Bengtsson's thesis on limes (*Tilia* spp.) clearly illustrates the importance and skill of Dutch nurserymen in the seventeenth century. By this date they were layering clones of the hybrid *Tilia europaea* and exporting transplants for landscape plantings to at least five European countries. Their dominance in the trade resulted in such trees becoming known in five languages as "Dutch limes".

Our lack of a detailed understanding of nursery practices ends with the outpouring of nineteenth-century gardening books that reveal everything that was going on at that time. A little later Victorian authors, with characteristic pedantry, bombarded us with specific and often unnecessarily intricate techniques for each of their favourite plants.

Today's version of these methods still fascinates people, as every TV gardening programme-producer knows. It is also requires skill, and nursery people identify themselves as members of a professional group in their own right. Around the world there are college courses, learned textbooks, numerous research departments and a few complete research stations given over to the subject. The practitioners have specialist conferences and organisations, of which the International Plant Propagators Society is the largest. In their day-to-day work, plant propagators apply and manipulate many of their plant's physiological processes, although when doing so they use their own terms rather than those of the scientists.

There is an alternative group to the tuber crops for the title of oldest man-made clone. These are the many and varied plants that may have been carried back in small numbers and planted in the vicinity of the home so that they were to hand when needed. It is argued that such a list would have included herbs for flavour, medicine and magic. Many such plants are herbaceous perennials with creeping rootstocks, while others are low shrubs. Many of the herbaceous types will transplant from bits of their rootstock. Given the same treatment, pieces of stem pulled from some shrubs will produce adventitious roots and form a new plant. We can still see this sort of casual vegetative propagation going on when herbaceous borders are rejuvenated and, albeit unintentionally, when householders dump garden rubbish on country road verges and in railway cuttings. The *New Atlas of the British and Irish Flora* records dozens of such escapes, including such garden favourites as bergenia, horseradish and montbretia.

There is a third candidate for man's early or even our first excursion into vegetative propagation, and it could even predate agriculture. It is the sprouting of protective barriers against wild animals. So popular have living willow fences and sculptures become that it is hard to avoid them, but watching some of the artists at work serves to remind us that you don't need much horticultural skill to root some woody species, and that tonight's "dead stick fence" can become tomorrow's hedge. So it could have been protection rather than food or medicine that taught mankind that cuttings root. The leafless tree and shrub stems used are typically between one and three years old, and vary in diameter from the thickness of a pencil to that of a broomstick. In the slightly refined form known as truncheons these hefty "hardwood cuttings" are still used. They are popular propagules in the tropics but may soon be appearing in a field near you. They are the recommended form of cutting for establishing, *in situ*, the high number of low-cost plants needed in flood protection schemes and bank retention, and for large-scale biomass fuel crops.

Whoever were the first to use a plant's powers to regenerate from vegetative fragments, there can be no doubt about the Roman understanding of most aspects of the craft. In *The Georgics*, Virgil writes of the natural regeneration of elm and cherry "cropping up from their roots", and then goes on to describe features of various nursery techniques, including the "pinned-down arches of the layer", and the propagules of some other trees that "need no root" and so can be as "safely committed to the soil [as] cuttings from off a high branch".

Grafting

Another surprisingly early form of vegetative propagation is as far away from these semi-natural methods as it is possible to be without resort to a laboratory; it is grafting. Grafting was almost certainly first used as a device for increasing the number of specimens of difficult-to-root subjects. The idea of controlling size is however recorded in writings from the sixteenth century. Like most good ideas it is obvious when you are told. Grafting in its basic form joins two plants together, the roots of one with the aerial parts of the other; these are known respectively as the rootstock and the scion. Joining them does not affect the genetic make-up of either, but this interdependence does influence the grafted plant's growth by nothing more complicated than the rate of production of materials and their supply along the conducting tissue that bridges the graft union.

There is no suggestion that grafting was a skill employed by the first cultivators; indeed it may not have been practised for several thousand years, but it certainly was in use by 1000 BC and it is referred to several times in the Bible. Virgil once again provides us with the best description, although he goes way over the top with claims of joining unrelated trees.

The ancients faced the same problem that dogs orchardists to this day: cultivars of tree fruits such as apple and pear do not breed true from seed, and most do not root easily from cuttings. The stems of two plants can however be fused together in a mutually supportive union. Just who had the way-out idea of joining two plants together and then pruning them to finish up with the top of one on the roots of the other is not known, but do it they did. Fusion only succeeds if each piece's cambium cells are brought into contact and the union made airtight. The ingenuity used to achieve this can be judged by the range of carpentry joints invented over the years: veneer, kerf, splice, whip-and-tongue, rind, saddle, wedge, crown, and on and on. Achieving the airtight seal is comparatively easy nowadays using plastic tape, but in the past produced some surprising home-made sealants; ingredients, taken from various receipts, included clay, cow-hair, resin, tallow, beeswax, fuller's earth, and everyone's favourite, fresh cow-dung.

As with so many of the most sophisticated skills of gardening, Northern Europe learnt its craft via the Mediterranean cultures, then probably lost the art for several hundred years following the withdrawal of Roman influence. As some splendid drawings illustrate, grafting returned north during the slow medieval renascence of husbandry techniques. It has remained a basic part of the orchardist's trade right up to the present day. Those wishing to understand either the biology or the carpentry of grafting can do no better than read *The Grafter's Handbook* by

Robert Garner. As *The Guardian* put it, "Mr Garner almost certainly knows more about the vegetative propagation of tree and bush fruit than any man on earth." Neither reviews nor compliments come any better!

Layering

The propagation technique that had great prominence among nurserymen up to the nineteenth century was layering. Today it is seen as slow to do, slow to give results (and then often rather poor ones) and costly. For over a thousand years it was the easiest method of multiplying hundreds of kinds of shrubs. The basic idea is simple; stems of many shrubs and not a few trees will produce adventitious roots if, after receiving a superficial wound, they are buried in the ground for a few weeks or months. Of course there is a bit more to it than that; the soil has to be kept moist and you have the problem of getting the stems down to the ground, of holding them there and of stopping them from waving about in the wind.

Cuttings

Nowadays it is uncommon to find a nursery propagating anything other than some rootstocks by layering; its earlier pre-eminent role has been over by the almost ubiquitous dominance of soft and half-ripe cuttings. The great problem with cuttings is that they don't have any roots! Or, put another way, the great problem with cuttings is keeping them alive until they have produced roots, at which stage they have re-established themselves as complete plants. Keeping cuttings alive means preventing them from shrivelling up. You have to stop the loss of moisture from leaves and soft stems being greater than the water uptake from their cut bases. The general rule is that the younger the shoot the softer its tissue, and so the faster it loses water. Keeping such leafy cuttings alive out of doors is virtually impossible, so they are rooted under cover in frames, in polythene tunnels, or now, most commonly, in purpose-designed and purpose-equipped glasshouses. The easiest way of making sure that the cut ends have all the water they need would be to treat the cuttings like a bunch of flowers in a vase. There is however a slight complication: the cut bases also need oxygen to start initiating the cell division that eventually leads to the development of roots. Somehow you have to contrive to have both water and air available, and that's where the choice of compost comes in. The other approach to achieving turgidity in cuttings is to prevent them from losing water in the first place. There have been investigations into methods of sealing the leaf pores with various spray-on films, but these have found little favour with propagators.

For some years in the middle decades of the last century it seemed that any advances in vegetative propagation would be concerned with environmental control and the chemical treatment of the cutting. A frenzy of international research produced papers on everything from plant ageing and the innermost workings of a plant's physiology on one hand to blueprints for mass-producing African violets on the other. A summary of the resultant recommendations would read something like this:

Find the cultivars that root the most easily.
Define the appearance of the most successful cuttings.
Grow mother plants to produce many such cuttings.
Make the cuttings carefully, exactly to the specification.
When required, treat the cuttings with growth hormones.
Put the cuttings into the correct compost.
Provide and maintain the right compost temperature.
Provide and maintain the right air temperature.
Maintain a very high atmospheric humidity.

Specialist nurseries were lucky; they had to meet those criteria for only a small number of different kinds of plant, and in many cases these were closely related. The general nursery, especially those with long and honourable reputations for a wide range of plants, faced an almost impossible dilemma. They appreciated the rightness of the research advice that different plants had different optimum requirements, but it would have been totally uneconomic to have divided up their propagation units to provide exactly the best for each kind. The search was on for the best compromise, broad-based facilities that took advantage of the recent research but could handle most of their stock list.

Composts and humidity control illustrate the search very well. Rooting substrates, as the textbooks describe composts for cuttings, have to do several things: hold water, release water and supply oxygen to the base of the cutting. They do not need to supply nutrients or anchorage, but they must be either sterile or at least unsupportive of the types of fungus that cause cuttings to rot. Historically, propagators had used either washed sand or a mixture of sand and peat. In the 1960s, an era when man-made materials were often seen as innately superior to natural, these were challenged by vermiculite and perlite. Both these new materials worked very well. They were certainly sterile, both having been made by processes that raised their temperature to several hundred degrees Celsius, but as a result they were costly and energy-consuming. After the honeymoon was over many nurseries returned to their earlier loves, albeit with very precise definitions as to the type, grade and mix of their ingredients. Today many of the most progressive establishments are once again using peat and sand. It looks a clear case of "What goes around comes around," but an increased appreciation of just what physical conditions are required has had a huge impact on results.

If the story of substrates turned out to be flirtation with new materials, managing humidity is a story of novel equipment and electronic control systems. The first humidification system was a sheet of newspaper and a garden boy with a syringe full of water. For well over a hundred years, leafy cuttings were sprayed over several times a day in summer to try and stop them wilting. Pots of cuttings were put into "closed cases" – frames with close-fitting lights built on glasshouse benches. The newspaper shaded the frames and helped reduce the power of the sun that might otherwise both dry out and cook the encased cuttings. Old newspapers haven't become more expensive, but garden boys, or their equivalent, have. Added to which, their best endeavours were not always successful, so as a last resort growers had to cut most of the leaves off their cuttings.

All this helps explain the huge enthusiasm for the arrival of "mist propagation" in the 1950s. The idea was to place cuttings on the open glasshouse bench and to spray them with very fine droplets of water immediately their leaves dried out. If the leaves remained damp then the water within the leaf could not evaporate. "Mist" could have several advantageous side-effects, as every student at the time learnt off by heart. The cuttings could retain more leaf and that, coupled with direct sunlight, now that the old newspaper had gone, allowed more photosynthesis. The evaporating water cooled the leaf. The compost would not become waterlogged but remained well aerated, as only small amounts of water were used. Everything was controlled by a moisture-sensitive switch known as an "electronic leaf". It would be unfair to say that mist was other than an excellent idea. It rooted millions of cuttings and is still widely used, but it certainly had its problems, the reliability of the electronic leaf being one and water quality another. If you had slow-rooting cuttings in a hard-water area you could easily finish up with petrified objects so encrusted with mineral deposits that they appeared to have been cast in stone. As an enthusiast for both the notoriously slow-to-root dwarf conifers and mist propagation, H. F. Welch, the author of *Mist Propagation and Automatic Watering*, faced just this problem. His response led to the development of the cation exchange "Water Witch".

After mist came fog. Here the droplets produced by high pressure filled the glasshouse and were so fine that they were intended not to settle but instead to wet the air rather than the leaf surface. This was another high-tech solution, but one with fewer management problems than mist, other than the crop and the staff disappearing every few minutes! It is not a pleasant atmosphere to work in, and vigilance is needed to ensure that there is no risk of legionnaires' disease.

All the time, alongside these engineering approaches to environmental control, the simple plastic sheet was being developed as a basic but dependable concept. To be a little more precise, it was a sheet of milky-white, semi-translucent polythene used to cover a tent within the propagation glasshouse. In the hands of skilled staff it produces excellent results. Containers of newly made cuttings are placed under completely sealed tents where the humidity is near to a hundred per cent. As the plants root, the humidity is slowly reduced and the light level is increased, both changes being achieved by nothing more sophisticated than cutting holes in the plastic sheet. In a way it is rather sad to see all those clever nozzles, compressors and controls abandoned for a few bits of thick wire, a sheet of plastic, a few clothes-pegs and a sharp knife. One secret of the plastic sheet's popularity is that a skilled propagator can tailor conditions to suit each batch of cuttings. At last there is a way of applying those specific research findings.

Micropropagation

All this interest was focused on the leafy stem cutting, the type of cutting that seemed to hold the future of vegetative propagation, but in the last few years this has had to share centre stage with a much smaller but more dynamic player, the micropropagule. Like its bigger sister it too responded to chemical treatment and environmental conditions, but in this case the chemicals turn out to be a cocktail of complex organic molecules that both nourish and control the cutting, while its living environment is inside a piece of laboratory glassware. To the traditional eye these in-vitro cuttings are as unfamiliar as their surroundings: stem tips each only a few millimetres long.

As the name micropropagation suggests, this technique uses tiny fragments of the mother plant. It is a two-part process. The first task is to remove the tiny propagule, made up of a few simple cells, re-establish it in its sealed, sterile world of a glass container and encourage it to increase in size. Once that has been achieved the tiny blob of plant life can be subcultured and the programme repeated to build up the clone. The second stage starts when the blobs are induced to bud off tiny shoots. These explants, as they are termed, are removed and treated as mini cuttings until they are complete with roots, shoots and leaves, and robust enough to grow successfully on the open glasshouse bench. There are many variations to this story, but all aim to mass-produce new members of a clone. It is not obvious, but the offspring of this high-tech method of propagation are all around us, from some of the crops we eat to very many of the flowering and foliage houseplants lined up on the florist's shelves.

Taken from a 3500-year-old temple mural at Deir el-Bahri, Egypt, this sketch shows slaves loading trees onto ships of Queen Hatshepsut's fleet at Punt on the Red Sea coast, making it the first illustration of international plant translocation.

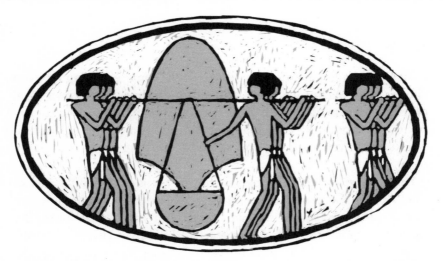

12 TRANSLOCATION: THE ACT OF TRANSPLANTING

Throughout this book I have referred to transplanting as one of the everyday activities of the cultivator and, although we don't have a word for it, the same goes for "trans-seeding". Translocation is at the very heart of man's manipulation of the plant kingdom for our own ends. We have seen that on a global scale it has redistributed virtually all the major crops, many across thousands of miles of ocean to continents far from their ancestors' place of origin. On a local level, enthusiastic gardeners exchange plants between gardens and from place to place within their own garden. Commercial growers move trees and shrubs several times within the nursery before they come finally to rest as part of a new orchard, plantation or amenity landscape. Long-term success in their new homes depends on a combination of the adaptability of the plant and the efforts of the cultivator to modify site conditions. In the short term it is down to some very basic biology.

It is said that for many people moving house is one of life's most traumatic experiences, but the ability to relocate and start life afresh on a new site presents the vast majority of plants with a far more unnatural and potentially life-endangering challenge. Seed dispersal is a natural strategy, and sowing seed imitates nature fairly closely, but there is no natural equivalent to transplanting. A few plants including some cactus break up and are blown or pushed to new locations, and trees and shrubs can sometimes re-establish having been uprooted in floods, but these are uncommon occurrences and plants don't depend on them as a dispersal mechanism. As we have seen, some creeping or even shattered stems sprout roots, and although that's certainly a form of vegetative propagation it is hardly transplanting. No, there's no doubt about it: transplanting simply is not natural. Yet it works, from pricking out the smallest seedling to moving large trees.

The need to prick out arises from our habit of sowing seeds so thickly that the resultant seedlings very soon suffer if they are not given more space. As we have seen elsewhere, both the skilled broadcasters of yesteryear and today's precision drills overcome the problem as, in a wasteful way, does thinning out. Pricking out is mainly associated with sowing in containers, where it goes back to Roman times when Columella advised doing it at the six-leaf stage, rather later than twentieth-century research would suggest. Today there is less and less pricking out done. On larger nurseries most bedding plants are precision-sown. Two advances may have helped growers to avoid this costly and laborious task: free-draining "sterile" composts and better light. Victorian manuals stress the dire consequences of the soil going "sour" in large containers. It is hard to get to the bottom of this particular worry. It could be that "sourness" referred to the presence of "damping off" disease fungi, as they are more rampant among closely growing seedlings. As to the value of improved light, anyone who has germinated seeds in their house will know how seedlings can flop over when the hypocotyl, the stem beneath the cotyledons, becomes etiolated; it can happen in a few hours of low light, and now as then, the only remedy is to bury the offending organ when transplanting the seedling.

Transplanting has been a standard part of many production programmes for centuries. It allows cultivators to produce young plants safely within the care of a nursery before moving them, spaced out across field, orchard or forest. Annual crop plants such as cabbage, Brussels sprouts, leeks and in some countries tomatoes, raised in seedbeds are lifted with little or no soil, graded and transplanted, spaced out in their final positions. It is the same idea with onion sets but in this case the immature transplant is a tiny resting bulb. Although the numbers per unit of land area are lower, young forest and fruit trees are transplanted from nursery to plantation, as are coffee, tea and rubber. On a global scale the prize for the greatest number of transplants handled in a year must go to either the foresters or the rice-growers; both deal with tens of millions of young plants every season. Each worker's daily output is almost beyond belief for the suburban gardener taking the whole of a Saturday afternoon to put in two dozen bedding plants. In Canada foresters manage seven thousand seedling tree transplants per day, but rice planters may do more than twice that number.

Handwork is still common where the terrain is difficult but, as you would expect, transplanting has produced its own machines: equipment capable of handling either bare-root or containerised plants and able to do it at high speed if the conditions are right and the fields well cultivated. It is very unlikely that the vegetables you buy will have had a trowel or dibber anywhere near them.

The dibber, I should say, is the archetype traditional tool for transplanting peg plants (bare-root plants with little more than a taproot). British dibbers look like a pointed stick with a tee-handle on one end. The French *plantoir* has a one-sided, slightly angled handle making it look something like an upside-down sawn-off golf club. Given that they were the masters of intensive potager cultivation, it could be worth while picking one up next time you are over there, although they may have changed shape since my 1900 reference was hot off the press.

With either model in the hands of a skilled worker, no that's wrong, the *hand* of a skilled worker, the job is done at walking pace. Stab into the soil, twist, pull out, clean hole left, in goes the plant from a bunch held in the other hand, in goes the dibber again at a slight angle alongside the first hole, push the soil firm against the root, twist and pull out, walk on. Don't stand up; of course your back aches, but you are not being paid to admire the view. Larger transplants or those with a ball of soil attached are usually put in with a trowel. Equipment tends to become ever more elaborate, but the modern trowel is compact and streamlined compared with its more cumbersome predecessor whose blade had a semicircular cross-section, which while useful for taking out a core of soil, must have been awkward for more general work.

For the agronomist a plant's ability to re-root after disturbance and root loss before the top suffers irreversible damage through a shortage of water is one of the most fortunate of the "miracles of nature". Producing roots on demand is standard practice in the plant world; only the main elements of a root system are permanent, the rest being short-lived and continuously replaced as a plant maintains or returns to its typical root/shoot ratio [g]. Young roots have a huge capacity to produce other roots which, unlike stems producing stems, they do without going through any complicated bud development. In most woody plants older roots manage to do the same thing, although it takes a bit longer. This regenerative ability is just as well, as transplants can lose huge amounts of root. In some experiments as much as ninety per cent has been retrieved from the seedbed, left behind when the young plants were lifted. It is the same with the larger trees and shrubs we are going to meet a little later, as Dr Tony Kendle found when researching the subject at Liverpool University. In one experiment we did at Bath University many years ago, we removed different amounts of root from two-year-old ash tree seedlings. You almost have to finish up with a cutting to be certain of killing such plants, provided they are looked after and not allowed to dry out. Such severe root removal was not an original idea. In 1896 in his book *The New Horticulture* an American, Professor Henry Martyn Stringfellow advocated planting apple trees that had had their roots cut off so that the transplant's new root system developed in harmony with the local soil formation. The technique has become known as "stringfellowing", perhaps because people felt that with such a drastic method it was safer to be able to pass the blame back to an identifiable inventor should anything go wrong. In fact it is on record that he got prize-winning results.

Nowadays we associate transplanting large tree and shrub specimens with the contemporary demand for instant results in the garden or urban landscape but sadly this has frequently led to a landscape of dead or moribund trees. Following an outstanding career in several branches of botany, Professor Anthony Bradshaw FRS dedicated much of his time and legendary enthusiasm to tackle this and other problems facing amenity horticulture as it ventured into ever more challenging sites. Tony Bradshaw's team showed that while vandalism, mechanical damage and waterlogging were significant problems on some sites, drought was a very common cause of transplant failure, typically exacerbated by the transpiration from weeds or turf growing around the base of the tree. Even when the soil moisture deficit is confined to the planting pit it can be disastrous as, regardless of whether the transplants are bare-root, balled and burlapped, or container-grown, they are all restricted to accessing the moisture held in less than 0.3 cubic metre of soil.

This impatience for instant trees is far from new; the wealthy and powerful of ancient Greece, Rome and even before that Egypt had large trees moved. Some measure of its importance can be gained from the formidable list of famous writers that addressed the challenge. It includes Xenophon, Theophrastus, Columella, Virgil, Seneca, Cato and Pliny. Their instructions are virtually identical to those we give today: take care over the size, depth and shape of planting pit, also the cultivation of the base of the pit and the preparation and nature of the soil backfill. Be careful to bind the rootball [g] and prevent roots drying out through wind or sun. Give the tree a similar orientation after moving, and thin out the crown. Did they, I wonder, also have problems with their contractors?

Planting pits for trees and shrubs are, or should be, only a transient feature in the life of any specimen. If the land beyond their edges is so unsatisfactory that roots cannot spread to colonise it, the site is simply in no state to receive transplants. In this respect it is conditions to the sides of the hole that matter most, as typically roots endeavour to spread laterally through the topsoil. Today we use various tools including subsoilers, rippers and chisel ploughs to improve soil structure on development sites, but few go so far as the famous American horticulturist E. A. Wilson recommended for private gardeners. His method of making planting pits big enough was both labour-saving and fun:

> Dynamite is cheaper than digging and in every way much better. Half to a whole stick of Atlas Farm Powder 40 per cent, inserted from 2 to 3 feet [60 to 90cm] down and exploded will loosen ordinary land 6 to 10 feet [2 to 3m] downward and outward. Excavating to the required depth is then easy and since the soil is broken in all directions the roots penetrate and ramify without obstruction.

Gardening is such a tranquil pastime.

So it has been known for a long time that what a transplant cannot cope with is its remaining roots drying out in transit between nursery and final site. Work done by a colleague of mine some twenty years ago showed that seedling birch transplants suffered, and some were killed, if their roots were exposed to a drying breeze for just twenty minutes. And yet almost any day in the late autumn you can see pick-up trucks driving at 70 m.p.h. with bundles of tree transplants hanging out of the back. Poor unsuspecting customers; sticking dead roots in a bucket of water at the end of the journey won't revive them. Once a dead tree, always a dead tree.

An elaborate strategy that dates back more than two hundred years is still occasionally used on older trees to try and stimulate the production of young roots before the plant is lifted. A year before the tree is to be moved a trench is dug around it about half a metre from the trunk, the roots severed and the trench backfilled with topsoil. This results in a considerable regrowth of new roots from the cut ends and from just behind them. The plant is, of course, re-establishing its root/shoot ratio referred to above and in a place were most of the new root can be successfully saved, often with the ball of soil intact, when the transplant is later taken up.

Root-balling had a long history well before *The Horticultural Register* of 1832 reported the success of a new device used to move large trees in Bushy Park. It was "suitable for specimens requiring ten or more men to lift them", indeed it could accommodate "as many men as can conveniently apply their strength to it as are wanted". Surely this must have been William Barron's famous apparatus – or a crib from it – as it was in February 1831 that it had first gone into action to move three 12m high cedars at Elvaston Castle. Based on the success of this move, Barron became famous as the nation's best-known large-tree transplanter. His record success was an ancient churchyard yew, which, according to *The Gardeners' Chronicle*, had a root-ball weighing over 50 tonnes. With the advent of today's lifting equipment, root-balls wrapped in hessian and wire-netting are still preferred to exposed roots. Nevertheless, as long ago as the end of the eighteenth century, bare-root specimens of mature trees were being moved successfully within estates when parks and grounds fell into the hands of the landscape movement. Several horse-drawn tree-lifters and transporters were developed capable of handling the ton or more of branches, trunk and roots involved in such massive undertakings. Lithographs of that time are notorious for their artistic embellishment, but one I have seen shows a 10m specimen on its side on a huge cart pulled by two horses. The several men on the guy-ropes are convincing, but I doubt the authenticity of the chap up in the branches!

Bare-root specimens experience exactly the same root loss trauma when they are containerised in the nursery prior to being transplanted into their final location. Only a few years ago this practice resulted in many deaths, but nurserymen have become very skilled in managing this kind of post-operative stress and now most transplants are back to being fine specimens within a few months. It is beyond the scope of this book to go into the many aspects of this work, but a balance between water demand and supply appears to be a key factor. Pruning away part of the canopy reduces water loss, while "at the other end" its controlled application is of equal importance. By the time the tree has fully recovered and is once again a vigorous transplant the container must receive several litres every day.

Sadly for huge numbers of transplants, this irrigation stops when they reach their final location and we are left with the familiar and totally predictable but unnecessary sight of the dying and the dead. More than half a century ago, E. A. Wilson warned us to "never let the demon drought assert himself". Clearly this need not happen. Transplants from containers to either larger containers or into the open land should hardly feel a thing, as the dentists say.

There are a few problems, however, and they are all related to leaving the plant in the original container too long. The most common is the difficulty of getting water into the mass of roots and soil that form the root-ball. It is easy to wet the surrounding fresh soil, but the water penetrates only slowly to the place where it is really needed. It is not uncommon to see a transplanted young tree with its leaves falling off with drought stress while the maintenance staff declare their commitment to tender loving care and point to wet soil.

The other problem only makes itself known a few years and a strong wind later: root spiralling. Roots typically grow out from the base of a plant, out and a bit down, but not straight down, at least not for long, even if they are parsnips! The container of course frustrates their internal sense of the horizontal and vertical. This results in roots spiralling round and round the inside surface of the pot. The plant is pot-bound. This condition not only brings us back to the watering problem but, supposing the roots now strike out into the surrounding soil, they leave behind a coil connecting them to the stem. As every camper knows, coils in guy-ropes are a bad idea; come a storm and the roots literally unwind and over goes the tree. As we shall see later (p. 339), designers are well aware of the problem and there are several designs of container that help prevent this root-spiralling

A recently planted example of a Wellsborne fan, a design devised to investigate the effect of increased density/competition on crop performance. When so treated African marigolds differ greatly in plant size, form, flower number and length of flowering season.

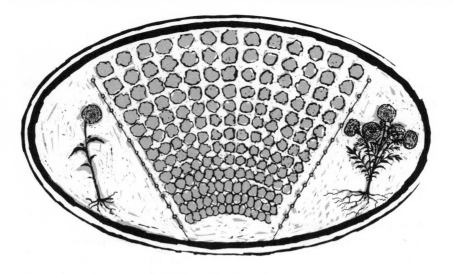

13 LIVING SPACE

ROOM TO GROW

"Give everything room to grow. See how much you can get out of your garden not how much you can get into it." So said Mr Middleton, the first broadcasting gardening guru. He owed his fame to his leading role in the "Dig for Victory" campaign of the Second World War, and this is one of the homilies that, as the nation's gardener, he or his scriptwriters came up with every week; it was, as usual, excellent advice.

It is an easy mistake to think of the needs of a single plant as the be-all and end-all of the requirements for a successful crop. The pitfall is to overlook the fact that crop plants live in a community – a community that until a very few years ago was made up of both their own kind and a few uninvited species from the local flora: weeds. Communal behaviour is the life-blood of ecologists; and their understandings of how individuals respond to the influence of their neighbours, be they of the same kind or unrelated, are known respectively as "intra-specific" and "inter-specific" competition. This knowledge transferred to the arable field has had a major influence on today's approach to agronomy. "How far apart?" is a standard query in any *Gardener's Question Time*, whether you are talking about apple trees or lettuces. It is just possible that the questioner is concerned not to waste space, but it is far more likely to be prompted by the justifiable fear that overcrowding will ruin everything.

If we try to put ourselves in the shoes (what shoes?) of the first cultivators it must have been a difficult concept to grasp that more seeds and seedlings did not mean bigger harvests, in other words that there was an optimum population density of crop plants per unit area. Perhaps the understanding that those other plants we know as weeds were causing real damage and crop losses was easier to grasp then. After all, the women would have been very aware of the problem of extra mouths to feed from the same cooking pot.

Intra-specific competition and crop spacing

Weeds, or if you prefer it non-crop plants, are often the most obvious players in the struggle for space that goes on within a crop, but nature does not differentiate between inter-specific and intra-specific competition. Indeed the struggle within the crop, between individuals of the same kind, is as a rule even more deadly because the individuals concerned all require exactly the same conditions.

From the agronomist's point of view, intra-specific competition can be a huge problem made no easier to bear because in most cases it is self-inflicted. One landowner avoided such a mistake by personally thinning a 100-acre (40ha) timber plantation. The notice he erected later informed passers-by that "This plantation has been thinned by John, fourth Duke of Bedford, contrary to the advice and opinion of his gardener." It is not clear if the notice was intended to exonerate the gardener but the trees' subsequent excellent growth no doubt embarrassed him.

I can't remember anyone ever suggesting that any of the vegetables we produced on the holding I was brought up on were too big. Marrows and beetroot could be too old, but that was a different matter. Maybe it was simply the food shortage during and just after the Second World War. Anyhow, things started to change in the 1960s and now small is beautiful, or to be more accurate some size less than plant-breeders have enabled the plant to achieve is.

Before we get into controlling the bit of the plant we eat, let us look at the extreme case of overcrowding when there are so many crop plants in a given area that they smother each other. Of course it is disastrous, but it very rarely leads to a total wipeout. What happens is that a small percentage of the individuals get some slight advantage at a very early stage. From this they pull away from their fellows on the basis of the old adage that nothing succeeds like success. The result is a kind of socialist's worst nightmare, with about ten per cent of the population getting all the environmental assets and the rest failing even to reproduce.

Avoiding such a state of affairs was well understood by the medieval seed broadcaster, in fact he or she did rather better than the early seed-drills which introduced the curse of rectangularity – lots of space between rows and too little in the row. Rectifying this depended on two things, getting the distance between the rows right and thinning out the plants in the row.

If you look back to the dozens of late nineteenth-century texts on vegetable growing you will find extremely precise row distances for all kinds of crops: 12 inches for carrots, 15 for leeks, 18 for parsnip and on and on. By 1907 British farmers were receiving similar advice via the Board of Agriculture and Fisheries leaflet number 169 that instructed them to sow mangels in rows from 26 to 29 inches apart and thin the seedlings to 12 to 14 inches between plants, depending on the row setting. It was these distances, still in use over thirty years later, that gave us our World War Two instructions as to how to Dig for Victory. For seed-sown crops, distances within the row were achieved by thinning out surplus seedlings, in other words either pulling up or hoeing off the surplus, work often done in several stages each stage to a set distance: first thinning, 1 inch; second thinning, 4 inches; final thinning 8 inches. It was not until well into the 1950s that such spacings were challenged, when the art of giving plants just the right amount of room become a science and in so doing provided the cultivator with a powerful tool to manipulate the size and form of the individual items that make up the harvest.

The fresh mind was that of Professor John Bleasdale, who saw that to supply the size of produce now popular with shoppers, growers should apply two long-recognised ecological principles. One was that, up to the point of overcrowding discussed above, the closer plants are to one another the smaller they will grow, and the other was that plants typically, and most efficiently, occupy circular territories. The advent of precision seed-drills made spacing out the seed possible while herbicides then just recently developed removed the need to hoe out weeds between the rows. For the first time, technical advances offered better crop-spacing than a skilled broadcaster had managed well over a hundred years before. John Bleasdale's work gave us the machine settings to deliver vegetables of the size the market wanted while making full use of the land

Arable farmers use the same reasoning to achieve the best results in terms of productivity per unit area, with everything from wheat to sugarbeet. The only difference is that the ecology expresses itself indirectly. No one is judging the size of the ears of wheat; what matters is the tonnage and quality of the grain. You might think it was exactly a similar story with the sugarbeet, but in this case there has to be a balance between the gross tonnage of all the roots and their percentage sugar content, and that can vary with root size.

Spacing also influences the morphology of individual plants. Most species do not produce side-shoots or branches if the space they would grow into is too shady to support photosynthesis. We have seen how seed-producers use this to prevent harvesting immature seed. Both the major harvests of woodland – timber and polewood – are best without side branches, and so are fibre crops such as jute and hemp. Different as these types of crop are, all use plant density to obtain the desired quality. Clearly, crop spacing influences not only the overall size, shape and prosperity of individual plants but also the proportions of their constituent parts. From the cultivator's point of view this provides a chance to manipulate the harvest index (the ratio of the harvest organ to the whole above-ground plant).

Controlling the size and shape of crop plants

Why work to make things smaller when the idea of husbandry has always been to *grow* plants? Typically, those blessed with a perception of quality look for an optimum size. This appears to be as true for apples and cabbages as for plays and orchestral concerts, but it seems there are exceptions. Today I went to the supermarket. Two mini-cauliflowers in a pack were lined up alongside extra-large cauliflowers, with normal specimens below them; all were of the same excellent quality promising the same flavour. Weight for weight, by far the most expensive were the minis, then came the extra-large and cheapest of all the normal-sized curds. While these differences may in part reflect production costs the reason why anyone would opt to pay more per mouthful of cauliflower curd from unusually small or large heads is I suspect something to do with fashion in the appearance of dinner-party dishes. I don't however have to guess how to achieve these size differences; it is all to do with spacing. When the harvest organ is virtually the whole above-ground part of the plant, as with cabbages or lettuce, controlling size is usually achieved by plant density as we saw in the previous section on competition.

Working to reduce the number of harvest items seems almost as perverse, but both flowers and fruits can be initiated in such numbers that if the reserves of the parent plant are spread between them, come the harvest none will have developed to our satisfaction. On these occasions, to achieve the required size, the cultivator resorts to pruning in the guise of disbudding or fruit thinning. Chrysanthemum exhibitors aiming for the largest and most perfect blooms carry this to the extreme of allowing only one or two flowers to develop per plant (see Chapter 5).

Concern for the size of the whole plant comes from two directions, namely fitting the plant into the space available and keeping it within manageable dimensions, for example when you are growing tree fruit.

Controlling size is mostly a problem in decorative horticulture, in protected cropping or in fruit-growing. Pruning either shoots or roots or both might seem to be the obvious answer, but it would be my choice of last resort. Among the better ways one may exploit is the phenomenon of genetic mutations known as dwarf forms. More are being found, but to date there are only a few shrubs where growers have noted and vegetatively propagated a mutant of dramatically reduced stature, such as *Viburnum opulus* 'Nanum' and *Cornus stolonifera* 'Kelseyi'. Decorative horticulture abounds with examples of carefully selected "short" cultivars of annual flowers, bulbs and other herbaceous perennials.

People have long wished to have crop plants that, left to their own devices, did not grow out of reach. The answer in the future is almost certainly in the hands of the geneticist, but for more than a century it has rested in the nursery, achieved by grafting. Sadly, little has been made of this technique in decorative horticulture. The drive to keep fruit trees within manageable dimensions provides the prime examples. Here the search for dwarfing rootstocks has produced dramatic results for apples, and the work continues to match these for other tree fruits. A vigorous rootstock sends a lot of raw materials upwards, whereas a slow-growing type delivers only a limited amount. The former boosts the scion's growth, the latter throttles it back. Reduced vigour is the effect that is usually needed in fruit trees, but in some ornamental shrubs the reciprocal arrangement provides a useful boost to inherently slow-growing but attractive types.

THE CURSE OF WEEDS (INTER-SPECIFIC COMPETITION)
Weeds

We know from their remains that weeds have been living alongside crops since the very beginnings of agriculture. Providing accommodation for some locals would not matter if only they did not try to take over and smother the intended plants. Every kind of crop is vulnerable, as competition for water, light and nutrients can kill young oak transplants as surely as wheat seedlings. I have put these three potentially lethal factors in this order, as water stress has played by far the biggest part in my own battle with weeds, owing to my involvement with transplanting trees and shrubs onto amenity landscapes. Just over one hundred years ago William Bear, writing in the *Journal of the Board of Agriculture*, reminded us that "experiments had proved that nothing is so deleterious to the growth of young fruit trees as letting grass grow closely round them". It still is, and that goes for all other kinds of woody transplants; it is time we took note! Our never-ending fight to control weeds has cost mankind millions upon millions of back-breaking hours of toil. Trying to outwit them by understanding their life style has spawned a special botanical discipline known as weed biology, while trying to kill them has resulted in a vast array of mechanical, physical, biological and chemical devices. All this and yet across the world weeds still flourish and account for massive crop losses.

Gurus who address amateur gardening clubs are fond of telling their audiences that a weed is "a plant out of place" – a definition first attributed to an American horticulturist, Professor W. J. Beal of Michigan State College. You could be forgiven for thinking that such a definition should suffice, but its only one of ten given in L. J. King's *Weeds of the World*. The rest home in on particular unpleasant characteristics such as "competitive and aggressive habits", "growing in an undesired location", "of wild and rank growth", "persistence and resistance to control or eradication", "having large populations", "useless, unwanted and undesirable", "harmful to man, animals and crops" and "unsightly in the landscape".

I am going to finish this outpouring of condemnation with two quotes, the first from the late Professor William Stearn, that most learned of botanists. In his view:

> Weeds are not so much a botanical as a human, psychological category within the plant kingdom, for a weed is simply a plant which in a particular place at a particular time arouses human dislike and attempts are made at its eradication or control, usually because it competes with more desirable plants, sometimes because it serves as a host to their pests and diseases or it is unpalatable or dangerous to domestic beasts.

Stearn, however, did not go on to warn us, as the sages of Suffolk warned George Ewart Evans, that our attempts to eradicate weeds are futile. They, he writes, held that all who cultivate the soil are cursed to struggle against them forever, after our eviction from Eden.

Well, not exactly all, as this second quote shows. It comes from the dust-jacket of F. C. King's *The Weed Problem: A New Approach*:

> A lettuce bed richly variegated with an assortment of robust weeds does not depress or alarm him. Over cultivation is his bugbear and to him a dug soil is a spoiled soil. Plants, like human beings, must live in groups and co-operate in a give and take system of economy that is for the good of all. Healthy weeds and unblemished plants are as often as not natural companions, and while the living weed is not necessarily stealing the crops' nourishment, but may even be contributing to it, the decomposed seed is bound to return to the soil the wherewithal for humus. The author believes in nature's method of a humus carpet in preference to dug-in compost, and if the weeds of this green carpet are not sufficiently abundant, he advocates the sowing of weed seeds.

It is true that studies in weed biology did not reach their zenith for another twenty years or so, but the basics were well enough understood by the world's cultivators and had been for thousands of years.

The typical harmful weed is one that alive, dried or in seed will pollute the harvest. For hundreds of years, corn-cockle poisoned our wheat, and ragwort our horses' hay. Today, any foreign foliage among the baby salad leaves might cause distress around the suburban salad bowl; indeed, so important is it to keep this harvest weed-free that growers go to the huge expense of sterilising the beds before sowing the saladings.

The idea of a plant out of place is most suited to the decorative garden, where locating each planting is a basic tenet of design, and even a few spontaneous specimens are said to ruin the effect of a planting – this in spite of the legion of serendipitous combinations of plants that add so much to the beauty of countless gardens.

Among monoculture crops, "out-of-placeness" clearly applies to every species other than one, but it is not a definition used by farmers, and I doubt if it was ever intended to include the idea of weeds as competitors for space and environmental resources. This role as competitor for water, light and nutrients is however the really serious issue and the one that costs mankind millions of tonnes of produce every day of every year. It makes weeds a major concern to agronomists worldwide, and supports the science of weed biology and all the branches of the industry of weed control which in their various ways wage war by mechanical, chemical, physical and biological means.

This war has gone on for thousands of years, in many cases against the same species, but so closely do the life cycles of weeds harmonise with our crops and cultivation practices that final victory eludes us. *Lolium temulentum*, darnel to us, was decried as a weed in wheat-fields by Dioscorides, complained of in the Bible, condemned by Roman farmers and superbly illustrated by an unknown Byzantine artist in AD 512. So we have been warned about this pest for more than two thousand years, but it is still there!

Weeds depend on us to provide them with a home. Very few are of any significance in even semi-natural parts of our countryside. So where do weeds come from? Those who specialise in the study of weed biology consider that such plants are recruited from two groups – plants, usually foreign introductions, that were once nurtured by man but are no longer wanted, and wild native plants that found conditions under cultivation much to their liking. Within both groups there are both perennials and annuals.

Only a very few perennials have become serious weeds of arable land as they are generally unable to withstand the combination of in-crop weed control and inter-crop tillage. Perennial weeds such as couch-grass and ground elder

(*Agropyron repens* and *Aegopodium podagraria*) are however the bane of plantation crops such as soft fruit and permanent decorative plantings from suburban hedge bottoms and National Trust rock-gardens to the massed shrubs of trendy housing estates and supermarket car park landscapes. Once established among the desired plants they are exceedingly difficult to eradicate by either chemical or mechanical means. The old gardeners' obsession with "cleaning the land" before planting remains fully justified. In many cases the weed's ramets are brought onto site in topsoil imported to "make up the planting beds" at the end of a development project. As I drive past heaps bristling with couch I can't help wondering if we really are the "Nation of Gardeners" we boast of being.

The annuals are mostly what ecologists refer to as "ruderals". In nature, some ruderals live in semi-desert conditions and seize their moment when the rains come. In nature, our annual weeds are far from conspicuous. They are short-lived, shadowy characters that lurk about as seeds waiting for an opportunity to pop up, grow fast, and set another crop of seeds before they are overtaken by either the climate or other members of the local flora. Of course, if you follow that kind of life style it is important to produce a lot of seeds and to be able to spread them round, as it is impossible to predict where favourable conditions might occur.

The number of weed seeds in long-cultivated land is truly amazing: ten thousand per square metre is regarded as a conservative estimate by most researchers. If weeds are allowed to seed the number builds up each year, as although seeds buried within the soil eventually die, many have a tenacious grip on life. Fallows and leys brought back into arable cultivation often sprout a cover of weeds from seeds left over from long ago. That's the reason why an unsprayed wheat-field can still turn red with poppy flowers even if it has been kept weed-free for years. Indeed it was the dramatic soil disturbance of the battlefields of Flanders that triggered the huge and now famous growth of poppies from seed shed in an earlier, peaceful time. We should not have been surprised; John Ray told us in his *Flora of Cambridgeshire* back in 1660 that poppy seeds are "still capable of germination after being kept ten years".

Each needs a space to grow in; in nature they can use any small patch of bare earth – the microsite we met earlier in Chapter 3.

When the cultivator comes along and makes a seedbed the whole area becomes one huge microsite – or should that now be macrosite? Up come the weed seedlings in their thousands in direct competition with the crop. When those seeds lying just beneath the surface get an appropriate signal, they have a good chance of a clear home run, free from competition. These signals can be light or fluctuating soil temperature, either of which tells the waiting seed that there is no blanket of leaves above them to smother them at birth should they be foolish enough to germinate before the coast is clear. Other environmental conditions tell the seeds which season it is, and if they get the right message they start to grow. Some, like cleavers (*Galium aparine*), germinate in the autumn and hang about as seedlings over winter, ready for a rush of growth in the spring; others remain dormant until spring and then complete their life cycle in just a few weeks. To be more accurate, it may take some species the best part of the growing season to do it, but others are so precocious that they even have flower-buds in the axils of their cotyledons.

You might think that weeds must be locals; after all, no one deliberately plants them or introduces them to their fields and gardens. Well, you would be wrong on several counts; of course there are local bad boys, but weeds are often foreigners brought along when crop seeds are imported. In some cases these accidents took place thousands of years ago but in others much more recently. One extremely pernicious example is a kind of swap that has taken place between South Africa and Australia. Each now has several members of the other's flora as some of its worst weeds, far worse than when at home. On top of this they both have our European weeds to contend with. In fact it is very hard to find an indigenous species in the fields of some Australian farms, so complete have been these overseas invasions. Charles Darwin remarked on the already evident problem of introduced weeds in New Zealand as early as 1834 during one of his excursions from the *Beagle*. He tells of two species that were deliberately introduced: leeks "as a flavour, by a French ship" and docks that "will for ever remain a proof of the rascality of an Englishman who sold the seeds for those of the tobacco plant".

As to setting out to plant them – well, that has happened and some people think it is still going on. Some species that were introduced as ornamentals or crops have become pernicious weeds. The very tenacious little *Veronica filliformis* which is now a common weed of lawns was introduced, indeed it was sold as an alpine for rock gardens as recently as the mid 1930s. A bit before that, a novel introduction in the form of a spectacular herbaceous perennial for the wild garden became instantly popular in large country-house gardens; nowadays we know it as Japanese knotweed! Today's worry is with the escape of water plants from ponds and aquaria into our rivers and canals where some might form huge masses to the detriment of the local plant and animal life. If we go back far enough, weeds and crops seem to merge; for example, oats and wild oats may have been gathered as one potential harvest. Now huge areas of our best cereal land are plagued with a residue of wild oat seed. Clearly we should take heed of such examples, but caution should not become a panic or trigger a witch-hunt against our rich exotic garden flora.

Weed control

For millennia the tillers of the soil have struggled to rid their land of these competitors; only in the last fifty years have they succeeded. In 1910 one farmer counted 29 species of "weed" in just 100 square yards (9m by 9m) of his cereal crop, 17 of which he described as "abundant". Today when you stand on the edge of a wheat-field and look into a mass of vegetation consisting of only one type of plant, the chosen crop, it is a five-thousand-year dream come true. Perhaps the longest of man's battles against nature is won, at least for that particular crop. If something has taken five thousand years to control, let alone eradicate, it is fairly obviously going to be hard to persuade the victors to give up their successful weapons, and so it has proved with herbicides.

Unlike most utterances of the anonymous rural sages that inhabit the folk literature of every country, "One year's seeding is seven years' weeding" is true, and remarkably accurate. The question has always been how to destroy the weeds without killing the crop at the same time. For the first few thousands of years, hand-pulling seems to have been favoured, unless you were the one doing the pulling. For the best results some farmers believed in "doing the work over the period of a waning moon and completing it by Midsummer Day". As an incentive to finish the miserable task of pulling corn-cockle out of spring wheat or "corn showing the Lent grain" as they would say, end-of-job "field feasts" were held and a competitive edge introduced by promising

311

the most industrious weeder the largest piece of cake.

Pre-seeding cultivations must have been of some benefit in keeping the weed population down. It was a common medieval practice to till the land several times before a spring cereal sowing, which presumably resulted in what we now call the stale-seedbed approach. The first cultivation encourages weed seed germination, while subsequent harrowings or hoeings destroy the seedlings while at the same time stimulating more to come up to be similarly destroyed before the crop is sown.

Cutting or slashing down the weed tops is a poor strategy. To start with, it is extremely difficult to do, as in most crops there's not enough room to swing a hook. Secondly, it is now known by experimentation to be almost a waste of effort, as even the remaining low cover of weed foliage suppresses crop growth. Farmers and gardeners may well have discovered this by simple observation millennia ago; however foresters did not, and it is still not hard to find this essentially futile activity taking place in among young trees "in a plantation near you".

Hand-pulling arable crop weeds is a task going back into the annual rites of every agrarian culture that has left us evidence of its crop husbandry. The species that got pulled seem to have been those that had the audacity to stick their heads above the crop, and that's the way it has been with all the aids ever since. For hundreds of years in Britain farmers employed women and children to pull the larger and more damaging species. From late medieval times onwards weeding tongs may have helped. They look like a blacksmith's pincers and are "to be used after rain", but I doubt if they were in general use. To be fair, hand-weeding included cutting as well as pulling. There seem to have been several kinds of cutting implement; the sickle or grass hook cut weeds above ground while the weed hook severed stems at ground level. To do this the worker first held down tall weeds with a forked stick, his "crotch", then cut them through with the weed hook. This long-gone tool had a narrow head shaped rather like half an arrow; sharpened on its inside edges it cut as it was pulled back towards the user. By the mid seventeenth century we find reference to augmenting hand-pulling and hooking by tools that attacked below ground, the spud and the grubber. The spud is a simple long-handled tool with a chisel-like blade used to stab at the base of large weeds, while the grubber levered the weed out of the ground, holding it between its two prongs. Although the field tool has long taken up museum residency having been replaced by the cultivator, it is still available in its diminutive form to grub daisies from the lawn – for those with an aversion to herbicides and weedy lawns.

Thistles, you should know, "must not be cut before St John's Day" (23 June). In Devon delay is poetically advised:

Cut 'em in May, and they come again next day;
Cut 'em in June and you cut 'em too soon.
Cut 'em in July and they might die;
Cut 'em in August and die they must.

I very much doubt it.

Stories of life in the country abound with the drudgery of hand-weeding docks, thistles and wild oats from cereal fields; Thomas Hardy's *Ruined Maid* was certainly not the only one "tired of spudding up docks", and it is not over yet. Last summer the roadsides of Wiltshire were resplendent in two shades of yellow, one from the flowers of ragwort, the other from the safety jackets of the chaps who were pulling up the plants in an attempt to stop them seeding into the surrounding fields. This is as much a bit of social history as an aspect of good agricultural practice. Ragwort is a "notifiable" weed; by law you must control it, as it is poisonous to livestock. For many years little if any notice was taken of this, but now there is a new and powerful voice in the British countryside: the middle-class horse owners, whose horses are at greatest risk. It is a brave weed or county highways officer that stands up to that lot. Ragwort is not only a British problem; it is one of the many weeds we accidentally exported to the Southern Hemisphere in sacks of agricultural seeds. Early in the twentieth century the government botanist for the state of Victoria in Australia put his own spin on hand-pulling the menace. He initiated prizes for the schoolchildren who gathered the most stems and within weeks he had twenty thousand; it sounds impressive but it is less than the seed produced by two large specimens.

Ploughing, or its garden equivalent, digging, between crops also helped to control weeds, but arable land could get so infested, particularly with creeping grasses, that tillage had little long-term effect and cultivators resorted to "paring and burning", or as the seventeenth-century writer Walter Blith knew it, "denshiring". This was a massive task consisting of first slicing off and heaping up the surface soil together with its weeds, their tops, roots, rhizomes and many seeds. Once dry this was burnt and the ash and partly baked soil spread. The very fact that it would burn shows just how weed-infested the fields must have been. The same technique was used to turn pasture into arable in which case there could be enough ash produced to return some nutrients and help reduce soil acidity.

Hoes

I strongly suspect that few archaeologists are gardeners; maybe they are away doing their own kind of digging at critical times of the year. The objects described as hoes shown in photographs and even in the cases in the British museum are a very mixed bunch, many of them ill-suited to weed control; they are, I think, examples of the tillage tools we have already met. Nevertheless there are within our museums, distributed among assemblages of old tools like some offering at a car-boot sale, the remains of some once very serviceable weed killers with blade settings similar to today's draw-hoes. They were more than capable of cutting weeds off at or below soil level. When and where the first weeding hoes were used remains unknown. They have been found in archaeological digs on sites spanning thousands of years, associated with both farms and gardens.

British farmers seem to have been unconvinced about these various mattock-like tools, in spite of their use during four hundred years of Roman occupation (see page 245). In these islands it was not until the nineteenth century that hand-hoes and horse-hoes gradually replaced hand-pulling the weeds growing within field crops. The reason hoeing was so slow to be adopted, in spite of its obvious advantages of certain death to the weeds and a fast workrate, was the risk it posed to the crop. Damage to crop roots can easily outweigh the good. The answer was to grow your crops in rows. Planting and seed-sowing in drills is a very old garden skill but, as we have seen in Chapter 11, translating it to a field scale had to wait for the invention of the machines of the eighteenth-century agricultural revolution. Some very well respected agricultural historians have argued that the improved control of weeds was the single most important contributory factor to the improved yields recorded from that time. Horse-drawn hoes were illustrated in books at least as far back as 1777. Their basic design changed little in the next 150 years: a number of blades set on a frame designed to cut weeds off just below soil level. Details proliferated, however, varying from region to region and to suit different soil types. There were even specific blades for the first weeding, fashioned to prevent the seedling crop suffering excessive root disturbance. Country parsons have always taken a keen interest in farm work, which in turn supplied their sermons with endless metaphors, so perhaps we should not be too surprised that it was a Reverend James Cook that speeded up the work by inventing a horse-hoe which by straddling the crop could weed several rows at a time. The horseman walked behind, steering both horse and implement in an endeavour to get as near to the rows of plants as possible without damaging them – clearly a task for a steady hand, a good eye and a very well-trained horse. Even the best horses went slightly off line at times, which was enough to drag the hoe into a row of plants (opportunity for another sermon). That danger was reduced with the introduction of the swing steerage hoe, whereby the front half followed the errant horse while the flexibly linked hoe blade assembly could to some extent be steered by the horseman.

By the start of the twentieth century the garden weeder, again often recorded in the staff lists as a "weeding woman", would still have been using a Victorian invention, "weeding talons", slipped over the fingers to scratch out weeds in gravel paths. Her more up-to-date sisters had a choice of weapon design; they could either push or pull. That is to say, both draw-hoes and Dutch hoes, or as the Americans called them, English scuffle hoes, were available. In the refined world of the productive garden and pleasure grounds the Dutch hoe scored on two counts. It could be pushed through the surface tilth and the stems of seedling weeds with hardly a ripple left on the surface to show where it had been. And while you walk forwards when using a draw-hoe, you go backwards with a Dutch hoe, so leave no footprints.

British market-gardeners benefited from an American import, the wheelhoe. The excellent "Planet Jr." was produced in a huge range of versions able to mount tools ranging from seed-drills to light ploughs, but at heart it was a hoe. Pushed along between rows of seedling it made fast, light work of small weeds on light land but hard if not impossible work on heavy clay. Very much a case of horses for courses – but without the horse. Steering the two-wheeled version when straddling a row of seedlings was both effective and fast, *if* you remembered to reverse the blades.

Farm workers hoeing young field crops had little real choice in the matter of tools. Conditions in fields were so tough that a draw-hoe was needed to hack through the stems of the largest weeds and cut through the remaining clods. Growing the crop in rows allowed the workers to hoe off weeds first on one side, then on the other. For the first time crops could be kept weed-free, but it was a time-consuming task. In a misguided attempt to increase productivity, some bright spark introduced the two-headed hoe, designed to do both sides of the row at once. Unlike the Planet Jr. this impractical tool was soon abandoned and is now a museum curiosity.

Cutting weeds off at the knees sounds a red-blooded approach to the problem, but it needs a little further qualification before we promote it as a panacea. First, this business of "at the knees": well, if a weed's equivalent of knees is anywhere near where I think it might be then it is far too high. A weed has to be severed below the first node, that is ideally through the hypocotyl, that transition zone that joins stem to root. It is then a case of "off with its head" and no buds left behind to sprout like a hydra and start the whole story all over again. Hoeing off seedling weeds before they have a detrimental impact on the crop makes excellent sense, but Victorian head gardeners took this to extremes, declaring that crops should be hoed before any weeds appeared!

The second reason why hoeing does not always work is that not all small weeds are seedlings; there are a class of herbaceous perennials that have learnt to make a very successful living existing between and alongside crop plants. Among the most notorious are couch-grass, creeping thistle and ground elder. These toughs both spread and sprout from underground parts and are quite capable of regenerating following at least four defoliations from the hoe during the course of a single growing season.

I am sorry to say that there is at least one more major drawback to using the hoe, apart from backache. As noted earlier, in order to germinate weed seeds require the kind of conditions that are usually limited to the top one centimetre of soil and disturbing the soil to kill one generation of weeds creates an ideal seedbed for the next. The stale-seedbed technique is a double-edged weapon.

You might be excused for thinking that hoeing was just a way of killing weeds. However, in the past, hoeing took on almost mystic qualities attributed to soil disturbance. The first enthusiast for inter-row cultivation *per se* I can trace was Jethro Tull. We have already met his enthusiasm for surface tillage as in his opinion a method of releasing plant nutrients. As part of that thesis he claimed that horse-hoeing not only killed weeds but, by disturbing the soil and cutting back crop roots, improved subsequent growth and yield. It was precisely in order to create rows and so get at the soil between the plants that he developed a seed-drill. Tull's praise of hoeing was no idle, throwaway remark. He experimented to establish the spread of the fine side roots of turnips before recommending a tillage regime that would surely cut most of them off! He was not alone, but had a formidable champion in William Cobbett. Cobbett had powerful convictions and an equally powerful way with words, so it is best he speaks for himself through the pages of *The English Gardener*:

> Beside the act of killing weeds, cultivation means moving the earth between the plants while growing. This assists them in their growth: it feeds them: it raises food for their roots to live upon.

While Tull and Cobbett claimed to have experienced the remarkably beneficial loss and replacement of their crop's roots, others championed a further benefit of hoeing, the production of surface dust. Such a dust-mulch was recommended as a way of conserving water in *The Principles of Plant Culture*, an American text published in 1916 for "beginners in agriculture and horticulture":

> Crumbling of the surface soil tends to prevent drought, since it greatly lessens the points of contact in the soil particles, and thus interferes with the rise of the soil water by capillary attraction to the surface where evaporation chiefly occurs.

Only a year later such ideas bit the dust at the hands of another American, who correctly linked the apparent success of dust mulching with weed control. It was not the dust but the cultivation needed to achieve it that did the trick. It killed the weeds that if left to grow transpired the moisture away. Little did any of them know how dust would come to symbolise the mismanagement of the Midwest's soils in the forthcoming Dust Bowl disaster, but to be fair dust bowls and dust mulches are very different things. The final part of the dust mulch story came with

317

the recognition of how little soil water moved upwards by "capillary movement"; the real "mulch" turned out to be the dry surface soil, dust or otherwise. As no less a figure than Professor Penman of Rothamsted put it, "To all intents and purposes no further water evaporates from a soil once its surface layer is dry."

Research in the twentieth century has not been kind to the root-cutting school. More carefully monitored work not surprisingly indicates that plants do not respond favourably to having their roots removed.

Every age brings new ways of tackling old problems and creates devotees who search far and wide for benefits. A side-effect of deserting the hoe for the use of herbicides is an undisturbed soil profile. The surface can look singularly unloved and even support a covering of moss. Dr David Robinson, the outstanding Irish horticultural scientist of the second half of the twentieth century, persuaded his colleagues to quite literally look into this. They froze soil profiles, cut sections and studied the all-important crumb structure. It was excellent: better than frequently cultivated land and full of thriving roots. In his formidably active retirement he went on to develop the use of herbicides in the management of an incredibly species-rich 4-hectare garden and arboretum. In the context of man the cultivator of gardens, parks and arboreta, David Robinson's potential contribution is massive. He combined the scientist's understanding of plants with a gardener's enthusiasm for their day-to-day husbandry. This in turn has thrown fresh light on the hidden world of the root zone, an area still so frequently misunderstood by those who till the soil. David Robinson argued that to optimise many vital plant–soil interactions, soil disturbance should be kept to the absolute minimum. His approach to cultivation was to control competition without tillage, and herbicides were his tools. What fun it would be if William Cobbett were to meet David Robinson in paradise. Both certain of their right, both with a mastery of language – the Age of Enlightenment against the age of science.

If you don't cut or spray off weeds, how else might you kill them? Well you can prevent them from growing in the first place. If you strike before the crop is planted you can use the wipe-out-all-plant-life approach. To sterilise the soil sounds horrific, but properly handled it is less like Armageddon than it sounds. The idea is to kill off weed seeds and fragments of plant capable of sprouting that are in the soil that is going to receive the crop. Apart from its use in "salad leaf" production referred to earlier, it is a technique most often found in protected cropping and container growing. When it uses heat one could argue that it goes right back to being one of the advantages of planting on the fire heaps following slash and burn. That benefit may fairly be described as incidental, but nothing could be more deliberate than the thirteenth-century German writer Albertus Magnus's recommendation to flood the soil with boiling water to kill off the roots and seeds of weeds prior to establishing a new crop.

Chemicals have been used as soil sterilents for over half a century, again usually in intensive production, but they are not easy to apply efficiently and must completely disappear before any crop can be planted. An alternative approach is to render the soil surface lethal to weed seed germination by using a residual herbicide. Another, far "greener" approach is to mulch with a weed-free material applied to a sufficient depth to ensure that weed seeds in the soil below remain dormant. Nowadays huge quantities of bark and woodchip are used, but this kind of mulching is by no means a new idea; Dr G. V. Jacks reckons it maybe "as old as agriculture". We know the Romans mulched vineyards with stones, and the technique was probably in use in England long before it was first recommended in our seventeenth-century gardening books. In this chapter we are most concerned with mulch's ability to suppress weeds. This of course eliminates their competition for water but unlike other weed control methods a mulch, including today's popular plastic sheeting, has the added bonus of conserving water by preventing evaporation from the soil surface.

Chemical control

There are plenty of chemicals that kill plants but there is at least one good reason why the vast majority cannot be used as a weedkiller. Some are too toxic to animals, some spread too easily in the soil, and others are very difficult to apply. My old colleague Dick Stephens, in his book *Theory and Practice of Weed Control*, introduces us to "amurca", claiming it as the first herbicide used within a growing crop. It is the residue from pressing the oil from olives. Apparently, first-century Roman farmers spread it beneath their trees "wherever noxious weeds grow". So it seems the first chemical weed control would have passed the most stringent scrutiny by the organic movement. Not so the next lot! Inorganic compounds were used by a few growers from the start of the twentieth century, though not many of them would be recognised as herbicides by today's young farmers: ammonium sulphate, ammonium thiocyanate, borax, calcium cyanamide, copper nitrate, copper sulphate, sodium arsenite, sodium chlorate, sodium nitrate and sulphuric acid. If these materials showed any degree of selectivity it was because the crop plant was shielded from them by its growth habit or by having a waxy coating on its leaves.

The era of organic herbicides started with discoveries in the 1930s but it was a decade later that research into the properties of auxins, naturally occurring plant hormones, led to the synthesis and testing of their close relatives 2,4-D and MCPA. Selectivity depending on the difference between the physiology of crop and weed had been established – in these cases between the monocotyledonous cereals and the dicotyledonous weeds. Although it is not the only strategy used, it remains the most important.

Today the use of herbicides plays a huge part in the production of cheap food. Even a brief study of their chemical properties and how they are used in crop production reveals massive differences in just how much, if at all, a consumer is likely to come into contact with the chemical. Those charged with assessing the safety of these materials to man and the environment are highly educated specialists independent of the users. They are charged with judging each on its specific properties and make their recommendations accordingly. Those who publicly condemn these materials usually group them all together in their wish to see a blanket ban. Their attitude owes more to their emotions than to logic or a grasp of biology.

Currently a potentially confusing link has been made between herbicides and genetically engineered crops. This has come about because breeders have produced some GM cultivars that are resistant to specific herbicides (a phenomenon already found in some naturally occurring mutant weeds). This resistance allows the field that such crops are growing in to be sprayed with the chemical, leaving the crops undamaged but killing the weeds. This is exactly what was intended, but if the chemical is correctly applied this can be so effective as to deprive any creature that feeds on such weed species of its sustenance. The question then is: Should weeds be regarded as part of an arable field habitat, with their effect on yield a required cost that must be paid to support biodiversity, or should crop lands be exclusively for maximum profitable crop production, with other areas managed for wildlife? I would favour the latter approach; however, if the answer is that some weeds should be tolerated then it should be obvious that it is *not* the use of a GM cultivar as such that prevents this and thereby "damages the environment": its use simply makes it possible to choose to remove weeds by applying a particular chemical.

Irrigation is one of the most ancient aspects of cultivation. This sketch shows an Egyptian worker lifting river water into irrigation channels by means of a shadoof, a technique almost unchanged for many thousands of years.

14 IRRIGATION

PLANTS' NEED OF WATER

Plants need water to stay alive and to grow larger. We all know that pot plants die when we forget to water them, and indeed some folks use some weird, wonderful and ingenious methods of trying to keep their favourite houseplants watered when they are away on holiday. Away from matters of life and death, a whole raft of experiments have shown that consistently well-watered plants grow faster and larger than those that are allowed to dry out. In addition they may well be better to eat, more crisp, and more succulent or tender.

Soft plant tissue is ninety per cent water, and water is the molecule from which plants derive the hydrogen and oxygen found in their tissues. The passage of water through a plant conducts all the soluble substances that the plant needs. Unlike the circulation of our blood, water movement in a plant is a one-way system. Put simply, it is "in at the roots as liquid water and out at the leaves as water vapour", in a process known as evapotranspiration [g]. Most of the vapour escapes through the stomata. These minute pores can be closed, but plants cannot make themselves truly watertight and in a severe drought all plants shrivel, even cacti. In extreme cases plants reach their "permanent wilting point" [g] and die, but this rarely happens out of doors with established crops in Britain.

To those of us living in the British Isles with their moist, temperate climate, bringing rain in all seasons, and dry periods measured in days rather than months, it might seem crazy to put irrigation into the list of basics of husbandry. The truth is that the transpiration stream carries huge amounts of water away from the soil, a fact that the old Ministry of Agriculture tried hard to impress on growers in the opening paragraph of the bulletin on irrigation first published in 1947: "In summer an acre of vegetation in full sunlight loses on average about 10 tons of water a day." And, again in summer: " Crops in this country use an inch of water or more every 10 days." Clearly it was felt that growers were not using enough water to get the best out of their plants. Measuring a plant's uptake and loss of water has a long and exalted place in the history of the plant sciences. Water relations, as the study has become known, occupy the first four chapters of *Vegetable Staticks*, Stephen Hales's seminal work on plant physiology. The very first experiment, carried out from 3 July to 8 August 1724, describes the use of a pot-grown sunflower to "find out the quantity [of water it] imbibed and perspired". Hales rarely expresses surprise or excitement, but having given various averages he cannot resist mentioning the record of 1lb 14oz [852g] transpired during twelve hours on one very warm dry day.

More recently and with concern for the worldwide picture of pending water shortage, the International Water Management Institute warns us that on average a wheat crop uses 1790 litres of water to produce a kilogram of grain. This is one of those statistics that needs a bit of further explanation. British wheat-lands have an average rainfall of around 70cm, but because of our cool climate we can get yields of between 7 and 8 tonnes per hectare without supplementary irrigation. That works out at less than 1000 litres per kilogram, and those 70cm provide surplus water to percolate down to top-up the aquifers [g]. That is fine, as are other agricultural and horticultural demands if they can be met from local precipitation. The problem is that a lot of wheat is grown in much drier places, with much higher rates of evapo-transpiration. So the real worry is the shortfall that must be made up from the area's water reserves. Of course, wheat is only one example taken from a whole range of crops; one estimate reckons that ninety per cent of all managed water is used to grow food, apparently most of it to irrigate grasslands and water the stock that supplies us with our meat and dairy products. Such a massive use of irrigation is depleting subterranean water reserves, damaging river systems and creating shortages for industry and human populations.

It may be hard for us to contemplate an agriculture where, year in year out, the land becomes parched. Yet this not only is how it is today across tens of millions of hectares round the world but also exactly the how it was from agriculture's earliest times. Had agronomy started in North-Western Europe the first farmers might have remained oblivious to the vital role of water in sustaining plant life. In fact, cultivation appears to have started where there was a real risk of the communities' food plants dying of drought. This is true not only in the Middle East but also in northern China, Peru and Mexico, sites each credited with the independent discovery of cultivation. The first cultivators' year was divided between the wet and dry seasons. In the dry times the grasses went brown and the rest of the vegetation slowly shrivelled up, except for that growing in the marshes and along watercourses.

From the very beginning of modern man, the relationship between water and the local vegetation had been clear for all to see. Professor Hillman's view is that agriculture developed in the Fertile Crescent under the impetus of an increasingly harsh dry climate. Under those worsening conditions, wild plant populations might have been aided by diverting water to them. After all, we only have to watch children playing on a gently sloping beach to remind ourselves how easy and appealing it is to direct water by scraping out shallow channels. Alternatively, the wild plants may have been moved to wetter locations. As we have seen in Chapter 3, it is even possible that relocating wild food plants to moister sites was man's first venture into agronomy. Of course either one or both of these strategies may not have been introduced until after cultivation was under way, but at least one expert regards the need to supplement a shrinking rainfall as having been a powerful stimulus to man's adventure into the world of cultivation.

Long before the first cultivators, hunter-gatherers in the seasonally dry regions across the world, from the Middle East and the Mediterranean basin to North and South America, would have known of the link between the coming of the rains and the regrowth of wild plants with its effect on the herds they hunted. Virtually every one of these pre-agrarian cultures developed rituals and ceremonies to try and bring rain. As Edward

Carpenter puts it, "If you want the vegetation to appear you must have rain; and the rain-maker in almost all primitive tribes has been a most important personage."

Given that the Old World sites are in areas of winter rainfall, it may seem strange that, well beyond the advent of farming, many of these ceremonies to induce rain were linked with the coming of spring. However, "spring" comes very early to those parts and I suspect that farmers were particularly keen to ask for sufficient continuation of the wet season to allow their crops to reach maturity before being shrivelled up by the summer drought. As the Athenians prayed, "Rain, rain, O dear Zeus, on the cornland of the Athenians."

In *The Golden Bough*, Sir James Frazer cites more than a dozen examples from around the world and across the millennia of man's efforts to recruit supernatural assistance to ensure sufficient water for the coming crops. Such ceremonies stretch from libations at the opening of the irrigation channels following the coming of the annual Nile floods to the Aztecs' pleadings to Tlaloc their rain-god even to the extent of sacrificing children. Such horrors make the dousing of plough-boys on their return from the fields in nineteenth-century Prussia seem a very feeble and distinctly frivolous cry for rain.

However devout they may have been in their own beliefs, from the earliest times farmers seem to have, at the very least, augmented their prayers for rain with the hard work usually associated with obtaining and distributing irrigation water. Indeed, it seems reasonable to suppose that in the semi-arid birthplace of farming early attempts to extend the size of the harvest by increasing the area under cultivation would have meant tilling increasingly arid sites, a useless pursuit without some form of irrigation.

DROUGHT AVOIDANCE

Finding moist soil and then locating arable cropping to make use of it still makes excellent sense, but in many areas it dramatically limits the amount of usable land. The difficulty of bringing this land into production has encouraged the development of alternative strategies.

Some farming systems, for example those around the Mediterranean and in vast areas of the subtropics, organise their arable cropping programmes to fit into the wet season and leave the land fallow during the annual drought – a straightforward enough solution if the onset and duration of the rains is dependable. There are alternatives to dodging the drought. One is to do everything feasible to build up and conserve water in the topsoil before sowing a crop. Such methods of "dry land farming" have been practised for hundreds of years, indeed Northern Europe's ancient two-field system of cereals and fallow is said to have been an unnecessary carry-over from its use in the drought-prone fields further south. Water-collecting fallows are still practised in many low-rainfall areas of the developing world, and has been for more than half a century by First World farmers. "Stubble mulching" has become a key technique; but it is a form of cultivation that would never win a prize at a ploughing match! Rather than the plant debris from the previous crop being buried it is left on the surface, where it works in the same way as straw, bark or wood-chip mulches do in the garden. It suppresses weeds and reduces water loss, but in addition reduces erosion by wind or water – the latter always a risk on ploughland when the drought is broken by torrential rainstorms. Mulching may seem a very simple operation, but it can produce complex and even contradictory results – typically when the advantages of drought and weed control are offset by a reduction in available nutrients. Almost fifty years ago, the prestigious Commonwealth Agricultural Bureau commissioned a review of the research into the mulching of vegetables, citing over 600 papers on some 30 kinds of vegetables from asparagus to zucchini; most reported positive advantages for drought-prone sites. Unlike the stubble mulching of agriculture, where a lot of the value comes before the crop is sown, most horticultural mulches go onto established plantings.

Throughout history, water availability has dominated much of world's crop production, and is today both one of the most studied aspects of agronomy and one of its most worrying future concerns. Nowadays water conservation techniques go hand in hand with the search for less-water-demanding and/or more drought-tolerant cultivars of the most important crops. Surprising as it may seem, it is possible to find cultivars of, for example, beans that actually drink less than their relations. This is good news in itself, but things may get even better when the plant-breeders have done their bit and transferred these abstemious qualities to high-yielding offspring.

Taken together, these diverse approaches could be thought of as making best use of local conditions. Several may yet prove to have huge long-term value, but today's typical response to a water shortage is, if possible, to irrigate. I see that in my haste to bring the topic of irrigation up to date I have written "today's response"; that's true, but irrigation is by no means a recent introduction. Thousands of years ago across the Middle East, Asia and the Americas, whole civilisations depended on it. It has been estimated that as far back as 2000 BC the combined Assyrian and Babylonian kingdoms irrigated some ten thousand square miles of land, fed from a permanent and well-constructed canal system. Putting your faith in an engineer rather than shamans or rain dancers to supply the water perhaps marked a significant step forward for several ancient cultures.

APPLICATION OF WATER

For most of the history of agriculture, growers have applied water by allowing it to run over the surface of the cropland. In some cases, such as the Nile floodplain, much of the farmland was inundated as the river level rose to spread a sheet of water over it at the onset of the annual floods. The trick was to plough and sow immediately after the waters subsided, in the hope that the land would retain sufficient moisture to sustain the crop during its short life cycle from germination to harvest. One way of improving the chances of this happening was to impound some of the floodwater behind low bunds in temporary reservoirs constructed within the floodplain. The water could then be drawn off to give the crops a few extra weeks of moist soil. Typically, early farming took place on lands subject to wet and dry seasons. During the rains the rivers that supported these early endeavours rose significantly, but not all produced the dramatic floods of the Nile.

Those rivers whose lower reaches ran between levees offered another and rather more controllable approach. As the waters rose between these elevated banks, farmers made temporary breaches in them to flood selected fields. In other cases, small tributaries were temporarily dammed upstream of the ploughland to overflow into canals that led to fields lower down the valley. This last approach reaches its most impressive and permanent expression in the long canals and huge aqueducts constructed by the Incas to bring waters from the Andes to their croplands in dry valleys and the semi-deserts below. These structures remain, for all that are lucky enough to visit them, some of the most magnificent of the early civilisations' civil engineering works. Amazingly, we have another, quite different piece of source evidence for the 3300-year-old irrigation layout for the farms around the Mesopotamian town of Nippur. A map inscribed onto a clay tablet has survived. It shows fields and both natural and man-made waterways; indeed it even names them in the cuneiform script, revealing field names uncannily like those recorded in 1989 in *English Field Names*: Field of the Baru Priest (Priest Field), Field of the Boundary (Boundary Field), Field Between the Canals (Canal Field) and even the exact same "No Man's Land". Apparently farmers see their surroundings in much the same way regardless of time or place.

All these approaches have one thing in common: the irrigation water flows to the fields by gravity. Without such a supply from conveniently located highlands, the water must be lifted from lakes, reservoirs or wells. At its simplest, that means buckets and human muscle power, but by at least 3000 BC in some places that task had given way to mechanical devices and animal power. Once the water reached the distribution channels the farmers faced decisions that required a real understanding of crop husbandry if they were to allocate it according to each crop's needs.

The early farmers of Peru watered their fields in the arid foothills of the Andes via a complex network of reservoirs, canals and aqueducts that brought water from the high mountains. It seems to us a massive task, but tell that to any riverside or delta dweller and they would point out that the mountain people had it easy; once they had built their constructions gravity did the rest. The farmers of the lowlands had to lift their irrigation water out of wells, cisterns or rivers to the fields above.

There are four-thousand-year-old Egyptian illustrations of workers bailing water into elevated irrigation channels, but mechanical assistance was at hand, or at least only a few hundred miles away. The first relief from this back-breaking toil came with the Assyrian invention of the shaduf, around 2200 BC. All across the world in China, India, Persia and North Africa ingenious

methods were then employed to lift the volumes of water
required. By the time of the birth of Christ, the Greco-Roman
world had developed pumps not unlike those still in use today,
and they also used that water-lifting invention beloved of
schoolboys, the Archimedean screw. These developments in
mechanical engineering provided far more water, but they still
required powering by animal or human muscles. The spread of
Islam following the demise of the classical civilisations of the
Middle East and Mediterranean regions utilised and developed
these devices, quite literally lifting irrigation to new heights,
particularly though the use of various forms of the noria, or
current-driven water-lifting wheel. With the Arab conquest of
Sicily and Spain these highly sophisticated crop and garden
irrigation systems of channels, storage cisterns and lifting devices
arrived in Europe to supply sites far from their water sources.
Undoubtedly the British climate helps engender the idea that
crop irrigation on a field scale is an optional extra. When it is used
it is usually pumped to spray lines, but across much of the world's
arable land there are millions of hectares of crops whose success
depends each year on regular watering, much applied by a wide
range of surface irrigation methods. Some in the Third World are
still very basic but more and more now use sophisticated devices
by which the amount of water per unit area is both controlled and
monitored. The American textbook *Irrigation Principles and
Practices* by Vaughn E. Hansen, Orson W. Israelsen, and Glen E.
Stringham gives surface techniques full coverage before
discussing the science behind the efficient and economic use of
water.

That most direct of irrigation devices, the watering can, may
well go back thousands of years. It certainly has a long European
history, during which time it has undergone several
transformations. An illustration from 1470 of a ceramic "water
pot" shows a spoutless object shaped rather like a truncated
amphora whose lower half is pierced with holes. You might think
that water must have started to run out the moment that it left the
dipping pool, but just over one hundred years later Thomas Hill
in *The Gardener's Labyrinth* explains why this did not happen:

> The common watering pot for the garden beds with us hath a
> narrow neck, big belly, somewhat large bottom, and full of little
> holes, with a proper hole formed on the head to take in the water,
> which filled full, and the thumb laid on the hole to keep in the air,

330

may on such wise be carried in a handsome manner.

It took him rather a long sentence to tell us, but it is clear that they knew the trick of "holding" water by air pressure; I wonder when and in what context this was first discovered.

By the mid seventeenth century most water-pots had flat bases and teapot-like spouts with built-in roses [g]; in at least one model the water ran from a nozzle at the base, but we know the flow could be controlled by placing your thumb over the top filling hole, producing "an ideal vessel for watering rows of seedlings". By 1824 the gardener illustrated in *The Book of English Trades and Library of Useful Arts* has a metal can whose basic form is still with us. The characteristic French watering can with its curved handle also dates from this time, but neither is the last word in good design; that was the brainchild of John Haws, whose 1885 application for a patent still described it as "a watering pot". With its long spout, near-perfect balance, and meticulously designed roses capable of producing a controlled spray, whose close fit ensured that there were no leaks or drips "to the annoyance of the person using it", it became and remains to this day the Rolls-Royce of watering cans.

Pot plants are sometimes watered from the bottom, on the cottage windowsill by standing the pot in a saucer of water and on a commercial scale by capillary matting spread over benches. This is either periodically flooded or kept constantly moist by wicks drawing water from reservoir tanks. The trick is to adjust the distance the water must be lifted by capillary action: too great, and insufficient water will reach the plant; too little, and the system will lead to waterlogging. Capillary watering in any form sounds very technical and thoroughly modern, so it may come as a surprise to read Thomas Hill's instructions written in 1577:

> Take Wollen cloathes or Lists and these like tongues cut sharp at the one end, which lay to the bottom of the pot, filled with water, the sharp end hanging forth, wel four fingers deep … [these] may through continual dropping hastily speed the increase of the … plants.

I take these instructions to mean "put strips of cloth into a water-filled container leaving 4cm hanging out. These strips will [by capillarity] lift the water over the rim of the pot, it well then drip onto the soil thereby irrigating neighbouring plants."

Before leaving "hand-watering", as the use of a watering can was known, I must mention the tool that gardeners once carried in the other hand: the pot-tapper. It was a simple handmade wooden mallet, often no more than a cotton-reel-sized block of wood on a bamboo cane handle, but when used it could accurately indicate which potted plants needed watering. As a root ball [g] dries out contact is broken between soil and container, allowing ceramic pots to ring when tapped with the same high-pitched note they produce when empty. In contrast, moist soil muffles the sound. Empty (or dry) vessels do indeed make the most noise, but sadly not if they are made of plastic!

Thomas Hill described how to irrigate a garden using "a great squirt" – a pump set in a tub of water. Vigorous pumping "causeth the water to ascend and to flee forth of the pipe holes on such height that in the falling, the droppes come down through the air breaking it in the form of raine"; of course the tub and pump had then to be moved to another bed. By the late sixteenth century there were a few gardens whose owners were wealthy enough and with gardeners strong enough to boast the use of the massively heavy and cumbersome leather hosepipes. At about the same time the French had produced the "*tuyaux à chariot*", a series of rigid pipes mounted on wheels whose flexible joints allowed the gardener to manoeuvre the cumbersome beast to the flowerbed in question, or so the inventor claimed! The flexible hosepipe we know today was a Victorian innovation, based at first not on rubber but, thanks to Henry Bewley's researches, gutta percha, a gum-like latex extracted from *Palaquium* trees from South-East Asia. By the turn of the century rubber technology was giving the gardener the kind of hosepipe that dominated the market for some seventy years until it was superseded by today's lighter and more durable plastics.

It is only in the last eighty years that we have been able to apply water under pressure on a field scale. This gave engineers the chance to design spray lines that produced artificial rain. Perfect – or is it? After the following list of problems you may be excused to think it best to hunt out the nearest shaduf and a willing donkey. It is not at all easy to achieve an even distribution of water over a crop by spray jet, partly because any breeze carries the spray downwind, leaving half the field distinctly wetter than the other. Another problem is that most nozzles wet a circular area, and it is impossible to join up several of these as an even cover over a whole field. If you fly over large areas of the American prairies you see a very simple solution to that difficulty: make the irrigation engine so large that it waters a whole "field", and make the fields circular.

Finally, as if these difficulties were not enough, there is the size of the drops. Too small and they drift away and evaporate before reaching the ground, and even if that doesn't happen they don't carry the energy to travel far from the nozzle. If water droplets are too large they hit the surface with such force that they destroy the soil crumbs, reducing them to their constituent fine mineral particles. This causes the surface of the soil to "cap", that is to produce a crust that can impair germination and impede the entry of water and air. A good cover of vegetation breaks the potentially damaging force of the falling water and allows farmers to use much simpler equipment, which helps explain why the technique that produces the great circular patterns works on the prairie grasslands but not on young arable crops.

Overhead sprays are not the only contemporary water distribution method. More recently still, growers have turned to drip irrigation where water is released at ground level exactly where it is needed. This is not just in glasshouses, but by one American estimate on some 450,000 hectares of orchards of every kind of fruit tree from olives to apples. Drip irrigation requires a lot of expensive and elaborate equipment in the form of pumps, pipes, filters and nozzles, but once you have got the water to the plant the system starts to show its advantages. The water can be placed where it is needed, in the quantity required, without a great deal of loss through evaporation. The slow delivery rate allows each drip in turn to soak into the soil. This produces a volume of moist soil whose shape has prompted the name "the wet onion". Ideally the onion fits the crop plant's root zone, but its ratio of breadth to depth depends not only on the dripping speed but also on the nature of the soil. You get broad, flat "clay onions" and deep, narrow "sand onions". As you can see, irrigation has become high-tech, but as usual precision in performance requires precision in equipment and operation, commodities that are not always available in the Third World. Given the way water moves through soil and the increasing difficulty that plants have in obtaining water as soil dries out, you might think that the aim was to maintain field capacity throughout the root zone. Well, sometimes but not always, because as usual when dealing with biological matters things are not simple. First of all, some plants thrive on a level of drought stress. It controls the shape of the plant, helps resist pathogens becoming established and even triggers flowering in, for example, mangoes. The crop-producer aims to apply water when it does most good. By far the most critical time for transplants is immediately after they have been moved, before the newly arrived plant has extended its roots into the surrounding soil, whilst for directly sown crops it is as the seedlings emerge. Surface soil that was moist enough to allow germination to take place can dry out a few days later. The seedling is then caught with its root not yet having reached the moist layers beneath.

IRRIGATION SCIENCE

It may seem an exaggeration to describe watering as a skill, but ask anyone in charge of a pot-plant nursery and they will tell you it is. I have no doubt they would sympathise with this Egyptian lady's comments to her new employee some two and a half thousand years ago: "If you intend to be a gardener for me in my garden then you are to give water to it in the proper measure of twenty-eight hens of water to the pot." With one hen equalling 0.8 pints, that is 2.8 gallons (10.6 litres); they must have been large pots.

The two most frequently asked questions about irrigation by amateur gardeners are "How much?" and "How often"? To a large extent the first can be answered by reference to the soil type and the second by knowing the crop.

It is not possible to make the whole soil profile of the root zone "just a bit damp". Water travels down through the soil layer by layer and, apart from going down cracks and worm holes, its progress depends on each level reaching and exceeding field capacity. At that time the surplus water escapes the hold of the surface tension around the soil particles and moves down to the particles immediately below. This stately progress continues until the soil mass above the drains is wet, or until the water reaches the water table that marks the top of the saturated zone.

In Britain it pays to irrigate field crops about three years in five.

This does not mean that you start immediately you have sown the seed and keep going until harvest, but it does indicate that there will be periods during the growing season when the crop will be significantly affected by drought stress. As we have seen, the consequences of that stress vary according to the crop's stage of development.

Irrigation programmes are calculated to apply enough water to wet the whole root zone of the crop in question – no more, no less. Too much and it drains away, too little and the lower roots go without.

Much of present-day irrigation is not to be found in the world's semi-deserts or on terraces clinging to mountain slopes but in rather less dramatic and extreme settings. Areas with only a short rainy period or those that get much of their moisture remaining as an aftermath of having been saturated by floods need irrigation to extend the time that the soil is moist if the aim is year-round cropping, while erratic rainfall may need occasional supplementation to achieve the steady growth required for a good harvest. This is particularly so if a dry spell coincides with what are known as critical growth periods such as the germination of most crops, the swelling of potato tubers and, very commonly in the amenity horticultural world, the transplanting of trees and shrubs.

British readers without gardens may be surprised to learn that in the driest parts of the South-East of England, irrigation of field-grown vegetable crops is economically worth while in 7 years out of 10, roughly the same frequency with which our lawns turn brown for a few weeks in summer. The phrase "economically worth while" reminds us that growers use irrigation for more than keeping plants alive; it can significantly influence crop size, in terms of both total yield and individual specimens, and the quality and earliness of the harvest. We might call this use of irrigation "the optimum harvest organ approach". Three other uses are "emergency only" often used in gardens when a planting seems in dire straits after some weeks of summer drought, and the more common "aid to germination", when seeds and emerging seedlings need a damp soil surface. The third common emergency is when the soil around a transplant's greatly diminished root system dries out. Tens of thousands of young trees and shrubs are lost every year in landscape schemes through this cause.

Irrigation, like most husbandry practices, has its myths: "Water only in the evening." "Irrigation water will scorch foliage." "Irrigation as opposed to rain will encourage the wrong kind of roots." And, most damaging of all: "Soak plants then let them dry right out." This last one starts with sound advice, because as we have already seen, water only moves through a soil profile as each horizon is saturated. It is the idea that plants, especially fast-growing young crops, will then benefit from a subsequent drought before their next drink that's such rubbish. Experiments some fifty years ago showed that lettuces experiencing just one short drought between waterings never catch up and produce a crop as good as from those regularly watered. Ideally, the vast majority of our temperate cultivated plants grow best with a constantly available supply of soil moisture.

Most temperate-region crops grow less well as the soil in their root zone dries out from field capacity. Typically, things start well enough in the spring following earlier rains that leave the soil at field capacity. Then a combination of surface evaporation and transpiration from the crop slowly reduces the amount held within reach of the roots.

Irrigation is not without its dangers. To quote Peter Salter in *Know and Grow Vegetables*,

> Gardeners are well aware that watering their vegetable crops gives better growth, better quality, and higher yields. This has led to the belief that all vegetables will always benefit from watering, and the more water that is given the better. This is not so. It is very easy to give too much water too often. Apart from the waste of water, time, and effort, watering unnecessarily may merely increase the growth of the plant without increasing the size of the edible part. It may discourage root growth (making the plants more drought-susceptible), it may wash nitrogenous fertilisers out of reach of the roots, and it may reduce flavour.

The skill is to apply water just before the point when the plants really start to suffer. Healthy young plants respond just as you would expect: they grow! But, once again, things are not as simple as they seem. We harvest different bits of plants: with some it's leaves, with others stems, roots, fruits, seeds etc. These bits respond differently to a good drink and not always as we would wish. For example while it is good that leafy harvests such as cabbage and lettuce increase significantly, so do the tops of carrots and red beet, but sadly not the roots we want to harvest. As for young peas and French beans, they seem to let large quantities of water go to their head! They put on masses of leafy growth which then fails to result in much if any increase in the number of pods. It turns out that green peas are most effectively irrigated when in flower and forming their pods.

The amount of water available at specific stages in a plant's seasonal growth cycle can influence the direction that that growth takes. That is important, because timing irrigation to coincide with periods of greatest effect on crop yield saves money and can organise the plant to direct its efforts towards the bit that we harvest. Studies on potatoes show how complex something so apparently simple as watering "spuds" can be. It seems that maincrop potatoes will respond to an extra drink whenever the soil moisture deficit [g] is around 4cm. Applying enough to bring the soil back to around field capacity can make a huge difference to the crop in a dry season, with yields increasing by almost a tonne for every centimetre of irrigation water applied towards a possible harvest of 40 tonnes per hectare. But if you investigate further you find it is not that straightforward. Plenty of soil moisture just before the tubers start to form tends to increase their number, while watering a little later when the tubers are the size of marbles increases the size of individual tubers. A further complication is that these niceties seem to be cultivar-dependent. However, keeping up the soil moisture from then on works for all types; by keeping tubers swelling steadily it reduces cracking and malformations.

Watering early potatoes is another story, with its own rules. If your aim is to be the first with "new" potatoes, water only at the marble stage; if you want a heavy crop and can wait a little longer then keep up the soil moisture throughout their growing period. This kind of information has enabled researchers such as those who worked at the then National Vegetable Research Station in the 1960s and 1970s to produce irrigation strategies advising growers how much water to apply to various crops, and when. Around the world other branches of commercial horticulture use billions of gallons of water to irrigate container-grown nursery stock and every kind of crop grown under cover in glasshouses and plastic-covered structures. In some areas the demand is so great that it has become the limiting factor in the industry's expansion.

Considering how vital and obvious the role of water is, it is surprising that it took irrigation science some hundred years after the study of fertilisers to get under way. Perhaps soil moisture was seen as part of the weather, a curse or blessing in the lap of the gods.

Irrigation may seem bedevilled with technical problems, but the idea itself is surely benign. However much people may worry about cultivators using man-made chemical compounds to fertilise and protect their crops, watering must be an innocent pursuit. You've guessed it – it's not. Over hundreds of square kilometres of the dryer parts of the world irrigation is rendering the soil useless owing to the build-up of salts. This salinity develops because the farmers never put on enough irrigation water to let some surplus pass down into the drainage system. The thinking has been that it is too precious a commodity to waste like that. But unfortunately if the system is not flushed out the traces of salt in the water build up in the topsoil, even to the extent of forming a crust on the surface with disastrous results for future crops. Many agricultural scientists consider that irrigation-induced salinity will become a huge problem and remove vast areas of otherwise fertile land from crop production. This has led researchers to try to produce salt-resistant cultivars; by coincidence, their success with tomatoes was made public some time between the first and second drafts of this section of the book.

This sketch of a modified espalier design comes from a nineteenth-century text. The espalier is one of a host of the then fashionable tree forms devised for training fruit against walls. Their success depended on a combination of pruning and training skills.

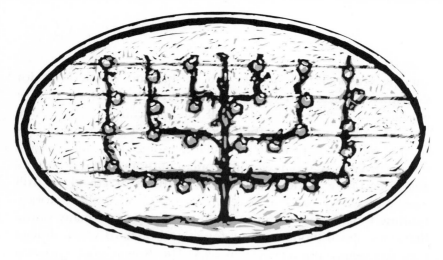

15 PLANT MANIPULATION BY PRUNING AND TRAINING

PRUNING FOR SHAPE AND YIELD

"Pruning is the removal of a part of a plant in order that the remainder may better serve our purpose." So says the author of *The Principles of Plant Cultivation*, first published in the USA in 1897. Surely there can be no better one-liner to summarise the craft before going on to explore all manner of such removals and parts, as this excellent old primer did!

Like the other husbandry activities that seem to be exclusively acts of man, pruning turns out to be going on all the time in nature. By this I am not referring to the kind of pruning you get after a litter of rabbits have made an overnight visit to a new planting of heathers, although the ability to regenerate from that sort of damage is inextricably linked to the biology of pruning. The sort of natural activity I am thinking of is the sloughing-off of the inner twigs and small branches of trees and shrubs that results in dead sticks, those fallen pieces of wood you find on a forest floor that in medieval times the peasants had permission to gather as firewood. It is by this auto-pruning that woody plants maintain their optimum shape, form and leaf distribution. Not only is the loss of surplus stems both natural and beneficial, but plants do it at the most logical place and have a mechanism to heal the wound afterwards. So the loss of bits is to some extent natural, as is the healing of the wounds and, in some cases, the regrowth after the loss.

Very few of our crop plants are left to grow as nature intended. Many are pruned and tied into the desired shape. Pruning is an ancient seasonal task within the husbander's craft, both for decorative effects and to control the growth and fecundity of woody plants. The pruning of all the major tree crops of the ancient world appears in their writings and art. We have murals of the Egyptians pruning grapevines some four and a half thousand years ago. Greek and Roman authors discuss the pros and cons of the various alternative methods practised on fruit trees and vines, and it is a recurring theme in biblical stories. Pruning tools – hooks, axes and knives – appear in many of the first book illustrations of farm, forest and orchard work, indeed they frequently dominate such lists. The Roman *falx vinitoria* could be described as a billhook with attitude; designed as an all-in-one cutting implement able to tackle thick stems and yet delicate enough to cut back tender young shoots, it was a sort of Swiss Army knife of its day. The billhooks and axes used at the tougher end of pruning have changed little in the last five hundred years, and the archaeological evidence suggests that we might extend that back by another fifteen centuries and still find much the same designs.

Pruning is second only to planting in the advice given to foresters in our early texts, starting with the most famous of all, John Evelyn's *Sylva* of 1664. By 1851 United Kingdom foresters had another *Sylva* to study, *The British Sylva, and Planters' and Foresters' Manual*, full of excellent advice based on sound biological principles. Curiously, no author is named, but whoever it was, in my book he stands alongside such pioneer scientific cultivators as Robert Thompson, who produced the excellent *Gardener's Assistant* eight years later.

The development of the pruning-saw and various forms of garden shears based on the scissor action brought more finesse to pruning in the nineteenth century, but the Marquis de Moleville's great invention, secateurs, don't appear in British gardening dictionaries by either name or design until very late in that century. With their adoption, the use of the old bloodthirsty weapons was slowly confined to forest and hedge.

Pruning had progressed from butchery to surgery, but recently modern tractor-powered equivalents to the slash and hack of the past have returned in the form of such weapons as a circular saw on the end of an hydraulically controlled arm, now in regular use in some of the world's most extensive orchards and plantations.

No species of plant requires pruning to survive in the wild. Cultivators use pruning as a way of shaping both crop and ornamental plants and manipulating individual plants to yield more desirable crops. For some the pruner's blade or the twine creates a new aesthetic not found in nature. Others get such treatment to improve their function as in the case of street trees and cattle barriers, while its most common use among crop plants from cucumbers to oaks and apples is to improve either the quantity or quality of the harvest. In other words, we prune plants to make them do or not do something they would do or not do if left to their own devices!

Pruning ornamentals is almost always about either controlling size or achieving a desired shape, be it "natural" or contrived. The sad and baffling thing is how often gardeners create ugliness. As a great friend and colleague used to say after making a landsite visit to a housing development, "Things would have been so much better if the gardeners had taken the day off."

Pruning in crop production is quite a different matter. It is about getting a harvest of the right quantity and quality every year. To achieve this, growers and researchers have come up with recipes – and there are usually several alternatives – for each crop. Fruit-growers typically aim to balance the size of the current year's crop with a fair production of new vegetative shoots whose leaves will support the current year's fruits, while their buds will be the start of future crops.

Controlling shape

Although I have written "controlling shape", it is more accurate in most cases to talk of creating it. It seems that mankind has a long-running love of forming nature into unnatural shapes. The Romans had a separate name for someone who cared for decorative pleasure gardens, "*topiarius*". For more than two thousand years, climbers have been twisted round wire forms, shrubs clipped into birds and trees bent and tied into twists and spirals. Tudor gardens had their estrades that look for all the world like Edwardian cake-stands, while pairs of plants are even now grafted into ladders and hearts. Of course this contrast, this contradiction in terms between nature and the man-made, this living artefact, can have a powerful design impact. Just think of the white-knuckle-pruned London Planes lining French boulevards or the slightly more elaborate pleached limes now back in fashion, but hardly new – as a close scrutiny of Geoffrey Chaucer's *Canterbury Tales* will reveal.

My favourite artificially shaped, as opposed to clipped, plant feature is the laburnum arch. The individual small trees are piteously bent and formed, but collectively they produce a stunning effect when the racemes of flowers hang down into the living tunnel. There are countless examples of topiary throughout the gardens of Europe; you can even buy one produced in Italy in the form of a bicycle. More dignified and far older examples nevertheless turn the William and Mary gardens in Levens Hall, Cumbria into a kind of Alice in Wonderland setting. Three hundred years of clipping have failed to keep the yew and box in scale with the formal design. The result is that instead of admiring a pattern of paths and beds with clipped accent points, you walk round dwarfed by huge geometric evergreen shapes.

Possibly the largest, and in their day, oldest trained plants were to be found in the villages of Northern Europe, where people venerated several species of lime, *Tilia* spp., as sacred to the goddess Freja, the patron of love, fertility, justice and trade. Beneath the canopy of the strategically sited "village limes", or *Dorflinden*, courts were held and wedding vows exchanged. But there was a problem: common limes have an excurrent growth habit with few if any spreading branches, yet the surviving records tell a very different story. In 1922 the canopy of the then 600-year-old-specimen at Neuenstadt in north Germany covered a remarkable 1.3ha. Surviving photographs show it to be the product of a change in growth form produced by centuries of training and pruning.

A hero of mine, William Robinson, most certainly did not approve of such plant sculpting, however old the practice. One of his less-known books, *Garden Design*, is dedicated almost entirely to raving against it. Given so much to quote from, I will limit myself to this from the extended title: "Clipping and aligning trees ... is barbaric, needless and inartistic."

The shapes and forms created to produce living sculpture and vegetable masonry may or may not be fine art, but the subject has a more serious, functional aspect than "trees mutilated to meet [the perpetrators'] views as to design" as Robinson puts it. Controlling size, shape and form can indeed contribute to achieving greater function and productivity. In traditional sylviculture the production of "pole wood" depended on pruning to both gather the harvest and stimulate the required regrowth. In Britain the resultant specimens typically took the form of either coppice stools, in which the plants were cut to the ground, or *pollards* that produced their shoots from the crowns of 2 to 3m high trunks. The vigorous almost straight shoots produced during each growth cycle of between 3 and 15 years had a multitude of uses appropriate to their size and species; these including fuel, hop poles, sheep hurdles, wattle infill of timber-framed houses and standby winter cattle fodder. We now cut only a very small area, mainly of hazel, sweet chestnut and willow, but once the millions of stools, both woodland and hedgerow specimens, included ash, oak, lime and holly.

A third tree form, more common in other parts of Northern Europe than in Britain, resulted from "shredding". Shredding describes the regular pruning of shoots regenerated from growing points retained along the entire length of the unbranched trunks of trees specifically managed to supply winter stock feed.

Frequently cut hedges become thicker, screen better, help create a more favourable microclimate and are more stockproof. For all these reasons, field hedges used to have their shape adjusted quite dramatically every twenty or so years; they were laid. Hedge-laying is one of those husbandry crafts beloved of those who don't have to do it for a living. I have in mind writers on countryside matters in the broadsheets, landscape architects, the Ramblers, and the nouveau-pseudo-rustics who come from the cities to live in the countryside.

In reality hedge-laying is a blood-and-guts sort of winter job in which an overgrown hedge, usually hawthorn, with the accent on the thorn, is attacked with a billhook. The idea is to remove most of the old canopy, cut out surplus stems and bend the remainder down so that they can be stacked or even loosely woven through stakes to make a living fence. In 1664 John Evelyn give an excellent description of the work, "with sharp bill and light hatchet", in a passionate cry to landowners to create stockproof hedges around their woods and so protect young trees from "the spoil of cattle".

To get the stems to bend down they are more than half cut through, slant-wise as Evelyn says, near the ground. As a result of this onslaught, regrowth springs from two places; just below the cut and along the length of the now almost horizontal stems. The shoots from the cut region are vigorous, vegetative types, as in a coppice. These will form supports for the hedge and ultimately be laid in their turn. The chances of getting a fair number of side-shoots from the laid stems is all to do with hormones as they say, and very neatly brings us to the kind of tree shapes produced by fruit-growers.

Fruit trees and bushes have long been trained into a number of standard shapes. Few if any of these originated in Britain, those that appeared in the eighteenth- and nineteenth-century walled gardens of British country houses being copied from the orchards of French and Low Countries aristocrats. Louis XIV's great potager at Versailles remains the supreme example of the craft of fruit tree training. Even the names of the trained forms were adopted with little change, as a dip into Le Potager du Roi's guidebook proves: *"espalier"*, *"cordon horizontal, oblique et vertical"*, *"gobelet"* and *"palmette"* are instantly familiar. *"Fuseau"* got translated into "spindle bush", but when we come to the more extreme tree-forms the British seem to have given up: *"pommiers en double spirale"*, *"poiriers en cercles verticaux"* and *"pechers en quadrillage"* were never our thing! Staying for a moment with terminology, it seems that it was the French who transferred the term "espalier" from its original meaning as the structure upon which trees were supported to the tree form itself. As we shall read later in Chapter 15, I have tried to give Louis Lorette his rightful place in the story of cultivation as the inventor of an outstandingly successful method of pruning, but his skill as a trainer of fruit trees deserves equal recognition, as photographs of his fruit garden at Wagnonville reveal.

Such three- or two-dimensional forms allow the crop to be picked from the ground and, as the old texts say, "present the fruit to the sun". In the case of temperate fruits, the 3D constructs are mainly based on spacing the branches to allow the sun's light and warmth to penetrate into the tree. It has long been common knowledge that the best-coloured and best-flavoured fruit comes from the outer reaches of a tree canopy. Each trained form had its following and a correct way of achieving it during a tree's formative years. Pruning, not tying, was at its core; these shapes were achieved by knowing what to remove, what to retain and above all at what point on each stem to make the cut. Regardless of the shape produced, the overall aim was the same. A tree whose form ensured that as high a percentage as possible of its fruits had a fine appearance and flavour. Not every kind of fruit requires the same open form of tree. For example under Mediterranean conditions citrus are trained to produce a tight head of shoots and foliage because dappled shade produces the finest fruits. The story is the same right across the world. Fruit-growers cultivating the fifty or so kinds of fruit that now grace our supermarket shelves struggle to produce trees, bushes and vines of the shape and form that, under their local conditions, give the desired harvest.

Before moving to life in two dimensions, I must find space for a brief mention of one of mankind's oldest and most loved bearer of fruit, the grapevine. Pruning this vigorous 50m climber to manageable and productive shape has been an annual ritual for at least four thousand years. It is not so much a case of which expert's style of training will you follow, as which civilisation's technique? Egyptian, Greek, Roman, medieval French, or to bring it up to date Australian, Chilean or Californian? (I am not certain that the last three are distinct civilisations but you get the idea.) Well, rather than go into any of these I have chosen to have a closer look at the Victorian British – practised not in vineyards of course but in vineries: glasshouses that produced some of the finest flavoured dessert grapes ever tasted. The transformation of this unruly vine into glasshouse conformity was a remarkable feat. Each winter the plants were reduced to one or more rods, permanent straight stems trained just below the roof of these lean-to structures. Every spring the rod sprouted side-shoots along its length; these carried the leaves and the bunches of grapes. Once the crop had been cleared the shoots were pruned back again, leaving only the gnarled rod.

Now we return as promised to the plant hormones known as auxins and their control over bud break. With effectively no knowledge of plant biochemistry, the gardeners in charge of these vineries observed that the nearer to horizontal those rods were in early spring the more evenly the buds broke along their length. Armed with this knowledge, every winter, until just before the buds swelled, they lowered the rods down from their growing season position just below the sloping roof. We now know that the improved evenness of bud break is due to a redistribution of auxins. As the *Oxford Dictionary of Plant Sciences* puts it, "Auxins cause the inhibition of lateral bud development in favour of apical buds." Once the stem is horizontal the gravitational force that "tells" the auxins where up is no longer directs them to the tip of the shoot, so lateral buds are no longer inhibited and new shoots sprout along the length of the rod. With the exception of grapes, by far the most unnatural fruit tree shapes are the two-dimensional or "flat forms" as the French called them. Today the most common are the espalier, cordon and fan. These and their many variations may be grown either against a wall or in the open, trained along wires. Regardless of location it is obvious that these flattened shapes insure that developing fruits are in a sunny, light position.

If the tree is on a wall then its flowers have some protection from spring frosts, and the radiated warmth from the wall helps ripen the fruit in autumn. These are not old wives' tales; wall fruit really does experience a microclimate that makes a difference, both to the chances of getting a crop and to its flavour. Sadly, fewer wall-trained fruit trees are planted nowadays, but you still see old espalier pears, many of which are approaching their hundredth birthday, covering the gable-ends of farmhouses. Until a few years ago the estate cottages in the village of Aynho in Northamptonshire all sported apricots, and many still do. It seems that the Cartwright family thought their tenants should have the pleasure of eating the same exotic fruit that their own gardens around the manor-house supplied; but woe betide the tenant that failed to look after his tree!

Each recognised shape is based on a construction blueprint dating back over three hundred years, but as you will soon discover if you try it, things never exactly follow the rulebook when you work with living plants. To get the desired result takes patience, skill and understanding. The result is magnificent even if you did not get a single fruit, a very unlikely tragedy. The skills are not lost; George Gilbert, now retired but previously in charge of fruit-growing at both the RHS Gardens at Wisley and Long Ashton Research Station, teamed up with Ian Fretwell, the head gardener of an estate in Yorkshire and together they have clothed the walls of the kitchen garden with elegant, fecund specimens.

Once the tree is shaped, attention turns to making it fruitful. Again we learnt our craft from the French. Slowly over three hundred years there developed an understanding of where and how the all-important flower-buds of apple and pear trees developed. Each type of shoot was named and our horticultural vocabulary enriched with "brindilles", "dards", "bourses" and "lambourdes". By the end of the nineteenth century, complete pruning systems were established. Paul Champagnat described these together with the then recent alternative proposed by Louis Lorette, the curator at what has become the Lycée Agricole et Horticole at Wagnonville, near Douai in the Pas-de-Calais. According to Georges Truffaut in the preface to *The Lorette System of Pruning*, this alternative was "not at first acceptable to the orthodox school of three-bud pruning". Indeed it was not: there were even "a few professional gardeners who, not unskilfully, tried to demonstrate the practical impossibility of the new methods," while "other prejudiced mockers merely made obvious jokes at M. Lorette's expense". But the reputedly modest M. Lorette had the last laugh: his ideas influenced fruit tree pruning for half a century. In the early 1920s Louis Lorette wrote his own exposé on his method of pruning, a work full of extremely convincing photographs deemed so important in Britain that it was translated by the secretary of the Royal Horticultural Society.

The pruning of fruit trees is held in such mystery by most amateur gardeners that it tends to eclipse all the other varied applications of cultivating by the use of sharp instruments. These range from the forester who "brushes up" young trees to remove their lower branches to prevent knots in the future timber, via the bonsai-grower nipping off extension growth and surplus shoots to topiary artists and suburban gardeners clipping their front garden hedge. All those wielders of secateurs, trimmers, loppers and pruning saws come quickly to mind, but there are still others among the cultivators using "plant surgery" to cut their way to a successful crop who all depend on the same biology, but wouldn't call what they do pruning. Whether it is side-shooting tomatoes, disbudding carnations, stopping chrysanthemums, pinching out sweet peas, shearing over young shrub transplants, coppicing hazel or even cutting the lawn, these, like pruning, all depend for their effect on a few basic biological responses. Cutting off the tips of strong shoots, including leaders and watershoots, removes their apical dominance, the biochemical control the tip has to suppress the growth of lateral buds. With that control removed, several buds break into growth, resulting in a much twiggier canopy than would have been the case. So we get a dense hedge or more stems on our young shrub or several shoots on our chrysanthemum plant. But as a quick inspection of a neglected hedge will show, the plant will return to its natural stem pattern and number within a few years.

Plants however have their own ideas about which shoots are leaders and respond very differently to the loss of others. Hence it is possible for a forester or fruit-farmer to remove stems from the inside of a tree or shrub canopy without any new shoots appearing. Indeed, removing the tips of some smaller, often lower, branches of, for example, pines and willows is enough to convince the specimen that it is time to abandon that particular stem because it is not pulling its weight, i.e. it is not producing as much through photosynthesis as it is using up through its respiration.

Coppicing to produce willow withies, cutting sugarcane and trying (and failing) to get rid of unwanted sycamore trees are all examples of where pruning stimulates replacement shoots as the plant attempts to re-establish its root/shoot ratio. Back in Chapter 1, I touched on the "new" idea of cropping some tree species for biomass, a technique in which the shoots from coppiced stumps are cut every few years, dried, turned into woodchips and used among other things as fuel in large-scale furnaces. It is a form of "green energy" for the industrial world. The Third World uses the same post-pruning biology to produce much of its fuel for cooking and heating. Historically the source was hardly a crop, more the struggling survivors of repeated spasmodic attacks with axe, panga or bare hands by the staggering total of 2.5 billion people worldwide who depend on firewood to supply between 50 and 100 per cent of their fuel needs. Gathering and carrying this massive demand, estimated to average one tonne per person per year, brings drudgery to the – typically female – users and the slow destruction of vast areas of woodland habitat. One estimate shows that a community's demand for firewood "from the wild" can take more than four times the land needed for food crops. The establishment and management of plantations of trees and bushes capable of sustainable regeneration after various forms of heavy pruning could at least halve that figure. The successful cultivation of such firewood crops is one of the most pressing challenges facing cultivators across the world. To this end the US

National Academy of Sciences produced *Firewood Crops*, an excellent publication whose authors have achieved the rare feat of combining a series of hard-hitting, poignant photographs with a rigorous technical text.

Root pruning

Given that roots are the vital collectors of water and mineral nutrients, it may seem strange to ever consider cutting them off as a husbandry technique. To be honest, it is more a practice from the past, and not much practised now except when producing large tree and shrub transplants. Before the days of dwarfing rootstocks, the vigour of fruit trees, especially those grown in glasshouses and against walls, was commonly controlled, that is to say reduced, by cutting through some of the main roots. In some cases the whole plant was dug up, the roots cut back and the tree replanted. More often, soil was scraped away from round the base of the tree and some of the exposed roots cut back. It was clearly a sufficiently common practice in the seventeenth century for John Evelyn to discuss "ablaqueation" [g], as it was termed, without explaining what the word meant. It was important to be able to get at the main roots, so to ensure that they radiated out from the trunk and remained near the surface for a short distance, fruit trees were planted over a stone slab. This system of root pruning reduced the vigour of the fruit tree and the physiological stress usually had the added benefit if causing it to develop extra fruit buds.

Root pruning is more often a necessary evil, as we saw in the transplant story. On occasion however it is carried out with scant regard for the owner of the roots. And that is when roots are considered to be a menace to other plants, to drains or to buildings. In every case water lies at the heart of the problem. Neighbouring plants are droughted by larger specimens. Pipe runs that are already damaged are invaded for their moisture and can be completely blocked by the resultant root mass produced by some trees and shrubs. The risk to buildings is again caused by localised water removal when some soils shrink to the extent that the foundations built upon them are unable to support a part of the structure. This vexed topic is has been thoroughly explored by Dr Giles Biddle and in *Tree Roots and Buildings* by D. F. Cutler and I. B. K. Richardson.

LEAF REMOVAL

Pruning away a lot of leaf can have several results. One general effect is of course to reduce the production of carbohydrates and so dwarf the plant, at least in the short term. This happens on a bowling green or a golf green, where the almost daily cut with the lawnmower has the effect of producing "bonsai grass". Incredibly, turf breeders have produced cultivars from the genus *Agrostis* that will tolerate the mower blades being set down to 0.3cm above the ground! In addition to the dwarfing effect such punitive pruning produces, the grasses are stimulated to struggle to produce replacement leaf growth and this harsh treatment may even increase the number of shoots, or "tillers" as they are called.

Total leaf removal can stimulate an extra flush of growth, causing buds to break that would normally have remained dormant at least until the following year. This happens when insects strip the foliage from some trees and is used by nursery growers to encourage the cuttings of some trees to sprout. At a simpler level, leaf removal in tomatoes allows air to move freely through the crop and light to reach the green fruits and hasten ripening.

Pruning off dead flowers and immature fruits prevents the plant using its reserves on the very demanding pursuit of seed development. The plant may therefore produce another flush of flowers or in some cases develop a larger than otherwise number of flower-buds for the following year.

"Thinning" is the deliberate reduction of flowers, fruits or even stems. It allows the remainder to benefit from all the available reserves the plant has, and will continue to, produce. Botanists regard each organ as a "sink" in competition with its fellows for the products of photosynthesis. As every seeker after flower-show awards knows, to get prize-winning entries often means disbudding and side-shooting. As we have seen in Chapter 5, for classes requiring "monster specimens" only one fruit per plant is allowed to develop.

We can think of pruning as the surgery of husbandry or we can see it as the way to control size and number. If you chose the latter definition we have to have a look at chemical pruning. The simplest form of chemical pruning involves the use of materials that kill off or render dormant buds and growing points, those sites of cell division that biologists call meristems. Depending on whether the target is the terminal bud or the laterals, a successful application gives fewer or more side-shoots. If all meristems are equally affected then no more growth comes from the treated shoots.

Chemical defoliants, and I am not referring to the infamous "Agent Orange", are used to get nursery stock to drop its foliage in the autumn so that lifting can start. There are other compounds that cause young fruits to fall. If this may seem a strange ambition for a grower, in fact it's back to thinning down the number of fruits to insure that the ones you harvest are a good size.

Some of these chemical pruning agents work in the same way as compounds produced by the plant itself, called "growth regulators". They can be applied to alter growth form and shrink the overall size of a plant without removing any specific bit. You could call them "shrinking agents", and they are extremely useful in producing pot plants. Your Christmas poinsettia will almost certainly have been treated to let you fit it on the dining table.

I have two reasons for using the weevil as the symbolic insect pest. First, vine weevils cause huge losses in nurseries and amenity plantings; and, on a personal note, because I first met my mentor V. W. Fowler when he was studying them.

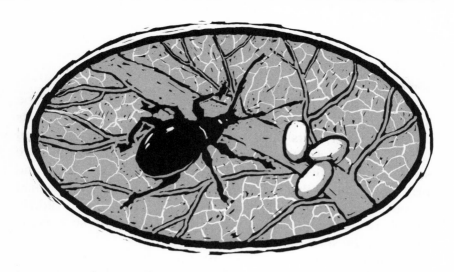

16 PESTS AND DISEASES

CONTROL OF PESTS AND DISEASES

Both herbivores and omnivores eat plants, and we are only one such species among hundreds of thousands. So we should perhaps be relieved that only a few of the others have managed to adapt to life among our crops well enough to cause significant damage to be deemed "pests". The bad news is that those that have cause massive losses if left unchecked. Efforts to control them have used millions of man-hours throughout our time as cultivators. Today even more millions of pounds are spent in a never-ending fight to prevent pests from lowering yields and reducing the exceptional quality demanded by supermarket shoppers.

Throughout their evolution towards modern man, our ancestors must have been aware that there were a lot of other mouths out there ready and willing to share our food. Indeed you can't really describe food as yours until the moment you swallow it. Over the millennia that we hunted and gathered, the most obvious competitors must have been the furry or feathered plant-eaters who moved in on a promising harvest just in front of us and cleared the lot, be it fruits, seeds or roots. It seems reasonable to suppose that our ancestors might have tried to protect promising patches of wild plants just as we do today's crops. Ecologists study animal territories as an essential aspect of behaviour, and fundamental to the concept of a territory are sex and a good food supply – home, sweet home. Could the protection of local future wild harvests by hunting, trapping, fencing or scaring have been some of our first acts of plant husbandry?

At what stage did we learn to recognise the ravages of the smaller competitors, the invertebrates? Surely plagues of locusts and some caterpillars must have made their presence felt even before we sowed crops. The very earliest farmers would have seen the destructive colonies of such groups as the aphids, and may have realised that by crippling the immature plant they had effectively destroyed the harvest. Slowly the small and the hidden must have come to be recognised as pests – creatures such as the mites and the subterranean root-eaters.

Just like animals, plants have parasites that live inside them; some are large like the Australian witchetty grub, which itself became food. These monsters must have been discovered centuries ago, but in contrast nematodes, bacteria, viruses and some fungi are extremely small and although the damage they cause was well known for thousands of years, some were not identified as the culprits until well into the twentieth century. Indeed the diseases they cause were very often attributed to supernatural forces and the work of witches.

If you suspected that the problems arose in the realms of the supernatural, that was surely the place to look for prevention or cure. Prayers have been offered for thousands of years to hundreds of deities. Most suppliants have asked for crops to be spared from the ravages of unidentified and mysterious agents of destruction. A few have been quite specific and knew exactly what the risk was, as when early Mesopotamian farmers begged protection from plagues of locusts.

Agricultural texts more than a hundred years old give very little space to pests and diseases, presumably because if you can't do anything about a problem it's not much use discussing it. Horticultural writers, with their focus on intensive small-scale cultivation, are ahead of their farming colleagues and early on offer some interesting treatments. Gervase Markham, in *The Second Booke of the English Husbandman*, published in 1635, devotes a whole chapter to "How to preserve all manner of Seeds, Hearbs, Flowers, and Fruits, from all manner of noysome, and pestilent things, which devoure, and hurt them." The problems are arranged in order of importance, so it comes as a surprise to learn that "of these enemies the worst and most violent is

Thunder and Lightening which in a moment killeth all sorts of

Flowers, Plants, and Trees, even in the height, and pride of their flourishing, which to prevent, it hath beene the practise of all the ancient Gardeners, to plant against the walles of their Gardens, or in the middest of their quarters, where their choysest flowers grow, the Lawrell or Bay Tree; which is ever held a defence against those strikings.

After thunder and lightening comes the following ecologically unsound list: Caterpillars – "filthy little wormes which lye about the leaves devouring them" – Frogges and Toades, Field Myce, Flyes, Greenfly, Gnats, Pismyers, Moales, Snailes and Moths. Control methods are as clear and as confident as any from the high days of DDT. To kill caterpillars "or prevent their breeding", sprinkle them with strong wine and ashes or envelop them in the smoke from smouldering old hay. The innocent, indeed beneficial, frogs and toads were banished by either burning "the fat of a stagge" or scattering a mixture of "kite dung and the shavings of an old hart's horne". Mice were poisoned with crushed henbane seed mixed with butter, or driven away by scattering the ashes of a cremated weasel. Flies were treated by alum powder or scared off by their own kind's ashes as "they will not dare to come neere them". Greenfly are next; if they "offend your garden" mix crushed Henbane, Houseleeke and Mints with vinegar. Gnats are smoked out by burning rosemary, mouldy hay or dry ox dung, as all such smokes are "very sharp and styfle as soon as received". Pismyers (ants to us) were even then being scolded with hot water. Moles were trapped or driven off by planting garlic or onions, whose smell was "deadley to these blind vermines". Snails, which were "as much offensive to gardens as any other crawling thing", had their abodes attacked with chimney soot, whereas the very pernicious moths were in an instant killed by the smoke from burning horse hoof pairings. To us a strange set of remedies, but some with more than a trace of good sense.

All this crop protection activity took place as an essential, time-consuming, routine part of crop husbandry, year after year, for millennia without a trace of a chemical spray. For several hundred years some very nasty chemicals have been used in poisoned bait, but it was not until the nineteenth century that insecticidal and fungicidal sprays were introduced. Some active ingredients came from the pharmacist's poisons store, while others were extracted from plants.

Some 225 years after the printing of *The Second Booke of the English Husbandman*, a different picture is presented by *The Gardener's and Farmer's Reason Why*. We begin to detect among some very traditional remedies a change that is usually attributed to the founding of agricultural chemistry. In what appears to be an echo from the past, readers are

> recommended in the case of almost all insects injurious to the horticulturist, to employ children in the summer months to destroy the moths themselves, giving a small premium for every ten or twenty they collect, and increasing the reward as the number becomes lessened. When taught where to look for them, they would discover numbers on the bark of trees; and if provided with gauze clasp-nets, would find it a most healthy and interesting occupation to catch them when made to fly, by shaking the trees and bushes in which they repose.

As an alternative to child labour, the author suggests an even smaller animal: "Fruit may be preserved from birds by a somewhat singular expedient, namely, the employment of cats." Apparently "the most perfect success" can be achieved using "four or five cats, each with a collar, and light chain and swivel, about a yard long, with a large iron ring at the end"; his informant claimed that

> as soon as the gooseberries, currants, and raspberries began to ripen, a small stake was driven into the ground, or bed, near the trees to be protected, leaving about a yard and a half of the stake above ground; the ring was slipped over the head of the stake, and the cat thus tethered in sight of the trees: no birds approached them.

Perhaps it would be more accurate to refer to "chemicals" rather than chemistry. Slugs and snails are killed by limewater, while pot plants are rid of red spider, scale, thrips and greenfly by sealing them in a box with crushed cherry laurel leaves (releasing prussic acid). Red spider are also "fumigated" with a combination of limewater and sulphur and aphids treated similarly with tobacco smoke. Gooseberry sawfly is attacked by limewater "thrown by a garden engine" (the first reference I have found to "spraying") and fruit tree insect pests by a mixture of sulphur and gas-water [g] plus soap, the latter still used today as a wetting agent. A band of tar softened with oil traps wingless female moths, and train oil [g] is painted on colonies of woolly aphid. Applying these early pesticides was evidently a problem;

dipping infected leaves and indeed whole plants was one way, application by paintbrush another, and for powders "there is a very useful instrument called a Boîte à Houppe manufactured especially for dusting flowers of sulphur over plants" – by the sound of it a "duster" or "puffer" and yet another French horticultural first.

Marked changes begin to appear in the literature towards the end of the nineteenth century. A retired professor of agriculture from Cambridge wrote a book, *Farm and Garden Insects*, that covered topics ranging from the internal anatomy of insects to their reproduction and classification and the symptoms of the damage they cause. While entomologists were studying the relevant insects in such detail, mycologists – or as they were then sometimes known, microscopists – were doing the same thing with fungi. The chemists were producing more compounds, equipment manufactures were producing spraying engines, and cultivators, particularly fruit and glasshouse growers, seemed keen to combine these developments into new methods of ridding their plants of pestilence. All this activity added up to growers using a formidable cupboard full of very poisonous items without much regard for the safety of their workers or the customers. Those who shun foodstuffs that have been treated with today's sprays, all of which have to undergo rigorous safety testing, should regard themselves as very fortunate that they were not living a hundred years ago. Of course, there was a good reason why people did not worry about such things in those days – ignorance!

By 1910 researchers had developed an even greater understanding of the biology of all kinds of pests. The life cycles of insects, the identification of disease-causing fungi, the existence of the nematodes farmers and gardeners know as eelworms, and bacteria were all documented thanks to the development of the microscope. The approaches of books such as F. V. Theobald's 550-page *Insect Pests of Fruit* and George Massee's *Text-Book of Plant Diseases* have a very modern ring about them, apart from the illustrations of people spraying in clothing more suited for a picnic on a hot day. Pest and disease control had moved on from the late Victorian era when compounds of mercury, arsenic and lead quite literally lay thick on the ground. Now fruit trees were being protected by such concoctions as the "Woburn Winter Wash", containing iron sulphate, lime and caustic soda, and "Lime-Sulphur-Soda Wash", containing lime, sulphur, caustic soda and soft soap. Application followed "spray programmes" which became a major part of the husbandry activities of fruit and glasshouse growers. Advertisements for the splendidly named "Bird Disguster" seed dressing appear during the first decade of the century; as was so often the case with "patent chemical formulations" of that time, it claimed a "two for the price of one" secondary function, in this case as a fungicide.

Most of these early chemical sprays were discovered by trial and error, the errors being borne by both plants and people. By far the best-known of these serendipitous discoveries is "Bordeaux mixture", a blending of copper sulphate and quicklime. As with all the best folklore, the story varies from teller to teller, the most fanciful being the spraying of grapevines with lime to stop boys scrumping the fruit. The lime reacted with the sprayer's copper containers to produce a deposit that controlled mildew. Of course, a good raconteur at a garden club meeting will make a lot more out of those bare bones, with appropriate cries of "Mon Dieu!" and "Voilà!".

I intended to leave the story there and move on, but the clear absence of any source of the all-important sulphur in this version drove me to look up a more authentic reference. This one comes from the 1940 edition of *The Scientific Principles of Plant Protection*:

> In 1882, Millardet, investigating the Downy Mildew of the Vine, observed that along the roadside at Médoc in the Gironde, certain vines bore leaves though elsewhere they had been defoliated by the disease. Attributing this persistence of the foliage to some treatment, he found on inquiry that it was the practice to daub the leaves of these particular vines with verdigris or with a mixture of lime and copper sulphate. For this reason, passers-by, thinking the fruit below would be similarly treated, would not touch it for fear of poison. Millardet followed up this slender clue and, in 1885, was able to announce the successful use of a lime-copper sulphate mixture as a fungicide against Plasmopara.

The value of the new fungicide, called Bordeaux mixture from the locality in which it originated, was rapidly established. The original formula gave a thick, slushy liquid, which had to be applied with a brush made of twigs, but improvements soon followed. M. Armand Cazenave's machine did not use either a pump or a nozzle but flicked the slurry onto the vines from the ends of a revolving stiff circular brush, rather in the way a dog showers bystanders after getting its coat wet. At about the same time M. Meyer produced a modification of the knapsack sprayer that most certainly had a nozzle, pipes and a pump. It was the latter item that singled it out from its competitors. The pump was built into the operator's shoes; spring-loaded, they worked like two pairs of bellows as the sprayer walked between the rows of vines. It was recommended that the rubber hose leading from the shoe-pumps to the spray tank ran up his trouser-leg to prevent it becoming entangled with the vines. Sadly, M. Meyer's "pedomatic apparatus" was soon superseded – most commonly by the "Éclair" designed by M. Vermorel, a brass worker from Villefranche, who improved both the parts that had given most trouble, the pump and the nozzle. Spraying the thick mixture was still difficult, but by now "*le sulfatage*" had become an annual routine on virtually every vineyard.

I cannot resist opening the story of crop protection in the twentieth century by mentioning information given in no less an organ of government than the *Journal of the Board of Agriculture* for December 1905. Under the heading of "Remedy for Flea Beetles", it reports on some research in Germany advising that seeds of susceptible plants be covered with a thin layer of white sand. Apparently, the whole secret of the method lies in the bright colour, which the flea-beetles dislike. The instinct of self-preservation, which here plays a part, warns the beetles that when they spring from the plants onto a light-coloured ground they will be at once seen and devoured by their natural enemies, the birds. The sand also hinders the beetles in their movements as it shifts from under their feet so that they become tired and are more easily caught.

By the mid 1950s the understanding of disease-causing organisms had grown to include the role of viruses. These organisms are so small that before the development of the electron-microscope they could only be detected by the symptoms they caused. Pest control was now attempted through an ever expanding and far more complex set of molecules typified in many people's minds by DDT (dichloro-diphenyl-trichloro-ethane, but including BHC (benzene hexachloride)). The all-prevailing cry seemed to be to spray early and spray often!

The story of crop protection in the twentieth century was one of overconfidence to a point of arrogance, but it was also driven by wishful thinking. Agronomists of all persuasions knew all too well the losses caused by pests and pathogens and the ever increasing demand for blemish-free produce. The idea that by simply "spraying" they could be rid of them was irresistible.

In spite of this, it is only fair to point out that the recommended control measures from this time included numerous references to very "green" approaches such as the search for resistant varieties, rotation, hot-water seed treatments, rigorous hygiene in the interval between crops, trapping creatures before they could lay their eggs and sterilising propagation equipment. Not a bad list, but it was the dire warning of the massive increase in chemicals that came from the pages of *Silent Spring* published in 1962 that is remembered.

If plant-eaters are found throughout the animal kingdom, so their preferred dining location is equally spread over every part of a plant. In researching information for this book, I have become convinced that there are a few books should never have been allowed to go out of print, just regularly updated. Fox Wilson's *The Detection and Control of Garden Pests* is one such. He breaks down damage symptoms by location and appearance. A glance at the contents gives a good idea of what cultivated plants in British gardens are up against: attacks on bulbs, corms and tubers; roots; stems; buds; foliage; flowers; fruits; seeds. No part of a plant is safe and the range and type of damage is no less comprehensive. Foliage alone may suffer from some thirty symptoms; it may be: blackened or browned; blistered; bloated; bronzed or rusted; chlorotic; damaged by clean-cut holes; coated with honeydew and sooty moulds; curled; discoloured; dropping; excessively hairy; spotted by frothy masses; galled; mined; mottled; pitted; puckered; rolled; scalloped, scaly; scarred; scratched; severed; silvered; skeletonised; spotted; spun together; wilted; or covered with woolly masses.

These categories of damage are caused by over a hundred different creatures. Are they all pests? Clearly Fox Wilson thought so, and so did the members of the RHS who sent him the damaged specimens. To some extent a pest is in the eyes of the beholder. If you are exhibiting chrysanthemums then the smallest damage to flower or foliage is a disaster. If plants are in a herbaceous border the owner is likely to be more tolerant and a shrub that's part of the structure planting in a housing estate will have to be half consumed before its plight is noticed. Commercial growers also have to decide what constitutes a pest – a decision often forced by the marketplace. Today's society seems to be pulling in two directions. We want to live with nature and not use toxic substances, and yet we demand flawless produce.

The connection between pestilence and the daily tasks of husbandry starts with the erection of physical barriers around crops to keep out marauding beasts and the employment of children to scare birds, an occupation that is recorded from medieval times until well into the nineteenth century. Efforts from arm-waving to shouting and throwing stones were mechanised by the arrival of the clacker. There's an odd connection between this piece of rustic equipment and the early days of the Home Guard in the Second World War. Real ammunition was far too precious to use on training exercises, but the troops needed to know they could be under fire from enemy machine-gunners. Short of shouting "bang-bang-bang!" very fast, the problem seemed intractable until someone came up with an enlarged addition of the clacker that generations of country folk had used to frighten birds off crops. Another piece of equipment joined the real Dad's Army; I know the story's true because the chap who made it worked for my father and I had a go with it before it went into service.

Shooting is the more obvious link between guns and birds, and I have little doubt that the sound of the shots did more good by scaring off the rest of the flock than by killing one or two of the raiders. This brings us neatly to the use of explosive bird-scarers. Today these devices bang away every few minutes when a timer produces a spark that ignites a mixture of gas and air. Surprisingly, back in 1857 you could buy something that did the same job, the "Rook Battery". It took the form of a circle of 24 very small brass cannons primed with blanks poking out from beneath a metal cone. Each fired in turn as a very long saltpetre-soaked fuse reached its touchhole. Now that really is the kind of bird-scarer I would have liked to have tried out, and so I guess would Captain Mainwaring!

Trapping of both small mammals such as rabbits, mice, voles and rats used all sorts of ingenious self-closing cages, as well as a range of barbaric spring-traps and snares. Birds suffered the same fate once inside their specially designed cage-traps, or fell for the use of bird lime, an extremely sticky goo that trapped them if they landed on anything covered with it. Hand-picking of such pests as caterpillars seems to have been restricted to horticultural crops in Britain, but it reached field scale use in other parts of the world and it is far from having died out completely in the Third World.

CROP PROTECTION IN THE TWENTY-FIRST CENTURY

An in-depth study of the way crop protection may go in the coming years is beyond the scope of this book. However, I don't wish to finish with this topic without some reference to today's practices and how they impinge on the work of contemporary cultivators. To do this, let's look at two approaches to crop protection, spraying and biological control.

It is possible that there are people who sincerely believe that farmers and growers really do slosh vast volumes of deadly poisons all over the countryside without regard or concern. The reality is very different, however, and very much safer for all concerned. I recognise that no amount of writing by me or anyone else will influence those who have closed their minds to the use of what they quaintly term "chemicals". However, in the hope that many readers still have an open mind I recommend they read the current *UK Pesticide Guide*. (Well, not all of it, as they could be at serious risk of death through boredom; concentrate on the first few pages that summarise the relevant legislation.) The Food and Environmental Protection Act 1985 (FEPA) and Control of Pesticides Regulations (1986) (COPR) introduced statutory powers to control pesticides with the aims of "protecting human beings, creatures and plants, safeguarding the environment, ensuring safe, effective and humane methods of controlling pests and making pesticide information available to the public". Control of pesticides is achieved by COPR, which lay down the approvals required before any pesticide may be sold, stored, supplied, advertised or used. In addition to this, the Control of Substances Hazardous to Health Regulations (COSHH) apply to pesticides, and no one is allowed to store, sell, advise on or apply pesticides without a certificate of competence.

Safety dominates the regulations, not only by prohibiting the use of materials deemed too dangerous, but also by minimising risk to people, both users and customers. All the chemicals have to be approved for each particular use, crop and pest; they must be applied at a specified rate at specified stages in the growth of the crop and only by a certificated operator. That said, it is of course impossible to legislate effectively for either stupid or wilful acts of misuse; however these materials are very expensive, so no one in their right mind who has to pay for them is going to deliberately exceed the effective dose.

Today's crop-sprayers are very sophisticated and expensive pieces of kit, often computer-controlled. They are designed to receive the concentrated pesticide in a way that eliminates the need to handle open containers. Within the machine this is mixed with and diluted by the appropriate amount of water; the resultant liquid is then pumped under pressure from the spray nozzles, which discharge it at an exact rate and droplet size over a known area of the crop. Tractor-mounted sprayers are designed so that the discharge rate is linked to the speed of the tractor. At the end of work they cut off the spray without dribbling extra liquid onto the soil.

The deliberate application of various forms of biological control is a very exciting development in which cultivators exploit and reinforce a species' most basic need, to obtain nutrients. It is by no means a new idea; there are some very ancient examples, but one I particularly like dates from 1677. John Worlidge recommended killing caterpillars on trees by releasing a bag full of ants onto the branches, having first ringed the trunk with tar. Then, he claims, "when they cannot go down by reason of the tar rather than they will starve for hunger they will eat up all the caterpillars".

The utilisation of nature's food-chain, whereby the plant-eaters are prey to carnivorous predators, remains the most common approach. Another aspect of the same strategy is to introduce disease-causing parasitic micro-organisms, diseases of the pest that is!

The use of predators has to start with finding suitable species and learning how to breed them in captivity. The grower can then release small populations among an infected crop, where he hopes they will feed on the pest, breed and multiply. The use of suitable pest-specific diseases has a lot in common with biological warfare. The infection is sprayed onto the pest, kills it and spreads to others.

Biological control has a very green ring to it; not surprisingly it is hugely popular, indeed essential, among those who do not use chemical means of pest management. It should not however be dismissed as unscientific – on the contrary it is a very logical approach to the reality that we are never likely to wipe out a pest species but we may be able to control its numbers sufficiently to effectively remove it from being regarded as a significant problem. It may come as a surprise to find that as long ago as 1943 Hugh Nicol wrote an excellent small book, *The Biological Control of Insects*. Published by Pelican Books, an imprint of Penguin, it was clearly intended for a wide readership, but I think they were a little optimistic to include the wartime request to "leave this book in a Post Office so that men and women in the armed forces may enjoy it". Biological control techniques set hunter against hunted or even instigate death by germ warfare. It is one gruesome story after another, but among them the sexual approach stands out as both deadly and deceitful. In this category comes the use of sterile but still sexually active males; when released in sufficient numbers they may greatly diminish a pest's breeding potential. Another technique is to lure either sex to their doom in traps bated with pheromone sex attractants. There is an interesting twist to this approach: use the appropriate attractant to bring in potentially very beneficial natural predators to the site of the infected crop. Chemicals derived from catmint seem capable of calling up lacewings over long distances – great for your crop, hard luck on the neighbours who will lose their help and total confusion for the local cats!

I am not sure that hiding your crop plants among other species counts as biological control, but it is an approach that deserves a mention if only because it illustrates how some "old wives' tales" so beloved of "green" gardeners turn out to work but not for the reasons they think. The believers in companion planting will tell you that the companion plant prevents pests from colonising the crop, either because the insect is repelled by the companion's smell or because the smell masks the smell of the host. According to Stan Finch and Rosemary Collier, two scientists at Horticulture Research International, the key is not smell but colour, appropriately enough green! Apparently, although insects are first attracted to an area of vegetation by the smell of a suitable host plant, they land anywhere upon its mass of green foliage but not on bare ground. Then they use plant odour to tell them if they have landed on a suitable food source for their offspring; if they have not they fly off. It seems that companion plants simply add more foliage, thereby reducing the chance of the insect hitting on a suitable host. The researchers found that all kinds of leaves were equally effective, from a sowing of clover to the local weeds and, most extraordinary of all, the cardboard leaves of artificial plants, provided they painted them green. While on the subject of pest control by companion planting, we might note that its devotees make some additional claims. Soft fruits interplanted with perennial stinging nettle bear heavier crops and resist disease, while foxgloves, in addition to reducing diseases, improve the storage qualities of potatoes and apples. Clearly our researchers still have plenty of claims to investigate.

The risks associated with the use of pest control materials have been endlessly debated in books and through the media by both the informed and the ignorant, and I do not intend to continue this here. My interest in crop protection is as part of the cultivation process, of which it has come to take a greater and greater percentage of production time and cost.

The development of crop protection materials and the methods of applying them are one thing, but all the regulations and clever design are of no value unless they work; so do they, and if not why not?

The answer to the first query sounds suspiciously political; the second is scientific. Does it work? Yes and no. In the short term, most pesticides are effective if you follow the maker's instructions, as it says in the textbooks. Even under field conditions populations of pests are dramatically reduced below the point where they can be reasonably described as a significant pest. But then the fungus, the nematode, the insect, the bacterium all start to reappear in ever increasing numbers. You could almost believe in that old myth spontaneous creation.

This is where the science comes in, in the form of a branch of biology known as population dynamics. Professor Leonard Broadbent was fond of pointing out that in theory one (they don't even need two) greenfly could become the founder of a colony of a hundred million offspring in a month. There are many reasons why this does not happen "in the field", but nevertheless it is the phenomenal breeding rate of these organisms that makes them such pests, and explains why it takes only a very few survivors to rapidly rebuild populations after applying insecticides. So if poisons aren't a long-term answer, will any other approach work any better? The present generation of crop protectionists think something will; it is called "pest management", and it involves a lot more ecology than earlier attempts.

We are only at the beginning of this revolution and certainly in no position to summarise the changes that such ideas as integrated pest management, various forms of biological control, and inbred resistance will ultimately produce. What is certain is that agronomists have a lot to learn, but that's the easy bit; as ever the hard part will be to change a time-honoured way of thinking. The changes now being researched and indeed introduced on a field scale require cultivators to admit that they cannot totally dominate nature but must coexist with their old enemies.

It is ironic that agronomists are being told that they must cooperate with conservationists because today's methods of crop production can drive many species to extinction, while at the same time other biologists are telling them that throwing all those deadly substances at pests is futile because they will always come back. Future changes to crop protection will not be as simple as swapping one chemical for another or even throwing the sprayer away altogether, which is unlikely to happen. Foresters, arable farmers and horticulturists will find that the adoption of the new approaches to pest and disease control will change many long-held practices that go right to the heart of our cultivation systems. Integrated pest management uses both chemical and biological methods in a series of moves to load the dice against the pest throughout the time that the crop is at risk. It is an approach that makes much higher demands on cultivators than simply following a spray programme, but in the current climate it is likely to get a fair hearing and be judged by results. Its appeal to those who dislike using chemicals but do not exclude them is twofold: it uses fewer sprays and, as the ones it does use are generally pest-specific, they are considered to do fewer damage to the environment.

Guidance by ecologists might require far more than adjusting the spray programme, and could extend to such surprising approaches as changing field patterns and shapes, altering crop layouts and having different forms of headland, some with beetle banks and other devices enabling them to act as nature reserves for beneficial pest predators. Maybe farmers in the future will sow two or more crops together and even employ some plants to act as traps or give an early warning to the neighbouring crop that they are being eaten. If you think the ecologists have some way-out ideas, you can hardly imagine what the geneticists are dreaming up. Plants that disguise themselves by producing the wrong smell, plants that were once an insect's favourite food now becoming unpalatable or even toxic, plants that render the pest sterile, plants that are too tall or too short for the pest to find them, plants whose leaves are too smooth for the pathogen to sit on.

Most of these ideas are not original; they have been around, and some have been in daily use, for a very long time. They are the devices plants already use; without them the world's vegetation would have been wiped out millions of years ago, long before the mammals appeared, let alone man. What today's scientists are thinking about is how to transfer nature's "good ideas" from one species to another, to those crop plants that could do with having their defences improved. If all this sounds as if crop protection, one of the basic activities of the cultivator, is about to become redundant and disappear, I must point out that these same scientists keep stressing that throughout the evolution of the land flora and fauna the two sides, pests and hosts, have kept pace with each other in an endless war, and it is likely to remain the pattern whether we join in or not.

SPRAYING TODAY

On many people's reckoning I should not be alive today, and I don't have in mind past students who had to resit exams. No, I am thinking of the safety-conscious who are about to read of my upbringing. On our holding we had a fruit-tree sprayer c. 1930. 15 years later it was still in use many times a year. Spray days went like this. Put on old raincoat – open concentrate container and pour content into measuring jug – pour into 40-gallon drum and fill with water. Stir with stick – dip in bucket – carry to sprayer – lift chest-high and pour in, dodging the biggest splashes – pump sprayer, or direct spray from end of leaking lance. Depending on wind direction and skill and "humour" of colleagues, regularly spit out excess spray – wipe spectacles etc. At end of day remove coat ready for tomorrow, wash hands and cycle home. We liked using DDT; it had a nicer smell and taste than lime sulphur and it didn't turn you yellow.

These horrendous days are thankfully long gone. Only our past ignorance can excuse them, but to me they have a value as a contrast to today. In spite of everything we did, we did not die, indeed I don't remember ever being sick. I do not write that as a boast but to make a point about today's extremely high safety standards. There are controls at every stage for each crop: the materials you may use, their concentration, their timing relative to harvest and the method of application. The maximum spray deposit levels allowed in one helping of fresh fruit must be less than a millionth of what we collected at the end of each day. And the chemical compounds used are safer. Relax and enjoy!

Chemicals can be used in two ways, either to protect a plant against the establishment of a pathogen or to eradicate one already present. Prevention is said to be better than cure, and so it is, but using previously available chemicals to achieve it was responsible for some of the most massive spray programmes. Five or more applications per season were required to do the job. No wonder the search for eradicants continues.

It is not just the safety of the consumer that is considered; current regulations also set out to protect the operator and the rest of nature – "the environment". The chemicals now permitted are less toxic to many forms of life other than the target species. They are used in the minimum effective amounts and their application is critically timed to be both effective and safe.

Today's spray equipment ranges from the small-scale, fiendishly uncomfortable, unsophisticated and awkward to use knapsack types to field-scale tractor mounted kit. These large, state-of-the art machines are a far cry from the "wheelbarrow hand-pump" model of my childhood. This is not the place for a full design manual of even one model, but a list of some of the common features will, I think, make the point. The spray concentrate is no longer handled. It is delivered in a container that can be opened only after it has been attached to the pipework of the sprayer, or else comes in a water-soluble sachet fed directly into the spray tank. Following the maker's instructions the number of concentrate packages is matched with the volume of water in the tank to achieve the desired spray concentration. A built-in agitator ensures that the concentrate and water are thoroughly mixed and remain so throughout the spraying operation. Output is controlled to give a known amount of spray per unit area of crop. The nozzles are positioned to give even crop cover and droplet size, determined by pressure and nozzle design to reach the target area but not drift across the countryside. To some, these developments will appear to be massive strides towards a safer and more responsible use of crop protection materials; to others, they represent the development of even more frightening killing machines.

Garden historians tend to think of bell cloches protecting a few early sowings on borders and hotbeds, but the caption on the frontispiece of The French Garden *from which this sketch was made notes that there were ten thousand in this field.*

17 CULTIVATION IN PROTECTED ENVIRONMENTS

HISTORY

Tender loving care is all very well, but building your plants a house and keeping them warm with their own central heating seems decidedly over the top. And yet there are today well over 7000 hectares of glasshouses in Northern Europe while in Spain alone there are more than 100,000 hectares of plastic structures growing out-of-season horticultural crops.

Broadly speaking there are three reasons for going to all this trouble: cultivating plants too tender to stand conditions out of doors; getting "out-of-season" harvests; and protecting delicate fruits and flowers from the wind and the rain. The alternative, of growing things in other parts of the world and then transporting the results has for long brought us our oranges and bananas and recently, as a result of ever rising heating fuel costs, a greater and greater percentage of our florists' flowers, tomatoes and other salad crops. Nevertheless as the figures above show, after some three hundred years the skills of the under-cover grower in the cool temperate world are still with us.

In gathering material for this book it has surprised me how early are the first references to many materials and practices. Protected cropping is just such an example. As horticulture's undercover activity it has operated behind a surprising range of translucent materials. On a small scale, the ancients are said to have used thin sheets of talc as well as the mica mentioned below. Many centuries later, oiled paper became a cheap if ephemeral alternative to glass. The journals of that most patient of naturalists Gilbert White nevertheless show him to be an impetuous gardener. He frequently had to resort to oiled-paper tents to protect vegetable seedlings sown weeks, if not months, before Selborne was safe from frosts. I guess that if he were alive today he would be an enthusiastic user of plastic sheeting. This material having in the last fifty years overtaken glass in many parts of the world to become the most common crop cover, we will have a closer look at it on page 387.

Two thousand years ago Tiberius, poor chap, fell ill. Maybe his doctors didn't know how to cure him and prescribed something so way-out that its efficaciousness could never be investigated. Their dietary recommendation was a cucumber a day. Perhaps to the medics' surprise, and thanks to their "specularium", the emperor's gardeners supplied the prescription throughout the winter. It seems tender plants were grown in these structures in what may be described as a hollowed-out hotbed, but it is not so clear what transparent material covered it. Most authorities suggest thin sheets of muscovite, the translucent form of mica, but certainly not glass, as the Romans did not have that for another two hundred years. It seems that very few of even the wealthiest Romans took up protective cropping, and Seneca may have been voicing a widely held opinion among his down-to-earth fellow-citizens when he criticised such efforts as contrary to nature.

One and a half thousand years later, Northern European nobility seems to have had a particular penchant for citrus fruit. Their determination to grow them goes back at least as far as Lord Burghley's efforts in 1561 to construct a building to overwinter orange trees. For the next three hundred years the gardeners of the wealthy developed the skills required to fruit many kinds of citrus in specially built orangeries. Indeed you needed great skill to produce oranges in an orangery; no doubt many are excellent pieces of period architecture, but most are far too dark for good growth. The earliest had no windows; the first were fitted early in the seventeenth century in a giant temporary building erected each year to overwinter the Elector Palatine's collection of 400 trees. For the most part, orangeries remained gloomy places, the standard solution to this lack of light being to keep the plants in huge boxes and carry them out to summer on a sunny terrace. The gardeners at Versailles became famous for their skill in managing this growing system, which they practise to this day, indeed the square sided, wooden Versailles design of container is still made, although nowadays rather more are sold for suburban patios than for royal orangeries and in some versions plastic has replaced wood!

In 1680 the Worshipful Company of Apothecaries erected their first glasshouse at Chelsea, the first of several managed and filled with exotic economic plants by the great Philip Miller. Given the importance of botany in the education of medics, it should be no surprise to find medical men prominent among glasshouse pioneers in both the Netherlands and England. By the early years of the eighteenth century Drs Richardson, Uvedale and Boerhaave had all built "stoves" and by the mid seventeen-hundreds wealthy individuals across Northern Europe had joined the more adventurous botanic gardens in growing a wide range of plants under cover so that they and their house guests might enjoy some of the newly arrived "curiosities of the vegetable kingdom", "introduced into this kingdom from the hot regions of the terraqueous globe", as Richard Steele put it in his *Essay Upon Gardening*. In 1746 Lady Petre's great stove at Thorndon in Essex was said by fellow collector Peter Collinson to be "the most extraordinary sight in the world", whose plants were so well grown that their "magnificence and the novelty of their appearances strikes everyone with pleasure".

At first the stoves that housed these decorative plants were partly glazed south-facing, lean-to buildings heated by open fires, some held in wheeled braziers – a somewhat hazardous method for both buildings and staff. Professor Bradley warns us to take care, as "Several men have been choked ... and sparks from them have set fire to the house." As the century progressed designs incorporated much more glass and far more satisfactory and less hazardous methods of heating. The required temperature was achieved by warmth radiating from the flues of furnaces located in the service buildings to the rear of the stove. The flues either were built into the back wall or ran beneath the floor. Other designs used beds of "tan", the slowly fermenting oak bark chips that had been used to tan leather. By one method or the other, or a combination of both, plus a generous nightly cover of straw mats, temperatures of around 20°C were maintained throughout the winter. Incidentally, that is exactly the figure aimed for today in most tropical departments in European botanic gardens.

The Dutch deserve the credit for the first stage in the development of the modern glasshouse. As early as 1737 they had published details showing almost fully glazed designs, very different from the English stoves of that time. Eventually we caught up, helped by that rarest of combinations, a professor of botany who knew how to cultivate plants. The man in question was Richard Bradley FRS, the chap who warned us of asphyxiating the gardeners. He held the chair of botany at Cambridge from 1724 to 1732, but it was before that, in 1718, that he wrote *New Improvements in Planting and Gardening*. I guess that today academics aspiring to a chair in any science at Oxbridge would save that title for their retirement!

Ahead of his times, as a professor should be, he told his readers:

> There is nothing more difficult in the management of exotic plants than the right understanding of conservatories, so I think it is necessary to prescribe such rules for the building and ordering of greenhouses as I have found to forward the welfare of plants, and as have yet been but little regarded or understood.

After this blanket condemnation of contemporary efforts he goes on in a more positive note to recommend better light, ventilation and the use of moderate rather than excessive heat. He even admits that in the past he had destroyed many specimens by virtually cooking them. He tells us he "could hardly venture them out of the hot beds in the most extreme heat of summer and in the winter half roasted them with subterranean fires". All good stuff, but the professor has gone down in the annals of Cambridge University for less honest attributes than his confession to tender plant mismanagement. It was said by his fellow dons that he was appointed on the strength of a fictitious recommendation and an empty promise to fund a new botanic garden, that he was completely ignorant of Latin and Greek and failed to give his lectures. My guess is that he could have got away with those crimes; I think it was the use of the word "gardening" in the title of a scientific paper that blackballed him!

Over the next hundred years designs improved so much that by the middle of the nineteenth century glasshouses had developed into forms easily recognised by today's horticulturists.

"Green-houses" overwintered the supposedly half hardy "ever-greens" that were being introduced from milder climes. From their general layout, specially designed structures were introduced in response to the increasing enthusiasm for cultivating edible plants, particularly fruit. Pineapples, melons, cucumbers, grapes, figs, peaches and nectarines: each of these crops had its own basic design of house, with catalogues of the time offering a huge range of styles within them. Northern European gardeners had to learn to manage the products of this building boom. The plants they housed were no longer grown only in containers but in raised beds, borders and pits, each filled with a soil mix specially selected for the crop. Cultivating the plants must have been a huge challenge, helped no doubt by the many periodicals and books published on the subject. It is clear from surviving letters that head gardeners made good use of the newly introduced penny-post to correspond with each other directly and to air their worries and triumphs more publicly via the editor's postbag in the many gardening periodicals of the time.

These early, and one must say, generally successful attempts at protected cropping can teach us a lot about how far the art of cultivation had got by the time we reach the start of the application of science. We don't need to be either historians or archaeologists to get this insight, although both disciplines have contributed a lot to our understanding. The interested layperson can simply pick up one of the hundred or so books, in French, Dutch or English, that were written by head gardeners during the nineteenth century; they are still about in second-hand bookshops. Two things strike me when I read these old texts: how far empirical but accurate observation got them in their quest to grow tender crops, and how literate these people were. The following quote from Mr Daes, gardener at Arundel Castle to His Grace the Duke of Norfolk, in the *Horticultural Register* of 1831 shows what I mean on both counts:

> Gentlemen, I beg to send you an account of a magnificent Brussels Apricot tree, growing in this garden. It is trained against a south-aspect flint wall, and completely covers [it being] forty-eight feet [14.4 m] long by twenty feet [6m] high; the stem, a foot from the surface, measures three feet three inches [1m], it there divides into three leading branches. I last year gathered 1800 very fine ripe fruit from it.

Wall fruit was technically "outdoors", but could receive protection in a number of ways. To avoid the flowers being damaged by spring frosts, straw or reed mats were put in place each night, while some trees were given the added protection of an overhanging canopy. That could be either a permanent feature, or something erected when needed, according to one advertisement "an attribute found most convenient, it being easily detached or attached at will". In practice it was attached twice a year, in spring when curtains hung from the outer edge of the canopy provided frost protection for the blossom, and in late summer to keep the wet off the ripening fruits. The most extreme form of assistance for wall fruit came in the form of heated walls. Long zigzag flues were built into them to carry the smoke and hot gases from fires situated at intervals along their base. Like the mats, they were only used when needed to keep the tree's flowers frost-free, but even that indicates the huge level of care lavished on such crops.

The logical development of the "fruit protector" was the wall cover or case. It was a permanent structure but with detachable sashes rather like a flattened glasshouse and the protection provided was complete. The final development in the quest for early fruit of the highest quality was the orchard house. Invented by the famous nineteenth-century nurseryman Thomas Rivers, it was a basic glazed, unheated wooden structure. Its secret lay in part in the recognition that many fruit trees require a cold dormant period followed by a warm growing season in which the crop can develop safe from the vagaries of the British summer weather. Its other requirement for success was a mastery of growing fruit trees, including apricots, peaches, plums, cherries and pears, in pots. That entailed skills in pruning, feeding and training that verged on the production of fecund bonsai. Rivers and a rival nurseryman, J. R. Pearson, each wrote a book entitled *The Orchard House*, and both authors devote most of their effort to this challenge. Pearson gives Rivers credit for the original idea but then goes on to describe the latter's design as "having the appearance of a covered drying ground and suggestive of a laundry" – a comment no doubt intended to keep his rival out of any stately house garden!

If rivalry over the design of a glasshouse for several kinds of fruit strikes you as somewhat small-minded then my last example of specialist design may seem positively nerdish: the gooseberry house. It is promoted both for the private garden and the commercial grower by Samuel Wood in *The Forcing Garden* because he thinks that "Any doubt about getting gooseberries large enough for tarts by Whitsuntide with numbers of persons is quite a serious thing." There is nothing unusual about its dimensions or glazed roof; the surprise comes when you look at the sides – there are none. They have been replaced by clipped hedges of box or "Siberian Arborvitae", chosen to "admit a softened air current through the house so that there is never the danger of suffocating the trees."

This is the point where in the pursuit of the craft of cultivation we bid farewell to the wealthy garden-owners and leave them to enjoy their glass "ranges", their palm houses and their grand conservatories. Undoubtedly their gardeners continued to achieve very impressive results. They have left us with no small residue of human stories, but they added very little more to the development of the glasshouse industry.

The first ventures into large-scale commercial glasshouse cropping took place during the second half of the nineteenth century, with notable British pioneers based along the South Coast of England around the town of Worthing. To start with, the structures were no larger than some of those in the great private gardens; for example one nurseryman, Mr Head, grew grapes for market in two with a combined length of some 60m. By 1870 these pioneer efforts were eclipsed by George Beer's five, each nearly 50m long, growing crops for the London market.

By this time glasshouses were being factory-produced by such companies as Foster & Pearson, "Horticultural Builders, Established 1841", and heated by hot water circulating in cast-iron pipes. Their generously illustrated catalogues are a mine of information, although in every case the commercial glasshouses are preceded by pages and pages of ornate "conservatories" supplied to both the aristocracy and the *nouveau-riche* industrialists for whom an interest in horticulture seems almost as *de rigueur* as the employment of a butler. At the turn of the century commercial glasshouse growing was well established, with G. W. Piper alone having 105 glasshouses covering 16 acres (6.5ha) of land. The twin aims in those early days were to provide luxury, slightly exotic and or out-of-season produce; the mainstays were grapes, melons, cucumbers, winter lettuce, early strawberries and, some time later, tomatoes.

The Worthing growers certainly did not have it all their own way. Clusters of glasshouse nurseries developed round several cities, those for the London market being concentrated particularly in the Lea Valley straddling the border between Essex and Hertfordshire. Locations were partly determined by soils and nearness to market, but the ready supply of horse manure from the city stables must have been a big attraction, if you see what I mean.

The Channel Island of Guernsey has one of the best-documented glasshouse industries anywhere in the world. It started with the export of some 4 tonnes of grapes per annum in the mid years of the nineteenth century that rose to over 2000 tonnes around the time of the First World War. Slowly, from then on, tomatoes replaced the grape as the island went on to become one of the largest tomato-producing areas in the world. Around fifteen per cent of the island was covered with glasshouses or vineries, as they were and still are known from their grape-growing days. At its peak, in the 1960s, the island exported more than 57,000 tonnes of tomatoes a year. Sadly, nothing lasts forever and the industry fell victim to international competition, relatively high production costs and especially to all that Southern European sun.

Helped by one of the most effective research and advisory services anywhere, the larger growers once again redesigned their glasshouses and changed crops. There is now a flourishing glasshouse flower growing business with freesias as an island speciality – horticultural product worthy of setting alongside anything produced by the famous Guernsey cow.

The horticultural history of the USA demands its own study, but I have two reasons for including a brief reference to it at this juncture. The first is the large scale and high level of development reached in the closing decades of the nineteenth century. By that time, a number of growers on the East Coast were producing large tonnages of tomatoes and three crops of winter lettuce per year, some with the aid of "the electric light" in the form of "2000 candle power arc lights suspended outside the glasshouses". The second reason is the amount of applied research into protected cropping being carried out at several universities. Right in the thick of the action, which was described with crystal clarity in his work *The Forcing Book* from which the above quote comes, sat that indomitable giant of American horticultural progress Professor L. H. Bailey of Cornell University in New York.

GLASSHOUSES TODAY

Some glasshouses and plastic-clad edifices are very basic constructions, whereas at the other end of the scale the most sophisticated cost in the region of a million pounds per hectare. Most of that huge sum goes on internal fittings and environmental control. Glasshouse growers are the control freaks of agronomy; if a modern cereal-producer seems a long way from the children's book image of Farmer Giles then these chaps are on a different planet from Adam the Gardener and Mr McGregor. Glasshouses cost a lot to build and a terrifying amount to heat. To make a profit the quality has to be excellent, and you need a lot of produce – and I mean a lot. Tomatoes are cropped at 500 tonnes per hectare per year while cucumber growers would expect 550,000 from a similar area. To begin to understand how such huge and totally unnatural yields are achieved we need to go back to the chapter on basic biology.

First, the plant has to have the potential to perform at this level, in other words the right genetic make-up. That's a job for the plant breeders and it is obvious they have succeeded. Then the grower takes over; the challenge of getting a plant to flourish in a glass- or plastic-covered structure is different from that faced out of doors, whether the growers are dripping with sweat in the vast cropping glasshouses of Venlo or gently perspiring in the Biomes of the Eden Project. The first objective is to remove the limiting factors that would otherwise throttle back the growth of the plant. Second, the plant has to be "directed" towards producing the bit that goes to market. Finally, the plants have to be kept pest- and disease-free.

So that summarises the aims; how are they delivered? Well, it would take a book to detail the operations for each crop, but a summary goes like this.

To remove the limiting factors ensure that the plants:
  never go short of water;
  always have the nutrients they require;
  breath an atmosphere with a threefold increase in the level of

carbon dioxide;

live in exactly the right temperature for each stage of their lives with a difference between night and day;

do not suffer through too high or too low humidity;

get as much light as possible, even if this means artificial illumination when they are young.

To target the fruits rather than other parts of the plant, the staff must side-shoot, de-leaf and eventually stop (pinch out the tip of) the plant. There's even help with pollination either by the use of vibrators or by introducing bumblebees.

Keeping the plants healthy is not just a matter of wallowing in spray chemicals. Preventative actions are far more cost-effective. These include using sterile material as a root substrate, sterilising the irrigation water, preventing pests entering the glasshouses and trapping those that do, and even in some circumstances dressing the staff in white coats to reduce cross-infection.

Following the eclipse of traditional wooden designs in the 1950s, the modern commercial glasshouse in its various forms can be thought of as a succession of pieces of apparatus. First comes the building itself, typically a very simple steel frame supporting an aluminium shell including the glazing bars, ventilators, lights and many of the heating pipes. The glazing bars hold the glass. Within this structure comes what the construction industry call second fixings.

At ground level the crop may be growing in the soil, but it is much more likely that the floor of the house has been sealed off with either concrete or plastic sheet and grow-bags positioned or some form of trough constructed to hold the synthetic compost in which the roots grow. Pipes designed to automatically deliver irrigation water are plumbed in. They may be joined by other pipes below the surface running off the heating system to raise the temperature of root zone to a pre-set level, yet another aspect of the environmental programme.

The final layer of equipment is the sensors and the controls managed by computer. Between them they monitor the environment and activate the appropriate apparatus when things start to deviate from the pre-set programme. They can work the heating, vents, irrigation, carbon dioxide discharge, humidity and lights. The modern glasshouse goes a long way towards controlling the weather and changing the climate.

Anyone with even a passing interest in economics must by now be asking, "Can this pay?" To which the response must be: "That's a very good question." This form of crop production is very much like most manufacturing industries; the most dangerous state to be in is trapped part-way between low-cost simplicity and high-tech complexity. Sadly, many who found themselves in that position have gone out of business over the last 25 years, but as the most progressive glasshouse growers testify, technical developments can still make some food crops profitable.

Before leaving economics and returning to the safer ground of cultivation, I should point out that it is not so much that the public might totally refuse to pay an economic price for their produce that concerns glasshouse growers but the availability of similar products grown out of doors or under plastic in warmer places. If anything finally kills off the glasshouse industry of Northern Europe it will be the jumbo jet freighter.

The ability to haul tonnes of fresh produce half way round the world for a few pence per kilo has done four things to my industry. It has shrunk the glasshouse sector and made the remaining growers invest in high-tech equipment to increase productivity. It has introduced the public to a range and continuity of fresh produce hitherto undreamed of and it has spawned an export industry of high-quality horticultural crops in places where previously there was simply no history of intensive cultivation of any kind.

It would be impossible to make any worthwhile use of all this equipment if we did not know the specific and precise needs and responses of the crop plant being cultivated. Glasshouse husbandry is the very best area of agronomy to illustrate the link between research findings in plant biology and crop cultivation. For the first time we know in depth just how a crop plant will react to the way we treat it. And we have the control to deliver those treatments either separately or in combination, as cocktails of environmental stimuli. If this is true, as I believe it to be, it is perhaps surprising and I think hugely reassuring that among all the growers I know, the one who stands out as the most successful user of all that science and technology spends hours just looking at his crops. But of course, he is not just looking; he is doing what generations of true agronomists have done, maybe for eight thousand years: he is reading his plants. Call it tender loving care if you wish, say it's experience, point to his professional qualifications, but what matters at the end of the day is that David can detect changes in a plant for good or ill before they become apparent to other people. He is a cultivator.

LOW-COST, SIMPLE PROTECTION

From the outset of protected cropping, people were looking for cheap, simple ways of giving at least the basic benefits of protection, often in the form of shelter and warmth at the start of the season. As early as the seventeenth century, oiled paper cloches were used to cover melon and cucumber seedlings, while the garden frame did a slightly up-market version of the same task. Strictly speaking, a frame describes the complete structure; the removable glazed cover is the light.

Today's amateur gardener probably regards the frame as rather inconsequential, possibly because it is much more pleasant to have a greenhouse where you can share the warmth of an artificial environment with your plants. In the eighteenth and nineteenth centuries, things were very different. A drawing of the Potager du Roi at Versailles shows several of the garden's many "quarters", each of around 400 square metres, covered by a total of well over 100 frame lights. Yet other quarters were similarly filled with hundreds more simple double-span glazed structures that look for all the world like Dutch lights covering hotbeds.

The frame played an important part in the development of commercial "protected cropping". Many were heated, at first by surrounding trenches filled with fermenting farmyard manure, later by a hot-water system. In various specially adapted designs, they grew luxury fruits including melons, pineapples and early strawberries. Later, other designs were produced, specifically for named crops. One such was the ground vinery, also known somewhat disparagingly as "The Curate's Vinery". In its simple form it is little more than a long double-span cold frame, but there were more elaborate versions such as that recently discovered at Trewidden in West Cornwall, in which the double-frame superstructure covered a slate-lined trough, turning it into a miniature form of the pit house [g] described below. A solitary vine planted just outside one end of the structure was trained within as a single rod suspended along the length of the ridge.

Some flowers also had specifically designed frames, the best known being the Victorians' favourite, violets. Eventually double-span frames became large enough for the gardener to join the plants, not by building up their sides but by digging down to provide an underground central walkway. Entered by steps at each end, these low structures were known as "pit houses". They were cheap to build and heat, and soon became one of the Victorians' most versatile glazed structures. They were used for propagation, producing bedding and pot plants as well as pineapples, melons, cucumbers and, later on, tomatoes. Their narrow path and steps ruled out the use of one of the gardener's few labour-saving devices, the wheelbarrow. Within such narrow confines it was a challenge to manoeuvre even a stretcher-like handbarrow [g] loaded with precious pot plants.

For over three hundred years glass cloches have been used to "bring on" early summer salads and the first vegetables. As far back as 1629, John Parkinson in his book *Paradisi in Sole, Paradisus Terrestris* writes of growing melons in "great hollow glasses like unto bell heads". The last of these bell cloches can still be seen in restored walled gardens, survivors of what was once an army occupying acres of land such as the field of ten thousand shown in the frontispiece to C. D. McKay's *The French Garden*. Each cloche covered one or more seedlings, and each had to be moved to ventilate the plants on hot days, to weed and to water – truly a case of hand-work. I can not leave the bell cloche without dealing a blow to the myth of its knob. The top of some cloches certainly had knobs but many carried only a scar produced when the glass blower separated the finished item. It is a pontal mark, as found on a hand-blown wineglass. Long after these cloches went out of use in commercial horticulture the idea spread among garden writers that this scar was where a knob had been struck off, as ever in such stories "by the garden boy", to prevent it working as a burning glass and tracing a scorch mark on the plant beneath! I have some of these cloches and looking at them I can't imagine how anyone could do this without breaking the whole thing. In case anyone has a cloche with a knob on, let me finish by pointing out that you *could* pay extra for such things; they were used in propagation nurseries for ease of handling. My guess is that the "garden boy" would have been in trouble if he *had* knocked the knob off. If you are brave enough to try and you succeed please let me know.

It is time to return to the main story of cheap and cheerful protected growing. The early decades of the twentieth century

saw two new forms of mounting glass over plants: the
continuous cloche and the Dutch light.

By anyone's reckoning the continuous barn cloche is a fiendish
idea patented by Major J. L. H. Chase in 1912. Four sheets of glass
are held together by three bits of spring wire. The operation of
assembly needs strength, dexterity, courage and the absence of
the health and safety officer. The barbed wire of the First World
War could have held little fear for the inventor. They are a
horticultural equivalent of the till in the TV comedy *Open All
Hours*. Writing from personal experience, I think I would rather
try and knock the knob off one of those bell cloches than
assemble a barn cloche.

Once assembled, continuous cloches worked well, advancing
crops by up to a month. The skill in cloche production is to keep
the things in action for as much of the year as they are useful

TWO-STRIP CLOCHED CROPPING SCHEME

STRIP 1	STRIP 2
1. Lettuce (Oct–Apr)	2. Dwarf beans (Apr–May)
3. Frame cucumbers (Jun–Sept)	4. Lettuce (sown Aug) (Sept–Nov)
OR	
1. Lettuce intercropped with peas (mid-Apr–May)	2. Tomatoes (Oct–early Apr)
3. Melons (Jun–Sept)	4. Tomatoes laid on straw (Sept–Oct)
OR	
1. Lettuce intercropped with carrots (mid-Apr–May)	2. Early tomatoes (Jan–Apr)
3. Late tomatoes (early Jun–Oct)	
OR	
1. Peas or broad beans (Nov–Apr)	2. Marrows (mid-Apr–May)
3. Melons (Jun–Sept)	4. Lettuce (Oct–)
OR	
1. Spinach or autumn-sown lettuce (Sept–Feb)	2. Strawberries (late Feb–Jun)
3. Cucumbers (Jun)	

and not to have to move them more than is necessary. A plan of
campaign is called for, and who better to supply it than Major J.

L. H. Chase? It is based on dividing the land up into strips, each wide enough for a row of cloches and a path. The cropping area consists of two or three such strips side by side, depending on the cropping plan. This form of intensive production requires a clear head and attention to the calendar. For the benefit of beginners to cloche gardening, I have included the five alternative cropping options, but have made it as easy as I can by choosing a "simple two-strip system based on one row of cloches". So the Major's orders are shown in the table opposite.

Things get more complex juggling with three possible cloche positions, and as Chase points out: "The possibilities of intercropping must not be overlooked." Intercropping is the growing of two or more crops simultaneously on the same plot. Typically the plan is to arrange things so that the harvesting of one makes room for the other to develop fully. If the first to be harvested is very fast-maturing, such as some leaf salads, it is called a "catch crop". If novices felt they needed help they could always join the Chase Cloche Guild (two shillings and sixpence per annum) whose monthly bulletin contained reports from its headquarters at Chertsey where some thirty-five thousand cloches were in use The cloche and Dutch-light enthusiasts of the twentieth century were by no means the first to use such ruses to intensify production. The Neat House market-gardeners in the early seventeen-hundreds were skilled exponents, with mixed plantings of cauliflowers and coleworts and sowings of radish and carrots. Intercropping is classed as one of the several approaches to what is now called "multiple cropping", a concept we first met under the very different conditions discussed on page 147.

To me cloches and Dutch lights represent the very essence of the skills of intensive market-gardening. Those seeking nostalgia should get hold of a copy of the Major's book *Commercial Cloche Gardening*. Although they no longer have a role in commercial cropping they are still a worthwhile item in the amateur's vegetable garden – but wear strong gloves!

A Dutch light, like the side of a cloche, is only a single sheet of glass, but it has the huge advantage for the user of being set in a wooden frame; no more need for those gloves! They arrived on our shores in the inter-war period, introduced by Dutch market-gardeners that had settled around Cuttingham, just north of Kingston upon Hull. There British growers learnt the value and flexibility of these simple basic units that could be arranged to make continuous long runs or joined to form larger "structures". Whole fields were covered and between 1930 and 1950 dedicated cropping systems using a vast range of crops grew up around their accommodating simplicity. If the Dutch lights were simple, the cropping systems were not; alternate and continuous-cover programmes with either one or several crops growing together, but maturing in sequence, required strict programming in some of the most intensive cultivation systems ever practised in British horticulture. Not only were there crop sequences to consider, but, for disease control, the rotation of the land between sequences. Then there was the requirement to build and dismantle the glasshouse-like structures formed to accommodate taller crops. The complexity of the cropping scheme from A. R. Carter's *Dutch Lights for Growers and Gardeners* published in 1956 makes the one for cloches seem simple. This plan uses two successions of crops (five in all) covering exact areas and in exact locations, produced on two adjacent strips of land. Based on the seasonal demands of the crops, the Dutch lights spent their time alternating between these two strips, sometimes in the form of frames, at others as glasshouse structures. There is a greater total area of land under cropping than the Dutch Lights can cover as frames (which is itself four times as much as when assembled as structures). If you have followed me this far you will have realised that a crop may spend varying periods of its life in the open or beneath frames or within structures. No wonder British growers are at times in awe of their brothers across the North Sea. Highly labour-intensive, Dutch lights could not resist the next generation of protection providers and by the late 1960s were in terminal decline.

In hindsight, Dutch lights can be seen as part of a final fling to develop protected cropping in the traditional market-garden. The other two ideas were the polytunnel and the mobile glasshouse.

THE MOBILE GLASSHOUSE

The mobile glasshouse was, and still is, a splendid idea. The first were built in the last decades of the nineteenth century, and as Ronald Webber tells us, they were neither pipe dreams nor miniatures. One a wooden, double-span structure measuring

"97ft. by 41ft. [30m × 12.5m] weighed 20 tonnes and could be moved in a few minutes". Some fifty years later, at the start of his career, one of this country's most creative engineers, the late Sir Ted Happold, revisited the concept.

The idea grew out of the fact that many crops need protection for only part of their growing season and that it should be possible to select a cropping series such that their needs followed one after the other. By planting them in adjacent "glasshouse-shaped" blocks and designing a robust and movable structure, a glasshouse could be pulled on rails over each in turn – typically, three or four crops a year. One of its more surprising features was that the rails formed the base of the house, the dolly wheels being held on rows of short piles set permanently into the land. Of course, the ends of the glasshouse had to lift clear of the crop that was about to be enveloped, an exercise that produced a terrifying number of creaks and groans as the gable end swung up – the ideal time to be called away to deal with an urgent enquiry.

Sadly, this ingenious idea fell victim to the difficulty of making intermediate technology profitable. Many of the general public may feel uncomfortable with the way crop production has become more and more high-tech, but the unfortunate truth is that the industry is littered with examples of good, simple ideas that proved unprofitable in the face of either more and more sophisticated developments or else very basic solutions such as the "polytunnel".

PLASTIC-CLAD STRUCTURES (POLY HOUSES)
Polyethylene plastic sheeting became available in the 1950s. From the start this completely novel material seemed to offer real advantages. In reality, production under plastic sheet has presented the glasshouse industry of Northern Europe with a stark and all too visible reminder of the dilemma growers in these parts face in our ever increasing demand for all-year-round, blemish-free, cheap produce. Can they compete with areas to the south that need only this cheap form of winter/spring protection?

As I have pointed out, we have known for a very long time that plants will grow successfully in transparent buildings. At first only the very rich could afford to build them and they commissioned architects to produce plant palaces: the orangeries, stove houses and palm houses of the eighteenth and nineteenth centuries.

That understanding has finally led us to cropping under plastic structures. At the outset they were seen as either the largest ever garden frame or the cheapest ever greenhouse. Of course they were neither, and plastic-clad structures or "polytunnels" as they became known, soon became recognised as new cropping environments with their own advantages, limitations and disadvantages to both plants and workers. Things started small; individual low structures known as polythene tunnels appeared on most market-gardens and nurseries. These developed into larger, often "multibay" buildings, much to the benefit of the plants and the comfort of the staff who no longer had their hair washed in condensation from the plastic sheet while bent almost double tending the crop.

These structures, now with much longer-lived sheeting, have become an important part of protected cropping in Britain and neighbouring Northern European countries, but it was further south that the plastic story really took off for early vegetable and salad crops. Huge areas of Huelva on the coastal plain of southern Spain have been covered almost without a break. From the overlooking hills the landscape seems to shimmer like some vast mirror, reflecting more light even than the sea beyond. Beneath this cover millions of lettuces, tomatoes and melons rush through their short lives before departing for the supermarkets of the North. Somewhat surprisingly, the march of the polythene sheet does not stop at the northern shores of the Mediterranean. There are thousands of hectares of the stuff in Israel, and if you look out of the aeroplane window as you land for your holiday on the Canary Islands you will see even more, like some vast tatty shanty town, covering bananas. It all adds up to the ugly face of intensive commercial cropping.

Longer life might have been the first big improvement in plastic sheeting, but it won't be the last. There is a lot of really imaginative research going on at Reading University under the leadership of Professor Paul Hadley. His group are looking at ways in which plastics can be used to filter light in such a way that the light that passes through them and reaches the crop is of the wavelength band that controls certain aspects of plant growth. It is theoretically possible that the very cover that protects a crop could also tell it how tall to grow. Even that is not the end of the story, because it might also protect it from diseases by stopping some fungus spores from developing. Such are the promises of the plastic houses of the future, but at present we have to face the big environmental concerns of excessive irrigation water and fertiliser use coming from Southern Europe.

THE DARK-HOUSE

After so much emphasis on the need for light and airy structures, it may seem strange to end this chaper on protected cropping by going into the dark world of the forcing-shed. "Forcing" is one of those terms that has had several meanings – indeed some writers use it to refer to most forms of protective cropping. Nowadays it generally refers to encouraging plants to produce succulent, blanched growths, often by putting them in a warm, humid and dark place. Forcing houses for rhubarb and chicory produce sufficient produce to make its presence felt on the supermarket shelves, but blanched seakale and asparagus are sadly no longer regularly available. They had their heyday a hundred years ago, products of the stately-home gardens that were harvested in late winter when the open garden offered little in the way of esculent luxuries. Either these harvests were produced when "roots" or "crowns" were lifted into specially designed heated "dark-houses" or they were gathered from within huge earthenware pots. As J. C. Loudon tells us, such forcing pots were "whelmed" over selected plants and kept warm beneath a thick covering of fermenting manure.

Grow-bags offer one way of isolating glasshouse crops such as tomatoes, peppers and cucumbers from the local soil. Providing the plants get ample water and nutrients they thrive in the small volume of substrate held in such containers.

18 CULTIVATION IN CONTAINERS

We have been growing plants in pots for a very long time – well not "we" if by that you mean the British or our immediate neighbours, because for most of this period we were not cultivating anything. There is a much-reproduced painting dated to around 1500 BC from a temple at Deir El-Bahri in Egypt, showing ships of Queen Hatshepsut's fleet loading containerised plants from Punt on the Red Sea coast. We are of course not certain that the plants had spent much time in their pots; it is possible that they had only just been potted up for the trip, a bit like some shrubs sold in dodgy garden centres even today. But this picture is not the only reference we have to Ancient Egyptian pot plants. Parks laid out in the reign of Ramses III certainly made use of large earthenware containers to grow specimen shrubs, giving pot culture a history of well over three thousand years.

Coming forward in time to the seventh century BC in Greece, we encounter pot plants again taking centre stage. The worship of Adonis included an annual celebration of his return from the underworld each spring, albeit this seems to have required some encouragement from Aphrodite. As part of these celebrations, the women made "Adonis gardens", which took the form of an arrangement of pots sown or planted with crop and decorative plants whose young foliage symbolised new life in the new season. It is said that although these gardens lasted only for the duration of the festivities they introduced the idea of pot culture, which became commonplace around dwellings in ancient Greece. From there, like so many sophisticated ideas, it spread to Rome.

Over this long time, growers have used every kind of container from half-coconuts and hollow bamboo stems to ceramic pots and brass jardinieres now revered as works of art. Perhaps the most famous of the "posh" containers is the "Versailles planter", an iron-bound wooden box with removable sloping sides designed to accommodate the citrus trees from the potager's orangery. More recently, nursery stock producers have used rather more down-market items including second-hand tin cans and plastic bags, while both amateur and professional glasshouse owners each bring a range of glasshouse crops to maturity in simple plastic grow-bags.

Containers have been filled with every kind of "soil", from Nile silt enriched with camel dung to those wonderful British formulations that helped herald the dawning of scientific horticulture, the John Innes composts. Others use only water, but unlike teetotallers permit "a little something" to be added to their hydroponic tanks.

As we have seen, translocation is a cornerstone of cultivation and huge numbers of potential transplants are produced in containers to aid to their mobility and to ensure that when called for they are not, as the saying goes, rooted to the spot. Remarkably, it is possible to confine a root system to a fraction of its natural spread without it being detrimental to the overall wellbeing of the plant. But such a confinement requires careful management of the compost and water supply if it is not to reduce the vigour of the rest of the plant. Mobility allows producers to space plants at their optimum density at each stage of their development, and to move them from one environment to another and finally market them as complete growing specimens. Flowering and foliage pot plants for home decoration are typically glasshouse crops, but as a visit to any garden centre or yet another TV programme on patio gardening will remind you, hardy garden plants are now very much part of this story.

In contrast to the open land, the prescribed world of the flowerpot allows growers to formulate and control virtually every aspect of the root environment, using what are really quite small amounts of compost. Growing in containers is very closely linked with protected cropping, as fewer and fewer glasshouse crops are grown *in situ*; indeed, the days when glasshouses were glazed sheds covering fertile land have long gone.

Well-thought-out container growing saves expensive glasshouse space and lends itself to automation. Indeed, it and its associated benching systems and high-tech equipment are an essential part of plant factories, the larger of which count production in millions of plants per year. It is a concept that sends shudders down the backs of practitioners of the three m's school of cultivation – muck, mystery and muddle. In the most highly equipped glasshouses, pot plants are sown, potted, lifted, moved, spaced, washed, labelled and packed by machine.

Decorative tender subjects are destined to be carried off as either foliage or flowering houseplants. The hardier types will go into garden centres for sale as garden trees, shrubs or border plants. In addition to these categories there are all those millions of bedding plants that appear every spring in all sorts of retail outlets from greengrocers to ironmongers and petrol stations.

Apart from all these specimens produced for the domestic market, there are a lot of crop plants that start their lives in containers, while others spend their entire existence in a sequence of production systems that isolates them from Mother Earth. They lead what might seem to be an almost science fiction existence, remote from even a trace of soil.

Container growing offers several advantages, but it is the problems that produce the most telling stories and no more so than in the case of the compost. I have not been able to trace when it was that gardeners first realised that garden soil, however good it was at growing plants in the open, was a nightmare in pots; however, that certainly must have been recognised when people started to give their own alternative recipes, which was at least as far back as the eighteenth century.

For the best part of two hundred years, growers blended light loam soils with rotted farmyard manure, leafmould and sand. Among the items added in smaller quantities were charcoal, mortar rubble, burnt clay and crushed bricks. All this, and in some cases much more, was mixed, it was believed, to meet the particular needs of specific plants. Two of my favourites are the requirement to use seven-year-old goose manure as an ingredient of the potting mix for incurving exhibition chrysanthemums, and a note in *The Magazine of Botany* by a Mr Green, gardener to Sir E. Antrobus, Bart, who grew epiphyllums in

> an equal quantity of light turfy loam and pigeon's dung and one

third sheep's dung; exposing the mixture one year to the influence of the summer's sun and winter frost to mellow. When wanted for use I add one third of sandy peat in both cases mixing them well together.

His reward, according to the journal's famous editor and infamous windbag Joseph Paxton, was "the most splendid we ever remember to have seen".

This era finally came to an end in the 1930s with the development of a standard potting compost at the John Innes Research Institute. This near-universal compost consisted of a prescribed ratio of carefully defined types of loam, peat and sand, to which was added lime and a specific formulation of a compound fertiliser supplying nitrogen, phosphorus and potassium. The John Innes Institute has gone on to employ hundreds of research scientists who have produced thousands of scientific papers which have contributed vastly to our knowledge of plants, but to the general public J. W. C. Lawrence and J. Newell's work on potting composts seems destined to be this remarkable institution's greatest triumph. Never have so many gardeners owed so much to so few.

But even the greatest triumphs must give way to the onward march of science, and the 1960s saw the appearance across Europe and the United States of loamless potting composts based on peat. From the University of California came the UC mixes of fine sand and peat. In Germany they favoured the addition of a little clay, while in Britain we developed 100-per-cent peat composts. Since that time some brands have introduced alternative organic substances to peat, in part to use otherwise waste materials and in part as a response to the "anti-peat" movement. No one can miss the success of these composts; it cries out every summer from shop fronts and lamp-posts in almost every city and town in Britain. Today's hanging baskets may have a heritage going back at least a hundred years, but they are massively better than anything of those times, and that is due in great measure to their composts and the slow-release, long-life fertilizer they contain.

The anti-peat campaign deserves some consideration. Lowland peat is formed if conditions prevent the dead vegetation of wetlands from decomposing completely. An organic layer builds up, contributing to a habitat that in turn supports its own specific flora. The large-scale drainage of such areas has been undertaken for a variety of reasons, but in almost every case agriculture has gained valuable land both for stock and crops – indeed such sites have produced some of the highest-yielding soils. In England the situation has been reached where such habitats and their plants and animals are endangered. The peat removal industry was not the initiator of this damage to wildlife; however, ecologists now consider that all England's remaining peat-based wetlands should be conserved. This of course precludes the removal of any more peat for whatever use. If however we consider the wider picture across the whole of the northern cool-temperate climatic zone, we find a rather different story. The region contains vast areas of peat-lands of various types in, for example, Finland and Russia. Here the question is not the conservation of an endangered final remnant but of land use, the percentage of a country, measured in millions of hectares, that should be left as untouched wilderness. Put into this context, peat for potting compost has an insignificant impact and in my view remains a legitimate industry when correctly located and controlled. The Finns were the pioneers both in the use of peat as a horticultural substrate and in studying its properties and behaviour. Based on the University of Helsinki, the work resulted in one of the great advances in container growing and is a rare example in agronomy, outside the world of agri-chemicals, of science preceding application.

Even before these developments people were wondering if they could dispense with soil-like substances altogether and grow crops in some inert material bathed in a nutrient solution. The answer was yes, in bucketfuls. The term "hydroponics" was coined in the USA by Dr W. F. Gericke in 1929, so his pioneering work to eliminate soil coincided with that at the John Innes Institute dedicated to finding the ideal soil-based substrate.

Gericke took his inspiration from the laboratory-based research into plant nutrition of two nineteenth-century German scientists, W. Knop and J. von Sachs, who are still remembered for the nutrient solution they formulated. It is not clear what turned Dr Gericke against soil, but in hindsight it is ironic that he experimented with outdoor waterculture systems where his ideas never took off, and overlooked their application to protected cropping where they have become so important. He constructed massive clay, wood or concrete water-tight tanks over or in the soil (nasty, old-fashioned stuff), suspended a "seedbed" made of organic material above it, filled the tank with a nutrient solution and sowed or planted his crops, everything from potatoes and carrots to dahlias and wheat.

Many kinds of system appeared after this pioneering work; each claimed the best results and superiority over the rest through design features regarded as essential by its exponents. Both growers and researchers became confused, doubtful or downright cynical, depending on their nature, when it was realised that these supposedly vital aspects were absent in the layouts of equally successful competitors. Those with no axe to grind began to see that there were as many successful hydroponic growing systems and substrates as roads to Rome.

The one name that cannot be left out of the story of hydroponic husbandry in Britain must be James Sholto Douglas, who is described on the flyleaf of his own book as "a member of an ancient and historically prominent Scottish family". Throughout the second half of the twenty century his writings enthusiastically promoted the idea of hydroponic cultivation for both amateur gardeners and professional growers, almost to the extent that one felt he mistrusted soil to continue to support plant growth, the job it had managed to do for millions of years. But Sholto Douglas was from the kind of background that happily mixes its missions, so at the same time that he is the leading voice in this most scientific of approaches to cultivation he also wrote *Alternative Foods: A World Guide to Lesser Known Edible Plants*, a book that one might immediately associate with a follower of a somewhat unconventional way of life. Long may the confidence that comes from such an ancestry produce such free spirits. To my surprise I learn that there is a flourishing following in "organic hydroponics", so I guess the liquid feed for pot-plants my father made from sacks of sheep droppings in a tank of water still has a place in the story of cultivation.

Roots seem to do their job pretty well any which-way if they are kept moist by a well-oxygenated film of water. This requirement having been satisfied, the rest of most hydroponic systems focused on the plumbing that supplied the nutrient solution to a bewildering range of moisture-holding substrates. These included straw, sand, gravel, rock wool, vermiculite, perlite and just water – still water in the case of "hydroculture", running water in the very successful "nutrient film technique" (NFT). For a few years in the early 1980s it seemed that NFT, by which a shallow "film" of dilute but very carefully concocted solution of plant nutrients was circulated round troughs holding the plant roots, might become a standard method of growing some glasshouse crops, particularly tomatoes. Research in Britain was centred on the then Glasshouse Crops Research Station at Littlehampton, but it was not long before scientists there were struggling to answer all the questions thrown up by over sixty hectares of commercial production while at the same time adding to the more than 150 research papers that this novel cultivation system had spawned. How different things were in the early days of Rothamsted!

Virtually all the systems designed to supply a nutrient solution to roots worked; the plants grew and produced a satisfactory harvest, but inevitably some methods just dropped out of favour. Overall, hydroponics has had virtually no impact on outdoor production, but it is a very different story under glass. In these highly controlled environments rock wool slabs moistened by drips of nutrient solution have grown in importance to become one of the main ways of producing some of our major glasshouse crops such as tomatoes, peppers and cucumbers.

Perusing each idea in any detail is inappropriate in a book of this kind; the important insight we get from all this enthusiastic search for an alternative to soil is just how far it is possible to go from natural conditions and still produce what are to all intents and purposes normal plants. Of course not everyone believes this, but here the key word is surely belief, or rather disbelief.

The story of potting composts is mirrored by the tale of the containers themselves. We have already met some of the largest with the most famous design, those used at Versailles to grow the Sun King's oranges. More normal-sized pots were thrown on a potter's wheel. By the middle of the nineteenth century there was a standard set of sizes ranging from a few centimetres across to around half a metre in diameter. Apparently every size was produced from the same standard lump of clay. It was first cut into equal pieces, each sufficient for one pot of the size required. The various sizes of pot became known by the number produced from the original lump or cast; hence in 1818, as William Forsyth tells us in his tedious book *The Culture and Management of Fruit Trees*:

In the vicinity of London, pots are denominated by the number contained in what the Potters call a Cast. They are delivered in at the price of from two shillings and four-pence to half a crown per Cast, which contains as under, viz.

The first size of	8	in the Cast is called	Eights
2nd	12	— do —	Twelves.
3rd	16	— do —	Sixteens.
4th	24	— do —	Twenty-fours.
5th	32	— do —	Thirty-twos.
6th	48	— do —	Forty-eights.
7th	60	— do —	Sixties.

The 1960s saw huge changes in plant pot fashions. Strangely, they are not talked about as much as the sexual revolution that was going on at the same time, indeed this note may be the first attempt to redress the balance. As far as the traditional British gardener was concerned, the ceramic pot had almost mystic properties; put a plant into anything else and you were courting failure. Then news started to filter through that the Americans were growing shrub transplants in tins, second-hand cans from the catering trade. Words failed the gardening establishment, which went into even deeper shock when the tins started to give way to black plastic bags and still the plants thrived; they simply did not understand that it was their duty as British stock to refuse to grow in the face of such philistine treatment.

At the same time, glasshouse pot plants were being put into ridged plastic pots, objects that, it was said, would not allow the potting compost to breathe or dry out as it should. These plants did equally well; the revolution was upon us, the earthenware pot was obsolete and tens of thousands went as hard-core into nursery roads. As ever, there is a final twist to the story: clay pots have now become "garden arty" – they are collectable and they are expensive. It is too late for those turned to rubble, but old potting sheds are well worth a visit.

At this point we might turn to other kinds of ways of containing roots, but before doing so there are some more pot-like objects worthy of our attention. My favourite is the "Spring Ring". This very effective and practical Australian invention for growing tree and shrub transplants does not try to direct the circling roots – it kills them! The Spring Ring consists of a sheet of stiff plastic moulded to give a dimpled surface like a miniature edition of an egg tray. The tip of each dimple is cut through. The plastic sheet is bent round and held in place to form a tube. When a plant's roots reach the sides, instead of going round and round, building up trouble for the future, they grow into the dimples where they are "air-pruned" when they try to grow out of the cut. New roots very soon sprout from behind the old root tip and within a few weeks a fibrous root system fills the container. Transplanting is simply a matter of uncoupling the plastic sheet and lifting out the plant by its rootball.

Pot-like containers are now made by compressing a whole range of degradable materials from sawdust to paper and peat. Another form of container that helps produce very small tree transplants with the right form of root system is the "Rootrainer". Intended for small seedling trees, it has two clear advantages over traditional pots. The sides are ribbed vertically to act as guides for the young roots, encouraging them to grow down rather than around. Rootrainers are hinged at their base so that they can be opened vertically to remove the seedling.

Ensuring that small seedling transplants retain a root-ball of compost and so avoid the worst of any transplant shock has produced a whole range of devices. Surely the prize-winner for lateral thinking is the soil block, which stands without the need for a container. The idea seems to have a long history, stretching back several hundred years if one counts the use in country estate gardens of inverted turf sods sown with melon seed. Setting aside both this practice and a few other odd examples, we arrive in Holland in 1946. To be precise it is it is our old friend Major J. L. H. Chase that visits the Netherlands, buys one of the primitive block-makers and returns with it to his market-garden in Surrey. Major Chase is a man of many parts, soldier, horticulturist and qualified engineer. Clearly the elegance of solving the plant-pot problem by discarding the pot appealed to his style of lateral thinking. He went on to become the soil block's champion, to develop much improved blocking machines that moulded appropriately formulated compost into cubes, and to be the co-author of *Soil Block Gardening*, the standard text on the subject.

The arrival of cheap plastic-moulding techniques helped the demise of the soil block. Small, usually square cells capable of being handled *en masse* became available. Known as "liners" in the nursery trade, they are the starter home to most of the cuttings that grow up to become our garden shrubs. Even larger numbers of transplants are needed to supply public and private gardeners' demands for bedding plants and, more recently, wildflowers such as dog daisies and cowslips. Every year many millions of such seedlings are raised in trays, each moulded to form a large number of individual containers each holding around a tablespoon full of compost. The resultant small transplants, known as "plugs" may be either potted on or planted directly into the open land.

Tackling the challenge of raising hundreds of thousands of rootballed seedlings for forestry plantations and field crops produced yet another ingenious solution to the quest for a cheap temporary container. The Japanese, who transplant their sugarbeet, turned to paper tubes produced *en masse* and joined together in a honeycomb-like form that packs closely into trays and is ideal for mechanical soil-filling and precision seed-sowing. Maybe the idea of using paper came from their skill with origami; however, unlike that craft this idea uses glue – in fact it depends on the use of two different glues, one water-resistant to form the paper tubes, the other, that initially holds the tubes together to form the honeycomb, water-soluble, allowing each seedling, in its tube, to be planted separately. The final trick is to use a paper that's strong enough to withstand mechanical transplanting but soon after degrades in the soil, allowing the roots to spread.

In the future crops may well change but the basic components of the science, craft and art of cultivation will surely remain the same, as they have from the beginning, eleven thousand years ago.

19 THE FUTURE

This book has tried to tell the story of how developments in cultivation have increased production and the quality of the harvest. Throughout there has been an assumption that each innovation has been both beneficial to those aims and economically sound. In recent years, and for the first time, not everyone would agree.

Cultivation is a subject with an eleven-thousand-year history. The majority of its hand skills were will developed at least five thousand years ago, many of them thousands of years before that. Mechanisation and the application of science have a history going back some 250 years, and yet almost every operation in today's production cycles in farm, forest and horticultural holding has been drastically changed in the last half century, and in many cases the whole crop relocated. The materials, equipment and power sources we use are all new, but the aims and objectives of the cultivator remain unchanged. The twentieth century was the age of investigation, verification and quantification of these ancient, basic acts of cultivation. The work showed most of them to be valid and effective. But by increasing our understanding of the way a cultivated plant responds to its environment and to our actions we are able to time its propagation and order its growth much more precisely to meet our requirements. We can now accurately predict the growth rate of timber trees, prescribe the optimum sowing dates for virtually all agricultural crops and anticipate their harvest time to within a few days. In horticulture, glasshouse crops of flowers are timed to the day, allowing the targeting of cut chrysanthemums for Mothers Day, or pot poinsettias for Christmas. Such understanding gives us the ability to programme and plan with accuracy, but the day-to-day needs of the growing crop remain as they have always been.

In several places in this book I have referred to the role of "tender loving care" in the story of cultivation. Talking to plants when cultivating them is to me just as natural as talking to a horse, cat or dog, albeit with plants it is of no practical value. In spite of my own eccentricity I take the more general interpretation of "tender loving care" to mean the traditional regular and close contact with growing "crops" from which follows astute observation of their condition and a rapid and appropriate husbandry response to any problems observed.

Such an approach remains to the fore in, for example, botanic gardens, among specialist collectors and not least in the hugely floriferous front gardens of some suburban homes. Nevertheless, it appears that many of the very best commercial crops and some excellent public parks such as those in the city of Bath are managed without this traditional approach. Indeed it would be ridiculous to pretend that crop husbandry has not become more remote for both the mechanised labour-force and its office-based management.

With our present knowledge of plant biology, particularly as it applies to major crop plants, programming work to meet their basic requirements is a relatively simple and straightforward matter, but like all living things, plants often succumb to circumstances and conditions quite differently from inanimate objects. In many ways the expression "tender loving care" summarises an understanding of that and the resultant need for constant vigilance.

This is why both successful amenity horticultural officers and commercial growers still invest in the close scrutiny of their "crops". They employ production managers, field walkers and specialists of various kinds, all charged with "keeping an eye" on the plants. Those that employ such monitors are well aware that they can be effective only if they detect problems at an early stage and that their observations are responded to quickly. Unforeseen occurrences and conditions must be dealt with speedily and effectively. Plants like humans sometimes need the services of an accident and emergency department, and it is perhaps in that provision that "tender loving care" remains a critical component of good cultivation.

Today there is a vigorous debate on the future of land use throughout Europe. As things stand, it seems that we do not need all the arable land we have to supply us with the food crops that can be most economically produced in our part of the world. Many people are shocked at the idea of a glut when people in other parts of the world are without, and we may yet find ways of distributing our harvests to more needy parts of the globe without destroying the stability of international trade. For now, the fact remains that cultivators in the developed world struggle to make money in the face of either the risk or the reality of (First-World) economic overproduction and overprotection. As things stand in many parts of Britain, few if any of our typical farm crops would be profitable if the subsidies were withdrawn.

Agricultural historians tell us that so-called marginal land has always gone in and out of production with fluctuations in profitability. Nevertheless, many well-respected people, from large-scale arable farmers such as Clifford Spencer to Melvyn Askew, head of the alternative crops and biotechnology group at the Central Science Laboratory, and Nick Starkey, the National Farmers' Union alternative crops adviser, believe we are facing changes far more fundamental than simply yet another adjustment to cultivation practices. They consider that today's "agricultural revolution" is on a scale that will produce a permanent, drastic change in land use.

None of these experts take such a pessimistic view as to predict the disappearance of arable farming in Britain. They seem to think that the most suitable land will remain in today's major crops, while at least another twenty-five per cent of good arable land will be devoted to the new industrial crops noted below.

One crop scientist has told me that he can foresee a time when the demand for industrial crops, led by fuel, will actually cause an increase in arable farming. But the more pessimistic believe that there will still be surplus ploughland, and our wider society worries over what will become of the cultural heritage that is our landscape. It seems that if we wish to preserve our lowland scenery in something like its present configuration we will have to pay some farmers to manage not only field boundaries but also "the bit in the middle", and it is not at all clear how they will be asked to do it. In the past in Britain, livestock farming has taken up any short-term and/or local slack in arable land use, and even where the stocking rates were low the animals prevented the land from progressing far along an ecological succession to scrub and woodland. In times of need such as the two world wars of the twentieth century, the land has returned to arable cropping. Today there seems little hope of livestock farming becoming an attractive alternative, except, notably, in the case of horses, whose grazing and feed have become a significant land use component in many areas. The EU's set-aside programme introduced in the 1980s did much the same thing, by subsidising the return of up to fifteen per cent of arable land to short-term fallow on a rotational basis, while a combination of the market place and subsidy payments made the rest of the land profitable to cultivate when under common field crops.

The concept of set-aside turns out to be more complex than "just doing nothing with the land for a year". To the farmer there is a risk of the build-up of weeds and weed seeds. However, to the ecologist these very weeds and the insects they harbour are a welcome, diverse food source to birds, while to the observer set-aside presents a scruffy, depressing air of dereliction and a foretaste of the British countryside bereft of the cultivator's care. It is generally agreed that a more permanent approach such as that available through Countryside Stewardship Agreements is preferable.

There seem to be three ways of tackling the problem of keeping arable land in production:

Increase demand for traditional crops.

Reduce yield per unit area.

Reduce the area devoted to over-produced crops by finding new crops.

The first of these options seems like a good idea, but is beyond the scope of this book, and its author!

The second is very fashionable with many in the "Green" movement", providing it is achieved using their methods. To most cultivators it is nothing less than a reversal of all they have struggled against for ten thousand years. Rewording it to "Optimise yield to give maximum return on effort and expenditure" would help. This wording has the merit of leaving the inputs open to either the organic or the mainstream approach.

We can expect a great deal of interest in this low-input, low-output strategy in the coming decades; let us hope that the debate is based not on emotion but the results of well-conducted research. Such cropping systems have much to support them in theory, but their profitability and long-term value will need demonstrating on a farm scale before farmers and growers are persuaded to commit to them. There is no evidence to suggest that the market will drop its evaluation of quality and its direct relationship to value. Whatever is produced will have to be worth buying.

How could such a policy affect the cultivation patterns and husbandry techniques required to produce the crop? Lower inputs could start with a reduced plant population per unit area, in which case money would be saved on seed but the work cycle would remain the same and the cost per operation would show only marginal savings due to a possible faster workrate. Reduced fertility due to lower fertiliser rates is the favourite yield-reducer. Again, equipment would be able to complete certain tasks in a slightly reduced time, with marginal cost reductions. Weed, pest and disease control could be reduced, but at a high risk of a very significant reduction in both the quality and quantity of the harvest.

Having seen the pitiful yields resulting from some or combinations of such reductions in husbandry inputs in both the old Soviet Union and the Third World, I find it beggars belief that such retrograde formulas could become the norm in this country, beyond a skilfully thought-out mix that reduced yield by, let us say, ten per cent. A most promising approach to achieving such a reduction without any form of neglect is reduced tillage – a technique exemplified by the equipment designed to produce a seedbed directly from stubble. Yields are lower than after ploughing, but costs and time are significantly reduced.

Surely it can be in no one's interest to allow unplanned-for reduction in production that might well trigger wild fluctuations in supply and demand and therefore in prices. Even if this can be prevented, we are still left with a fundamental question not encountered in other industries: "What do we do with the vacant land?" Are there any profitable arable crops for other than grade-one land? Can industrial and fuel crops replace food production? Taken overall, they probably can and will. Industrial arable crops are not new; cotton, flax and hemp have been with us for centuries. What is new is the use of naturally occurring molecules to form the basis of other products, such as plastics from starch and diesel engine fuel from oil-seeds. It looks as if there will be a few crops occupying large areas for such raw materials as starch, cellulose, fibres and some oils, and many small patches yielding specialist niche market products for, among others, the perfume, medicinal and chemical industries.

Considering future developments in the cultivation of arable crops must bring us to the vital but vexed issues embraced by that much overworked term "sustainability". We may leave cosmologists, astronomers, geologists, and evolutionary biologists to explain its long-term futility, and in the closing paragraphs of this book concern ourselves simply with a very brief consideration of the challenge cultivators face in attempting to maintain conditions while minimising, if not actually eliminating, the use of non-renewable resources. Without identifying it under this title, Britain has for over 150 years run a unique experiment on sustainability thanks to the foresight of those two pioneers of agricultural science J. B. Lawes and J. H. Gilbert. It is of course the famous Broadbalk Study at Rothamsted referred to on pages 33 and 221. To be fair, the zero-added-nutrient plots have also been deprived of the benefit of fallow and crop rotation, including the use of nitrogen-fixing crops, so we might regard them as the most extreme test of arable crop sustainability. Sustainability should not be confused with the concern over the use (or misuse) of materials that many people believe may be harmful to human health – that is a separate issue. Modern agronomy correctly executed within both farming and horticulture can maintain the land in excellent condition. Nevertheless, to do this both organic and mainline approaches import materials to achieve it. Sustainability must concern itself with these "imports"; they may include energy, water, fertiliser (both organic and inorganic) and "complex agri-chemical compounds". Water is being conserved by mulching, and in intensive horticulture much can be "recycled". Already there is an active programme investigating the possibility of breeding less-water-demanding cultivars of several crop plants. Fertilisers can be and are being more usefully placed and timed, and there must surely be far better use made of farm animal and human waste. As to the use of other agrochemicals, here it is not a case of running out of supplies but of minimising their use to prevent adverse long-term environmental impacts.

And what of the cultivators' contribution to the reduction of global warming, or more precisely the amount of carbon dioxide in the atmosphere acting as a greenhouse gas thereby contributing to the trapping of solar energy?

Plants through photosynthesis fix carbon and the source of that carbon is carbon dioxide. From this simple fact it follows that the more plant material, alive or dead, there is, the less carbon dioxide. Our planet has been storing photosynthetically derived carbon compounds for aeons, much of it in materials we now describe as fossil fuels. Such deposits represent a very small percentage of the carbon utilised by millions of generations of photosynthesisers; the rest was returned to the atmosphere through the decay of the entrapper shortly after its death.

It is all too clear how rapidly humans are releasing this store of trapped carbon, but while the use of biofuels is "carbon-neutral", that is to say that on combustion they simply release the carbon dioxide their source plants entrapped, it is not at all obvious how we can use plants to sop up the gaseous spillage we have already created by burning fossil fuels. To do that we would have to stop plant material decaying. In fact, both natural and farming systems keep only a small percentage of the carbon they utilise entrapped.

Some is held in durable plant parts such as the trunks of trees, other in the leaf litter and undecomposed organic matter on and within the soil, but this tends to be a finite amount that remains constant from year to year. To do better than that we need to harvest, remove and store plant parts for very long periods. The pioneers inside Biosphere 2 faced exactly this hazard when the plants within their sealed biome could not keep pace with the CO_2 released from the humus-rich topsoil they had imported. In a desperate effort to "balance the books" they stored huge stacks of dried leaves in the basement. Even supposing storage were a possibility, it's not without a fundamental drawback because as everyone in the organic movement knows, while the micro-organisms responsible for decay are unfortunately releasing carbon dioxide they are also making essential plant nutrients available. Thatched cottages, old haystacks, veteran trees, cathedral roofs and my father's abandoned packing-shed will simply not suffice.

I have tried to indicate how productivity-motivated agronomists might help to reduce the profligate use of resources, but I fear that such measures, in common with those advocated in other walks of life and sensible as they are, do not fully add up to sustainability. It is an objective that in the all-inclusive way it is currently described has not sat comfortably with arable cultivation ever since we set out to grow that extra blade of grass!

POSTSCRIPT

Since the completion of this text a sequence of events has dramatically changed the fortunes of arable farming and hence the importance of ploughland.

The potential demand for biofuel from arable crops and the purchase of a significant percentage of their harvest for that use has had a huge impact on world prices, thereby bringing cereal growing back into profit.

For the foreseeable future the challenge for European agriculture of what to do with surplus arable land has once again turned full circle to be replaced by a demand for its products. This time the cause is not war but the need to reduce the use of fossil fuels by turning to our cultivators to supply renewable energy provided by their crops through the process of photosynthesis. Jonathan Swift's words are once more vindicated!

BIBLIOGRAPHY

The following titles formed the main body of literature used in writing this book, some quoted from, others referred to only by title or author. Starting with Theophrastus they, in the various editions selected, span 2300 years of ever changing ideas and understanding. Some are among the most respected texts in their field; others should be studied as an historical record albeit that they contain some long superseded views on the craft, art and science of cultivation. The remainder should be approached with a mixture of amusement and amazement that such a down-to-earth subject should attract such exponents. All have contributed to my enjoyment and education.

AIKMAN, C. M. (1904) *Manures and the Principles of Manuring*. Blackwood, London

AINSWORTH-DAVIS, J. R. (ed.) (1920) Fream's Elements of Agriculture. Murray, London

AL-AWAM (Abu Zacaria Iahia) (2003 [c. 1150]) *El Libro de Agricultura de Al Awam* (trans. Mercedes Moreno and Agustina Bajo). Junta de Andalucia, Viceconsejería de Publicaciones y Divulgación, Córdoba

ALLABY, Michael (1998) *Oxford Dictionary of Plant Sciences*. Oxford University Press

ALLEN, Harry (1981) *Direct Drilling and Reduced Cultivations*. Farming Press, Ipswich

ANON. (1851) *The British Sylva and Planters' and Foresters' Manual*. Society for Promoting Christian Knowledge, London

ANON. (1860) *The Gardener's and Farmer's Reason Why.* Houlston & Wright, London

ANON. (1911) *Board of Agriculture and Fisheries, Leaflets.* HMSO, London

ANON. (1966) *The Horticultural Show Handbook.* Royal Horticultural Society, London

ASH, Harrison Boyd (trans.) (1948) *Columella on Agriculture,* bks 1–4. Loeb Classical Library, Harvard University Press, London

AYENSU, Edward S. (ed.) (1980) *Firewood Crops,* vols I and II. National Academy of Sciences, Washington, DC

BAILEY, L. H. (1908) *The Forcing Book.* Macmillan, London

BAILEY, Roger (1990) *Irrigated Crops and Their Management.* Farming Press, Ipswich

BAKER, H. G. (1965) *Plants and Civilization.* Macmillan, London

BAKER, J. O. (1947) *The Complete Market Gardener.* Garden Book Club, London

BAKER, Kenneth F. (1957) *The U. C. System for Producing Healthy Container-Grown Plants.* University of California College of Agriculture, Berkeley

BAKER, Margaret (1974) *Folklore and Customs of Rural England.* David & Charles, Newton Abbot

BALLS, R. (1985) *Horticultural Engineering Technology.* Macmillan, London

BARNES, Bernard (1982) *Man and the Changing Landscape.* Merseyside County Council, Liverpool

BARON, Robert C. (ed.) (1987) *The Garden and Farm Books of Thomas Jefferson.* Fulcrum, Golden, CO

BARRY, P. (1852) *The Fruit Garden.* Scribner, New York

BARTON, Lela V. (1961) *Seed Preservation and Longevity.* Leonard Hill, London

BAYLISS-SMITH, T. P. (1982) *The Ecology of Agricultural Systems.* Cambridge University Press, Cambridge

BECKETT, J. V. (1990) *The Agricultural Revolution.* Blackwell, Oxford

BEETON, S. (ed.) (1890) *The Garden: Its Preparation and Arrangement*. Ward Lock, London

BENDER, Barbara (1975) *Farming in Prehistory, from Hunter-Gatherer to Food-Producer*, John Baker, London

BENGTSSON, Rune (2005) *Variation in Common Lime (Tilia x europaea L.) in Swedish Gardens of the 17th and 18th centuries*. Doctoral dissertation, Swedish University of Agricultural Sciences, Alnarp

BENZIAN, Blanche (1966) *Manuring Young Conifers: Experiments in Some English Nurseries*. Proceedings of the Fertiliser Society, No. 94, London

BETTEY, J. H. (1977) *Rural Life in Wessex 1500–1900*. Moonraker, Bradford-on-Avon

BEWLEY, W. F. (1950) *Commercial Glasshouse Crops*. Country Life, London

BLACK, C. A. (1968) *Soil–Plant Relationships*, 2nd edn. Wiley, London

BLITH, W. (1652) *The English Improver Improved*. John Wright, London

BLOOM, Alan (1944) *The Farm in the Fen*. Faber, London

BLUM, Jerome (ed.) (1982) *Our Forgotten Past*. Thames & Hudson, London

BOISSET, Caroline (1997) *Pumpkins and Squashes*. Readers Digest, New York

BOND, J. R. (1923) *Farm Implements and Machinery*. Benn, London

BONNETT, Harold (1974) *Farming with Steam*. Shire, Princes Risborough

BOULD, C., HEWITT, E. J. & NEEDHAM, P. (1983) *Diagnosis of Mineral Disorders in Plants, Volume 1: Principles*. HMSO, London

BOWLER, Dermot G. (1980) *The Drainage of Wet Soils*. Hodder & Stoughton, London

BRACE, Harold W. (1960) *The History of Seed Crushing in Great Britain*. Land Books, London

BRADLEY, Richard (1717–18) *New Improvements in Planting and Gardening*. London

BRADSHAW, A. D., HUNT, B. & WALMSLEY, T. (1995) *Trees in the Urban Landscape*. Spon, London

BRETT, Walter (ed.) (1943) *The Smallholder Encyclopaedia*. Pearson, London

BRIGDEN, Roy (1983) *Agricultural Hand Tools*. Shire, Princes Risborough

BRIGDEN, Roy (1998) *Ploughs and Ploughing*. Shire, Princes Risborough

BRONOWSKI, J. (1973) *The Ascent of Man*. BBC, London

BROOKS, Robert R. & JOHANNES, Dieter (1990) *Phytoarchaeology*. Dioscorides Press, Portland, OR

BROTHWELL, Don & Patricia (1969) *Food in Antiquity*. Thames & Hudson, London

BROWN, Martin (2001) *England The Photographic Atlas*. HarperCollins, London

CARPENTER, E. (1996) *The Origins of Pagan and Christian Beliefs*. Random House, London

CARR, Susan & BELL, Mary (1991) *Practical Conservation Boundary Habitats*. Open University/Hodder & Stoughton, London

CARSON, R. (1962) *Silent Spring*. Houghton & Mifflin, Boston, MA

CARTER, A. R. (1956) *Dutch Lights for Growers and Gardeners*. Garden Book Club, London

CAUVIN, Jacques (1994) *The Birth of the Gods and the Origins of Agriculture*. Cambridge University Press, Cambridge

CHAMBERS, J. D. & MINGAY, G. E. (1966) *The Agricultural Revolution, 1750–1880*. Batsford, London

CHASE, J. L. H. & POUNCY, A. J. (1955) *Soil Block Gardening*. Faber, London

CHASE, J. L. H. (1952) *Commercial Cloche Gardening*. Faber, London

CLAUSING, Fritz (1983) *Rabewerk Cultivation*. Rabe Agrarsysteme, Bad Essen

COBBETT, William (1980) *The English Gardener*. Oxford University Press,

COBHAM, R. (1984) *Agricultural Landscapes Demonstration*

Farms. Countryside Commission, Cheltenham

COHEN, N. & MACQUEEN, H. (1993) *Science Matters: Genetic Engineering*. Open University, Milton Keynes

COOPER, Ashley (1989) *The Long Furrow*. East Anglian Magazine, Ipswich

COPPOCK, J. T. (1964) *An Agricultural Atlas of England and Wales*. Faber, London

COPPOCK, J. T. (1971) *An Agricultural Geography of Great Britain*. Bell, London

COUNTRYSIDE COMMISSION (1985) *Field Boundaries*. Cheltenham

COURTENAY, P. P. (1965) *Plantation Agriculture*. Bell, London

CROWE, Sylvia & MITCHELL, Mary (1988) *The Pattern of Landscape*. Packard, Chichester

CUTLER, D. F. (1981) Tree Roots and Buildings. Construction Press, London

DARWIN, Charles (1987) *The Voyage of the Beagle*. Marshall Cavendish, London

DAVIES, Bryan, EAGLE, David & FINNEY, Brian (1972) *Soil Management*. Farming Press, Ipswich

DAVIES, Jennifer (1987) *The Victorian Kitchen Garden*. BBC, London

DAY LEWIS, C. (trans.) (1940) *The Georgics of Virgil*. Cape, London

DE GIVRY, Jacques & PERILLON, Yves (1993) *Versailles, Le Potager du Roi*. J. D. G. Publications, Les Loges-en-Josas

DE ROUGEMONT, G. M. (1989) *A Field Guide to the Crops of Britain and Europe*. Collins, London

DEPARTMENT FOR ENVIRONMENT, FOOD AND RURAL AFFAIRS (2002) *Agriculture in the United Kingdom 2001*. Stationery Office, London

DEPARTMENT FOR ENVIRONMENT, FOOD AND RURAL AFFAIRS, Rural Development Service (2005) *Environmental Stewardship*. London

DICKSON, A. (1769) *A Treatise of Agriculture*. Edinburgh

DROWER, George (2001) *Gardeners, Gurus and Grubs: The*

413

Stories of Garden Inventors and Innovations. Sutton, Stroud.

DUNDONALD, Earl of [Cochrane, Archibald] (1795) *A Treatise, Showing the Intimate Connection That Subsists Between Agriculture and Chemistry*. London

DURANT, William (1935) *The Story of Civilization*. Simon & Schuster, New York

EARL, D. E. (1975) *Forest Energy and Economic Development*. Clarendon, Oxford

EDDOWES, Maurice (1976) *Crop Production in Europe*. Oxford University Press,

EDLIN, H. L. (1970) *Collins Guide to Tree Planting and Cultivation*. Collins, London

EMPTAGE, W. F. (1917) *Commercial Fruit Growing on the Small Holding*. Benn, London

ERNLE, Lord (1961) *English Farming Past and Present*, 6th edn. Heinemann, London

EVANS, George Ewart (1971) *The Pattern Under the Plough*. Faber, London

EVANS, George Ewart (1972) *Ask the Fellows Who Cut the Hay*. Faber, London

EVELYN, John (1676) *A Philosophical Discourse of Earth, Relating to the Culture and Improvement of It for Vegetation, and the Propagation of Plants, &c*. London

EVELYN, John (1972 [1664]) *Sylva, or a Discourse of Forest-Trees and the Propagation of Timber in His Majesties Dominions* (facsimile). Scolar, London

EWEN, A. H. & PRIME, C. T. (eds) (1975) *Ray's Flora of Cambridgeshire*. Wheldon & Wesley, Hitchin

FAIRBROTHER, Nan (1997) *Men and Gardens*. Lyon & Burford, New York

FENTON, Alexander (1986) *The Shape of the Past 2: Essays in Scottish Ethnology*. Donald, Edinburgh

FIELD, John (1972) *English Field Names: A Dictionary*. Sutton, Gloucester

FISHER, John, (1982) *The Origins of Garden Plants*. Constable, London

FITZHERBERT OF NORBURY, John (1882 [1534]) *The Book of Husbandry*, ed. W. W. Skeat. Trübner, London, for the English Dialect Society

FLAWN, Louis N. (1972) *Gardening with Cloches*. Garden Book Club, London

FOREST RESTORATION RESEARCH UNIT (FRRU-CMU) (2006) *How to Plant a Forest*. Chiang Mai University, Thailand

FORSYTH, William (1818) *A Treatise on the Culture and Management of Fruit-Trees*. Longman, Hurst, Rees, Orme & Brown, London

FOX WILSON, G. (1949) *The Detection and Control of Garden Pests*. Crosby Lockwood, London

FRASER DARLING, F. (1945) *Crofting Agriculture*. Oliver & Boyd, London

FRAYN, Joan M. (1979) *Subsistence Farming in Roman Italy*. Centaur Press, Fontwell, Sussex

FRAZER, Sir James (1911–15) *The Golden Bough*. Macmillan, London

FREAM, W (1893) *Elements of Agriculture*, 5th edn. Murray, London

FULLER, Thomas (1811) *Worthies of England*, 2nd edn. London

FUSSELL, G. E. (1949) *The English Rural Labourer*. Batchworth, London

FUSSELL, G. E. (1952) *The Farmer's Tools*. Andrew Melrose, London

GARD, R. M. & SHRIMPTON, C. (1972) *A Revolution in Agriculture*. Archive Teaching Units, University of Newcastle upon Tyne School of Education,

GARNER, R. J. (1947) *The Grafter's Handbook*. Cassell, London

GERICKE, W. F. (1940) *The Complete Guide to Soilless Gardening*. Putnam, London

GILBERT, S. (1682) *The Florists Vade-Mecum*. London

GLENNY, George (1862) *The Culture of Fruits and Vegetables*. Houlston & Wright, London

GOFF, E. S. (1916) *The Principles of Plant Culture*. Macmillan, New York

GREENOAK, Francesca (ed.) (1986) *The Journals of Gilbert White*. Century Hutchinson, London

GRIFFITHS, A. B. (1889) *Manures and Their Uses*. Bell, London

GRIGG, D. B. (1974) *The Agricultural Systems of the World: An Evolutionary Approach*. Cambridge University Press, London

GRIGG, David (1982) *The Dynamics of Agricultural Change*. Hutchinson, London

GRIGG, David (1995) *An Introduction to Agricultural Geography*, 2nd edn. Routledge, London

GROWER (1994) *Commercial Cut Flower Production*. Grower, Swanley

HALES, Stephen (1727) *Vegetable Staticks, or, An Account of Some Statical Experiments on the Sap in Vegetables*. London

HALL, David (1982) *Medieval Fields*. Shire, Princes Risborough

HALL, Sir Daniel A. (1931) *The Soil*. Murray, London

HANSEN, Vaughn E., ISRAELSEN, Orson W. & STRINGHAM, Glen E. (1980) *Irrigation Principles and Practices*, 4th edn. Wiley, New York.

HART, Edward (1981) *Victorian and Edwardian Farming*. Batsford, London

HARTMAN, John R., PIRONE, Thomas P. & SALL, Mary Ann (2000) *Pirone's Tree Maintenance*, 7th edn. Oxford University Press, Oxford.

HARTMANN, H. T. & KESTER, D. E. (2002) *Plant Propagation: Principles and Practices*, 7th edn. Blackwell, Oxford

HARVEY, John (1974) *Early Nurserymen*. Phillimore, London

HARVEY, Nigel (1976) *Fields, Hedges and Ditches*. Shire, Princes Risborough

HARVEY, Nigel (1980) *The Industrial Archaeology of Farming*. Batsford, London

HARWOOD, W. S. (1906) *New Creations in Plant Life*. Macmillan, New York

HEADLAND (pseud.) (1954) *Dutch Lights: Their Construction, Irrigation and Cropping*. Landsman's Library Publications, Hartford, Hunts

HEDRICK, U. P. (ed.) (1972) *Sturtevant's Edible Plants of the World*. Constable, London

HENDERSON, Peter & Co. (2002 [1898]) *Turn-of-the-Century Farm Tools and Implements*. Dover, New York

HIGGS, E. S. (ed.) (1972) *Papers in Economic Prehistory*. Cambridge University Press, Cambridge

HILL, Sir John (1812) *The Family Herbal*. Brightly, Bungay

HILL, Thomas (1987 [c. 1590]) *The Gardener's Labyrinth* (ed. Richard Mabey). Oxford University Press, Oxford

HILLMAN, G. C., Moore A. M. T. & Legge, A. J. (2000) *Village on the Euphrates*. Oxford University Press,

HITCHMOUGH, J. & FIELDHOUSE, K. (eds) (2004) *Plant User Handbook*. Blackwell, Oxford

HITCHMOUGH, J. D. (1994) *Urban Landscape Management*. Inkata, Sydney

HODGES, Richard (2006) *Royston Grange, 6000 Years of a Peakland Landscape*. Tempus, Stroud

HOLE, Christina (1976) *British Folk Customs*. Book Club Associates, London

HORN, Pamela (1976) *Labouring Life in the Victorian Countryside*. Gill & Macmillan, Dublin

HORT, A. F. (trans.) (1948) *Theophrastus, Enquiry into Plants*, vol. I, bks 1–5. Loeb Classical Library, Harvard University Press, London

HOSKINS, W. G. (1955) *The Making of the English Landscape*. Hodder & Stoughton, Sevenoaks

HOWITT, William (1971 [1844]) *The Rural Life of England*, 3rd edn (corrected and revised; reprinted). Irish University Press, Shannon

HURST, J. W. (ed.) (1931) *The Practical Smallholder: A Book of Reference for the Agriculturist, Allotment and Market Gardener, Poultry, Dairy, Fruit, General, and Live Stock Farmer*, 4 vols. Waverley, London

HUTCHINSON, Sir Joseph (ed.) (1969) *Population and Food Supply: Essays on Human Needs and Agricultural Prospects*. Cambridge University Press, Cambridge.

HUTCHINSON, Sir Joseph, CLARK, Grahame, JOPE, E. M. &

RILEY, R. (1977) *The Early History of Agriculture.* Oxford University Press, Oxford.

HUXLEY, Anthony (1974) *Plant and Planet.* Allen Lane, London

HUXLEY, Anthony (1981) *The Penguin Encyclopedia of Gardening.* Allen Lane, London

HYAMS, Edward (1971) *A History of Gardens and Gardening.* Dent, London

JANICK, Jules & SIMON, James E. (eds) (1988) *Advances in New Crops.* Timber Press, Portland, OR

JARMAN, M. R., BAILEY, G. N. & JARMAN, H. N. (1982) *Early European Agriculture.* Cambridge University Press, Cambridge

JELLICOE, Geoffrey & Susan (1975) *The Landscape of Man.* Thames & Hudson, London

JONES, William (1888) *The Gardener's Receipt Book,* 6th edn. Groombridge, London

KAIN, Roger J. P. & PRINCE Hugh C. (2000) *Tithe Surveys for Historians.* Phillimore, Chichester

KELLEY, Hubert W. (1983) *Keeping the Land Alive.* United Nations FAO, Rome

KENNEDY, John (1788) *A Treatise upon Planting, Gardening and the Management of the Hot House.* Dublin

KING, F. C. (1951) *The Weed Problem: A New Approach.* Faber, London

KING, F. C. (1952) *Is Digging Necessary?* Kendal

KING, Lawrence J. (1966) *Weeds of the World.* Leonard Hill, London

KIPPS, M. S. (1953) *Production of Field Crops,* 6th edn. McGraw-Hill, London

KROPOTKIN, P. (1912) *Fields, Factories and Workshops.* Nelson, London

KUHN, Herbert (1966) *The Rock Pictures of Europe.* Sidgwick & Jackson, London

LANGER, R. H. M. , & HILL, G. D. (1991) *Agricultural Plants,* 2nd edn. Cambridge University Press, Cambridge

LANGLAND, William (1912 [c. 1380]) *The Vision of Piers*

Plowman, modern version and introduction by Arthur Burrell. Dent, London

LARGE, E. C. (1940) *The Advance of the Fungi*. Cape, London

LAWRENCE, W. J. C. & NEWELL, J. (1939) *Seed and Potting Composts*. Allen & Unwin, London

LAWSON, Douglas (1992) *Hand to the Plough*. Ashgrove, Sevenoaks

LE SUEUR, A. D. C. (1951) *Hedges, Shelterbelts and Screens*. Country Life, London

LEIGH, G. J. (2004) *The World's Greatest Fix : A History of Nitrogen and Agriculture*. Oxford University Press, Oxford.

LEMMON, Kenneth (1962) *The Covered Garden*. Museum Press, London

LEONARD, Jonathan Norton (1974) *The First Farmers*. Time Life International (Nederland BV)

LEWIS, Joanna (2004) *Sovereigns, Madams and Double Whites, Fruit and Flower Pioneers of the Tamar Valley*. Tamar Valley AONB Service, St Dominick

LOEWENFELD, Claire (1964) *Herb Gardening*. Faber, London

LORD, Peter (ed.) (1979) *A Moorish Calendar: From the Book of Agriculture of Ibn al-Awam* (trans. Philip Lord). Black Swan, Wantage

LORETTE, Louis (1925) *The Lorette System of Pruning*. Hopkinson, London

LOUDON, Mrs J. (1851) *Instructions in Gardening for Ladies*. Murray, London

M., G. [Gervase Markham] (1614) *The Second Booke of the English Husbandman*. London

MABEY, R. (1996) *Flora Britannica*. Sinclair-Stevenson, London

MACDOUGALL, Elisabeth B. (ed.) (1986) *Medieval Gardens*, vol. IX, Dumbarton Oaks Colloquium on the History of Landscape Architecture. Dumbarton Oaks Research Library, Washington, DC

MACPHERSON, George (1995) *Home-Grown Energy from Short-Rotation Coppice*. Farming Press, Ipswich

MACSELF, A. J. (ed.) (n.d.) *Special Manures for Garden Plants*.

Collingridge, London

MADDOCK, James (1792) *The Florist's Directory, or a Treatise on the Culture of Flowers.* London

MALINOWSKI, Bronislaw (1935) *Soil-Tilling and Agricultural Rites in the Trobriand Islands.* Allen & Unwin, London

MANGELSDORF, Paul, C. (1974) *Corn: Its Origin, Evolution and Improvement.* Harvard University Press, Cambridge, MA

MARTIN, Hubert (1940) *The Scientific Principles of Plant Protection with Special Reference to Chemical Control,* 3rd edn. Arnold, London

MASSEE, George (1899) *A Text-Book of Plant Diseases Caused by Cryptogamic Parasites.* Duckworth, London

MAWE, Thomas & ABERCROMBIE, J. (1797) *Every Man His Own Gardener.* London

MAXEY, Edward (1601) *A New Instuction* [sic] *of Plowing and Setting of Corne, Handled in Manner of a Dialogue Betweene a Ploughman and a Scholler.* London

McINTOSH, Charles (1853) *The Book of the Garden*, vols I and II. Blackwood, Edinburgh

McKAY, C. D. (n. d.) *The French Garden.* Daily Mail, London

McMAHON, Bernard (1976 [1857]) *McMahon's American Gardener*, 11th edn reprint. Funk & Wagnalls, New York

MIDDLETON, C. H. (1942) *Digging for Victory.* Allen & Unwin, London

MILLER, Philip (1737) *The Gardeners Dictionary*, 3rd edn. London

MINISTRY OF AGRICULTURE, FISHERIES AND FOOD (1934) *Manures and Manuring.* Bulletin No. 36. HMSO, London

MINISTRY OF AGRICULTURE, FISHERIES AND FOOD (1936) *Salad Crops.* Bulletin No. 55. HMSO, London

MINISTRY OF AGRICULTURE, FISHERIES AND FOOD (1939) *Commercial Flower Production.* Bulletin No. 109. HMSO, London

MINISTRY OF AGRICULTURE, FISHERIES AND FOOD (1946) *Fruit Bud Development.* HMSO, London

MINISTRY OF AGRICULTURE, FISHERIES AND FOOD (1961) *Protected Cropping.* Bulletin No. 65. HMSO, London

MINISTRY OF AGRICULTURE, FISHERIES AND FOOD (1962) *Outdoor Flowers for Cutting.* Bulletin No. 190. HMSO, London

MINISTRY OF AGRICULTURE, FISHERIES AND FOOD (1967) *Bulb and Corm Production.* Bulletin No. 62. HMSO, London

MINISTRY OF AGRICULTURE, FISHERIES AND FOOD (1970) *Modern Farming and the Soil.* HMSO, London

MINISTRY OF AGRICULTURE, FISHERIES AND FOOD (1974) *Irrigation.* HMSO, London

MINISTRY OF AGRICULTURE, FISHERIES AND FOOD (1998) *Code of Good Agricultural Practice for the Protection of Water.* MAFF Publications, London

MINISTRY OF AGRICULTURE, FISHERIES AND FOOD (1998) *The Air Code.* MAFF Publications, London

MINISTRY OF AGRICULTURE, FISHERIES AND FOOD (1998) *The Soil Code.* MAFF Publications, London

MITFORD, Mary Russell (1893) *Our Village.* Macmillan, London

MOORE, H. I. (1946) *Crops and Cropping,* 2nd edn. Allen & Unwin, London

MOORE, Ian (ed.) (1968) *The Agricultural Notebook,* 15th edn. Iliffe, London

MOORE, Thomas (1881) *Epitome of Gardening.* Black, Edinburgh

MORTIMER, John (1707) *The Whole Art of Husbandry.* London

MUIR, Richard (1989) *Portraits of the Past.* Michael Joseph, London

MURRAY, Jacqueline (1970) *The First European Agriculture.* Edinburgh University Press, Edinburgh

NATIONAL ACADEMY OF SCIENCES (1974) *More Water for Arid Lands.* Washington, DC

NAYLOR, R. (2002) *Weed Management Handbook,* 9th edn. Blackwell, Oxford

NEWSHAM, J. C. (1914) *The Horticultural Note-Book.* Crosby Lockwood, London

NIALL, Ian (1977) *To Speed the Plough.* Heinemann, London

NICOL, Hugh (1943) *The Biological Control of Insects.* Penguin,

London

NICOL, W. (1822) *The Gardener's Kalender.* Longman, London

NIX, John (2000) *Farm Management Pocketbook,* 30th edn. Wye College, London

NUSSEY, Helen & COCKERELL, Olive J. (1909) *A French Garden in England.* Stead's, London

O'BRIEN, R. Dalziel (1956) *Intensive Gardening.* Faber, London

ORWIN, C. S. & ORWIN, C. S. (1967) *The Open Fields,* 3rd edn. Clarendon, Oxford.

PARK, H. G. (1947) *Late Flowering Chrysanthemums for Exhibition.* Warden, Hendon

PARKER, Rowland (1976) *The Common Stream.* Granada, London

PARTRIDGE, Michael (1973) *Farm Tools Through the Ages.* Osprey, Reading

PEACOCK, F. C. (ed.) (1978) *Jealott's Hill, Fifty years of Agricultural Research, 1928–1978.* ICI, London

PEARSON, J. R. (1865) *The Orchard House,* 3rd edn. *Journal of Horticulture and Cottage Gardener,* London

PHILLIPS, Henry (1823) *Pomarium Britannicum: An Historical and Botanical Account of Fruits Known in Great Britain,* 3rd edn. Allman, London

PILLEY, John J. (1881) *The Elements of Scientific Agriculture for Students and Farmers.* Gill, London

POLLINGTON, S. (2000) *Leechcraft: Early English Charms, Plantlore, and Healing.* Anglo-Saxon Books, Hockwold-cum-Wilton, Norfolk

POLLOCK, Michael (1984) *Shelter Hedges and Trees,* 4th edn. HMSO, London

PORTEOUS, Crichton (n.d.) *Pioneers of Fertility.* Clareville, London

POTTER, M. J. (1991) *Treeshelters.* Forestry Commission Handbook 7, HMSO

PRESTON, C. D. , PEARMAN, D. A. & DINES, T. D. (2002) *New Atlas of the British and Irish Flora.* Oxford University Press, Oxford

PRICE, Douglas T. (ed.) (2000) *Europe's First Farmers.*

Cambridge University Press, Cambridge

PURSEGLOVE, J. W. (1972) *Tropical Crops*. Longman, London

PUUSTJARVI, V. (1977) *Peat and Its Use in Horticulture* (trans. W. G. C. Krause). Turveteollisuusliitto, Helsinki

RACKHAM, Oliver (1976) *Trees and Woodland in the British Landscape*. Dent, London

RACKHAM, Oliver (1986) *The History of the Countryside*. Dent, London

RANSOME, J. Allen (2003 [1843]) *The Implements of Agriculture*. Old Pond, Ipswich

REA, John (1676) *Flora Ceres et Pomona*. London

REES, Sian (1981) *Ancient Agricultural Implements*. Shire, Princes Risborough

RENFREW, Jane M. (1973) *Palaeoethnobotany*. Methuen, London

REYNOLDS, Peter J. (1979) *Iron Age Farm: The Butser Experiment*. British Museum, London

RIVERS, Thomas (1873) *The Orchard House*, 15th edn. Longmans Green, London

ROACH, F. A. (1985) *Cultivated Fruits of Britain: Their Origin and History*. Blackwell, Oxford

ROBERTSON, John (1974) *Mechanising Vegetable Production*. Farming Press, Ipswich

ROBINSON, W. (1892) *Garden Design and Architects' Gardens*. Murray, London

ROHDE, Eleanour Sinclair (1932) *The Story of the Garden*. Medici Society, London

ROWE-DUTTON, Patricia (1957) *The Mulching of Vegetables*. Commonwealth Bureau of Horticulture and Plantation Crops, Farnham Royal, Bucks

ROWLEY, Trevor & WOOD, John (1982) *Deserted Villages*. Shire, Princes Risborough

RUSSELL, E. Walter (1973) *Soil Conditions and Plant Growth*, 10th edn. Longman, London

RUSSELL, Sir E. John (1942) *English Farming*, 2nd edn. Collins, London

RUSSELL, Sir E. John (1966) *A History of Agricultural Science in*

Great Britain. Allen & Unwin, London

RUTHENBERG, Hans (1971) *Farming Systems in the Tropics.* Oxford University Press, London

SALTER, P. J. & BLEASDALE, J. K. A. (1979) *Know and Grow Vegetables.* Oxford University Press, Oxford.

SANDERS, T. W. (1926) *Fruit and Its Cultivation.* Collingridge, London

SAUSSURE, Nicolas Théodore de (1804) *Recherches chimiques sur la végétation.* Paris

SCHAMA, Simon (1995) *Landscape and Memory.* HarperCollins, London

SCHUPHAN, Werner (1965) *Nutritional Values in Crops and Plants.* Faber, London

SCOTT-JAMES, Anne (1982) *The Cottage Garden.* Penguin, Harmondsworth

SHAW, C. W. (1889) *Market and Kitchen Gardening.* Crosby Lockwood, London

SHIGO, Alex Lloyd (1986) *A New Tree Biology Dictionary.* Shigo & Trees, Durham, NH

SHOLTO DOUGLAS, James (1976) *Advanced Guide to Hydroponics.* Pelham, London

SHOLTO DOUGLAS, James (1978) *Alternative Foods: A World Guide to Lesser Known Edible Plants.* Pelham, London

SMALL, James (1784) *A Treatise on Ploughs and Wheel Carriages, Etc.* Edinburgh

SMITH, J. D. (1996) *Discovering Horse-Drawn Farm Machinery.* Shire, Princes Risborough

SMITH, Kenneth M. (1960) *Plant Viruses,* 3rd edn. Methuen, London

SMITH, Thomas & RHODES, Jeffrey (ed.) (1954) *The Profitable Culture of Vegetables.* Longmans, London.

SMITH, Thomas (1911) *The Profitable Culture of Vegetables.* Longmans Green, London.

SOPER, M. H. R. & CARTER, E. S. (1991) *Farming and the Countryside,* 2nd edn. Farming Press, Ipswich

SPEAKE, Graham (1995) *The Penguin Dictionary of Ancient History.* Penguin, London

SPRAGUE, Milton A. & TRIPLETT, Glover B. (eds) (1986) *No

Tillage and Surface Tillage Agriculture. Wiley, Chichester

STELLY, Matthias (ed.) (1975) *Multiple Cropping.* American Society of Agronomy, Madison, WI

STEPHENS, Henry (1844) *The Book of the Farm.* Blackwood, Edinburgh

STEPHENS, R. J. (1982) *Theory and Practice of Weed Control.* Macmillan, London

STRINGFELLOW, H. M. (1896) *The New Horticulture.* Galveston, TX

STRUEVER, Stuart (ed.) (1971) *Prehistoric Agriculture.* Natural History Press, New York

STUART, David C. (1983) *The Kitchen Garden.* Hale, London

SUTTON & SONS (1898) *The Culture of Vegetables and Flowers.* Simpkin, Marshall, London

TAYLOR, Christopher (1975) *Fields in the English Landscape.* Dent, London

THEOBALD, Frederick V. (1909) *The Insect and Other Allied Pests of Orchard, Bush and Hothouse Fruits.* Wye

THICK, Malcolm (1998) *The Neat House Gardens: Early Market Gardening Around London.* Prospect, London

THIRSK, Joan (1997) *Alternative Agriculture: A History.* Oxford University Press, Oxford

THOMPSON, C. R. (1949) *The Pruning of Apples and Pears by Renewal Methods.* Faber, London

THOMPSON, Robert (1859) *The Gardener's Assistant.* Blackie, Glasgow

THOMSON, William (1867) *Practical Treatise on the Grape Vine,* 5th edn. Blackwood, Edinburgh

THORPE, I. J. (1996) *The Origins of Agriculture in Europe.* Routledge, London

TITOW, J. Z. (1972) *Winchester Yields: A Study in Medieval Agricultural Productivity.* Cambridge University Press

TRINDER, Barrie & COX, Jeff (1980) *Yeomen and Colliers in Telford.* Phillimore, London

TROW-SMITH, Robert (1967) *Life from the Land.* Longmans, London

TROW-SMITH, Robert (1973) *Man, The Farmer.* Priory Press, London

TROW-SMITH, Robert (1978) *Farming Through the Ages.* Farming Press, Ipswich

TUCKER, David M. (1993) *Kitchen Gardening in America.* Iowa State University Press, Ames

TUDGE, Colin (1988) *Food Crops for the Future.* Blackwell, Oxford

TULL, Jethroe (1733) *The Horse-Hoeing Husbandry.* London

TUSSER, Thomas (1931 [1580]) *Five Hundred Points of Good Husbandry,* ed. E. V. Lucas. Tregaskis, London

UNITED STATES DEPARTMENT OF AGRICULTURE (1961) *Seeds: The Yearbook of Agriculture.* Washington, DC

UCKO, J. & DIMBLEBY, G. W. (eds) (1969) *The Domestication and Exploitation of Plants and Animals.* Duckworth, London

USHER, G. (1974) *A Dictionary of Plants Used by Man.* Constable, London

VAN DER VEEN, Marijke (1992) *Crop Husbandry Regimes.* Collis, Sheffield

VAN EMDEN, H. F. & SERVICE, M. W. (2004) *Pest and Vector Control.* Cambridge University Press,

VAVILOV, N. I. (1992) *Origin and Geography of Cultivated Plants* (trans. Doris Löve). Cambridge University Press, Cambridge

WACHER, J. (1978) *Roman Britain.* Dent, London

WALLACE, T. & MARSH, R. W. (eds) (1953) *Science and Fruit.* University of Bristol, Bristol

WATSON, Andrew M. (1983) *Agricultural Innovation in the Early Islamic World.* Cambridge University Press, Cambridge

WATTS, Elizabeth (1866) *Vegetables and Flowers.* Warne, London

WATTS, Martin (1999) *Working Oxen.* Shire, Princes Risborough

WEARN, E. D. (1985) *The Flower Show.* Croom Helm, London

WEBB, William (1919) *Garden First in Land Development.* Longmans, London

WEBBER, Ronald (1969) *Covent Garden, Mud-Salad Market.* Dent, London

WEBBER, Ronald (1972) *Market Gardening, The History of Commercial Flower, Fruit and Vegetable Growing.* David

& Charles, Newton Abbot

WELCH, H. J. (1970) *Mist Propagation and Automatic Watering*. Faber, London

WHITE, G. (1977) *The Natural History of Selborne* (ed. Richard Mabey). Penguin, London

WHITE, K. D. (1977) *Country Life in Classical Times*. Elek, London

WHITEHEAD, R. (ed.) (1996) *The UK Pesticide Guide*. CAB International, Wallingford

WILKES, Peter (1978) *An Illustrated History of Farming*. Spur Books, Bourne End

WILKIE, Jim (2002) *An Illustrated History of Farm Implements*. Ian Allen, Hersham

WILLIAMS, C. N. (1975) *The Agronomy of the Major Tropical Crops*. Oxford University Press, London

WILLIAMS, C. N. , UZO, J. O. & PEREGRINE, W. T. H. (1991) *Vegetable Production in the Tropics*. Longman, Harlow

WILLIAMSON, Tom (2002) *The Transformation of Rural England*. University of Exeter Press, Exeter

WILLIS, Stephen J. (1954) *Weed Control in Farm and Garden*. Garden Book Club, London

WINSOR, G. W. , HURD, R. G. & PRICE, D. (1985) *Nutrient Film Technique*, Growers Bulletin No. 5. Glasshouse Crops Research Institute, London

WINSOR, G. W. , HURD, R. G. & PRICE, D. (1985) *Nutrient Film Technique*, Growers Bulletin No. 5. Glasshouse Crops Research Institute, Littlehampton

WINTER, E. J. (1974) *Water, Soil and the Plant*. Macmillan, London

WISEMAN, A. J. L., FINCH, H. J. S. & SAMUEL, A. M. (1993) *Crop Husbandry*, 7th edn. Pergamon, Oxford

WITNEY, Brian (1988) *Choosing and Using Farm Machines*. Longman, New York

WOOD, Alan (1950) *The Groundnut Affair*. Bodley Head, London

WOOD, Michael (1986) *Domesday: A Search for the Roots of England*. BBC, London

WOOD, Samuel (1898) *The Forcing Garden*. Crosby Lockwood, London

WORK, Paul & CAREW, John (1955) *Vegetable Production and Marketing*, 2nd edn. Chapman & Hall, London

WRIGHT, John (1891) *Profitable Fruit Growing*. May, London

WRIGHT, John (1920) *Profitable Fruit Growing*, 11th edn. Collingridge, London

WRIGHT, John (n. d.) *The Fruit Grower's Guide*. Virtue, London

WRIGHT, Philip (1961) *Old Farm Implements*. Country Book Club, London

WRIGHT, Sir Robert Patrick (ed.) (1908) *The Standard Cycolopedia of Modern Agriculture and Rural Economy*. Gresham, London

WRIGHT, Walter P. (1901) *Pictorial Practical Fruit Growing*. Cassell, London

YOUNG, Arthur (1969 [1813]) *General View of the Agriculture of Oxfordshire*. Kelley, New York

YOUNG, Arthur (1971 [1804]) *General View of the Agriculture of Hertfordshire*. David & Charles, Newton Abbot

In addition to the books listed above, papers published in the following journals have been consulted

The Journal of the Board of Agriculture
Biologist, Journal of the Institute of Biology
The Horticulturist, Journal of the Institute of Horticulture
Antiquity
Proceedings of the Prehistoric Society
The Garden, Journal of the Royal Horticultural Society
The Gardeners' Chronicle
The Horticultural Register & General Magazine (J. Paxton)
The Gardener's Magazine & Register of Rural & Domestic Improvement (J. C. Loudon)
The Farmers Magazine

APPENDIX:
WEIGHTS AND MEASURES

Books of this kind usually include tables relating to various units, now mostly obsolete, which past practitioners used to measure and monitor their day-to-day activities. Over the centuries land-work in Britain has used various systems of measurement together with a bewildering array of what I can only describe as specific items of known value. However, the quantitative value of many of the containers and assemblages used in connection with both materials and harvested crops varied significantly over time and from place to place, and thus although they were used as measures they defy conversion to any established system of measurement.

The following tables set out the bygone units commonly encountered for length, area, volume and weight. Relevant entries carry their frequently encountered equivalents in brackets. Others such as the hide cannot be so quantified and are described in the glossary. The table of commonly required metric equivalents should enable others to be calculated by simple multiplication.

Below the tables some miscellaneous measures are quantified and a small part of a contemporary paper indicates just how complex life was in the "good old days"!

Length
3 barleycorns = 1 inch (in)
4 inches = 1 hand
9 inches = 1 span or quarter
5 quarters = 45 inches = 1 ell (English)
12 inches = 1 foot (ft)
1 feet = 1 cubit
3 feet = 1 yard (yd)
6 feet = 1 fathom
5 yards = 1 pole, rod, or perch
4 poles = 100 links = 1 chain
40 poles = 220 yards = 10 chains = 1 furlong
8 furlongs = 1760 yards = 1 mile
3 miles = 1 league

Area
144 square inches (sq in, in^2) = 1 square foot (sq ft, ft^2)
9 square feet = 1 square yard (sq yd, yd^2)
30 square yards = 1 square pole, rod or perch
40 square poles = 1 rood
4 roods = 4840 square yards = 1 acre
640 acres = 1 square mile

Volume
1728 cubic inches (cu in, in^3) = 1 cubic foot (cu ft, ft^3)
27 cubic feet = 1 cubic yard (cu yd, yd^3)

Liquid measure
4 gills = 20 fluid ounces = 1 pint (pt)
2 pints = 1 quart (qt)
4 quarts = 1 gallon (gal)

Dry measure
2 gallons = 1 peck
4 pecks = 8 gallons = 1 bushel
8 bushels = 1 quarter
21 bushels = 1 cubic yard

Weight (avoirdupois)
16 drams = 1 ounce (oz)
16 ounces = 1 pound (lb)
14 pounds = 1 stone
28 pounds = 1 quarter
4 quarters = 112 pounds = 1 hundredweight (cwt)
20 hundredweights = 2240 pounds = 1 ton

METRIC CONVERSION OF SELECTED UNITS

Note: Some equivalent values are approximate; they are given to the customary accuracy.

Length: imperial unit to metric equivalent
1 inch = 25.4 millimetres (mm) = 2.54 centimetres
1 foot = 304.8 millimetres = 30.48 centimetres (cm)
1 yard = 914.4 millimetres = 0.914 m
1 pole/rod/perch = 5.03 metres (m)
1 furlong = 201 metres
1 mile = 1609.3 metres = 1.6 kilometres (km)

Length: metric unit to imperial equivalent
1 millimetre = 0.04 inches
1 centimetre = 0. 4 inches
1 metre = 39.4 inches = 1.09 yards
1 kilometre = 0.612 mile

Area: imperial unit to metric equivalent
1 square foot = 0.093 square metre (sq m, m^2)
1 square yard = 0.84 square metre
1 acre = 0.405 hectare (ha) = 4047 square metres
1 square mile = 259.2 hectares

Area: metric unit to imperial equivalent
1 square metre = 9.3 square feet
1 hectare = 2.47 acres = 11,954.8 square yards
1 square kilometre (sq km, km^2) = 247 acres = 0.386 square mile

Volume: imperial unit to metric equivalent
1 cubic foot = 0.03 cubic metre (cu m, m^3)
1 bushel = 0.038 cubic metre
1 cubic yard = 0.836 cubic metre
1 pint = 562 ml millilitres (ml) = 0.56 litres (l)
1 quart = 1.1 litres
1 gallon = 4.5 litres

Volume: metric unit to imperial equivalent
1 cubic metre = 35.29 cubic feet = 1.3 cubic yards
1 cubic metre = 45.2 bushels
1 litre = 1.78 pints = 0.22 gallons

Weight: imperial unit to metric equivalent
1 ounce = 28.4 grams (g)
1 pound = 454 grams = 0.45 kilograms (kg)
1 stone = 6.4 kilograms

1 hundredweight = 50.8 kilograms
1 ton = 1016 kilograms = 1.016 tonnes (t)

Weight: metric unit to imperial equivalent
1 gram = 0.035 ounces
1 kilogram = 2.2 pounds = 0.0197 hundredweight
1 tonne = 0.984 ton

MISCELLANEOUS MEASURES

The original unit of most weights and measures is said to be a grain of wheat from the middle of the ear and well dried; where this leaves the barleycorn (said to measure a third of an inch in length) is not clear!

A cord of wood is 4 feet by 4 feet by 8 feet = 128 cubic feet. A stack of wood is 3 feet by 3 feet by 12 feet = 108 cubic feet.

The "standard" bushel box measures 10 inches by 10 inches by 22 inches = 1.28 cubic feet or 8 gallons.

1 bushel of wheat or peas is traditionally assumed to weigh 63 pounds; barley 56 pounds; rye 57; oats 42 pounds.

1 gallon of water weighs 10 pounds, 1 pint (20 fluid ounces) weighs 1.25 pounds (20 ounces).

1 Scotch acre = 1.26 English acres.

A Gunter's surveyor's chain has 100 links and is 66 feet (22 yards) long.

1 truss of straw weighs 36 pounds. 36 Trusses = a load of straw.

1 ton of soil occupies 18–20 cubic feet (approx. 0.74 cubic yards or 0.54 cubic metres).

1 hundredweight per acre = 125 kilograms per hectares (1 pound per acre = 1.12 kilograms per hectare).

1 ounce per square yard = 2.7 hundredweight per acre (approximately equivalent to 30 grams per square metre or 300 kilograms per hectare).

1 tons per acre = 24 tonnes per hectare.

1 inch (30 millimetres) of water = 22,610 gallons per acre (4.5 gallons per square yard or 25.4 litres per square metre).

1 acre-inch = 102,800 litres.

1 centimetre-hectare = 100,000 litres.

1 are = 100 square metres.

The load is a frequently used but unquantified measure (e.g. farmyard manure per acre).

1 score = 20. When used to express weight 1 score = 20 pounds.

Temperature: to convert from degrees Fahrenheit (°F) to degrees Celsius (°C) subtract 32 and multiply by 5/9; to convert from degrees Celsius to degrees Fahrenheit multiply by 9/5 and add 32.

A short, abridged extract from the excellent paper "Weights and Measures" by Arthur Rogers, Head of the Intelligence Branch, Board of Agriculture, is in *The Standard Cyclopedia of Modern Agriculture*.

With a mixture of exasperation and tolerance Rogers reviews the plethora of containers and assemblages in common use at the beginning of the twentieth century and gives a clear indication of the complexity and chaos that surrounded agricultural and horticultural mensuration at that time.

> A sheaf of wheat is as much as will make a bundle of a particular size, often 12 in. in diameter. Ten inches is customary for barley and oats. Fourteen of these sheaves make a stook of wheat, 12 in the case of the two other kinds of grain. Sometimes a threave is made up of 2 stooks, sometimes 14 sheaves, and sometimes 12. In Northamptonshire 10 sheaves of corn make a threave, in Warwickshire 24, in Hertfordshire it used to be no less than 30. In the district of England which lies near the upper Thames, that is, Gloucestershire, Worcestershire, Oxfordshire, and Wiltshire, straw is reckoned by the bolting, a term implying in different places 12 to 24 lb. in weight.

If agriculture seemed chaotic horticulture was surely impenetrably complex:

> The sale of vegetables is conducted with the use of perhaps more peculiar terms than any other transactions in agricultural produce. Vegetables may be sold in bundles, tied in bunches, arranged in hands, packed in loads, flaskets, crates, hampers, pads, sieves, half-sieves, quarter-sieves, flats, molleys, prickles, feys, pottles, punnets, 2-hundredweight sacks, 1-hundredweight sacks, pea bags and half-hundredweight bags. .

INDEX